ELIZABETHAN FICTION

Elizabethan Fiction

EDITED WITH AN INTRODUCTION
AND NOTES BY

Robert Ashley

A N D

Edwin M. Moseley

HOLT, RINEHART AND WINSTON

NEW YORK · CHICAGO · SAN FRANCISCO
TORONTO · LONDON

Sixth Printing, December, 1964

Introductions and Notes
Copyright, 1953, by Robert Ashley and Edwin M. Moseley
Typography Design by Stefan Salter
Printed in the United States of America
Library of Congress Catalog Card Number: 52-13061
20540-0113

TO
CATHARINE
AND
VIRGINIA

INTRODUCTION

❦

A<small>N AUTHOR'S</small> contribution to the development of the novel is his particular addition to the previously established ways of describing individual behavior. In this connection it is natural that the English prose tale had its beginnings in the Renaissance, when attention to the individual in contrast to the social organism was becoming a characteristic attitude.

Medieval man conceived of the universe as an organic whole with every part in its ordained place, serving its ordained function. Of society it was similarly believed that each "member," that is, class, whether the nobility, the merchants and artisans, or the serfs, was essential to the whole and therefore equal in the sight of God. Each individual was bound by divine law, reflected of course in natural and human law, to perform his duty within the class of his birth. A man might change his station within his class: the gradations of the guild system, from apprentice to journeyman to master, allowed for this possibility, and a nobleman could acquire more land, hence higher status. But to move from one class to another, to assume pretentiously the manners of the class above or to debase one's self by marrying into the class below, was sacrilegious as a defiance of God's will and treasonable as a denial of the stated and tacit mores which manifested his will. The metaphor of the organism and its necessary members was derived from the physical being of the human individual, for whom, paradoxically, the medieval climate of opinion had so little concern.

Attention to the individual was a conscious concept of the new humanism, which was as much a nostalgic as a progressive intellectual movement; the individual was also the chief emphasis of the new bourgeois climate, which questioned and looked forward from the feudal milieu. The Renaissance as a revival of learning found its most zealous expression in the humanists. They approved of the translation of the classics, including the Bible, into the native tongues of the Western world, and they aimed at the creation of literature worthy of comparison with that of ancient Greece and Rome. Still, their motivation was more moral than aesthetic: they desired to arrive at ethical direction other than that laid down by the medieval Church and consequently at a new definition of the individual in relation to his society. But the humanists were not radical in their demands for social change: they worked for purification rather than the destruction or replacement of existent institutions; they were in effect the liberals of their time, wanting to analyze the discrepancy between current myths and actual behavior and to eliminate pretense. They constantly asked the questions: what is *true* nobility? what is *pure* Christianity? what is *ideal* kingship? using the familiar concepts of feudal organization and objecting only to the refutation of words by acts. They attacked ignoble noblemen, unChristian Christians, and unruly rulers, but they approved of each group in the ideal. They described seriously or they ridiculed abuses: they wrote essays on morality, dramatized utopias, satirized corruption, and even recorded behavior realistically, often by way of pointing out moral lessons.

That the humanistic criticism contributed to changes more drastic than the humanists intended is the familiar irony of the liberal position in every age. Wyclif, the English churchman of the fourteenth century, would still describe himself as an advocate of the true Church rather than an originator of European Protestantism. Sir Thomas More, preaching the sacrifice of the individual to the common good, consistently criticized abuses which were deviations *from* the feudal system and literally lost his head in defense of the medieval Church. Spenser lamented corruption at court but blamed it in part on change, and Shakespeare judged tragic heroes whose flaws were usually sins against the medieval values. Even Caxton, the first English printer, whose very trade helped to make literature available to the middle class, romantically yearned for the good old days before the disintegration of King Arthur's Round Table, dramatic symbol of the ideally functioning feudal system. It is, then, in spite of such conservative allegiances that the humanists contributed to a fresh conception of the individual so necessary for the development of the novel as we think of it.

The prose tales of Gascoigne, Lyly, Sidney, and Nashe are in the paradoxical tradition of humanism. Gascoigne's PLEASANT FABLE OF FERDINANDO JERONIMI AND LEONORA DE VALASCO (1575), was described as "translated out of the Italian riding tales" of a fictitious writer, Bartello, suggesting the romantic and melodramatic nature of the Italian novella. But the story is apparently Gascoigne's own invention: he had changed the English names and setting of an earlier version, THE ADVENTURES OF MASTER F.J. (1573), to more colorful Italian trappings and thereby had probably disguised an account of a personal experience. Ferdinando, Gascoigne's protagonist, invited to the dwelling of the Lord of Valasco for hunting, is expected to court the host's unmarried daughter Frances, but Ferdinando is attracted to Leonora, the wife of Valasco's son. After a period of urgent courtship, Ferdinando wins Leonora, but she soon rejects him when her secretary, secretly her paramour, returns to the estate. Jilted, Ferdinando departs at once; Frances, so enamored of Ferdinando that she has helped him gain Leonora, dies in grief; and Leonora continues on her amoral way.

Gascoigne's story revolves around a situation offering all of the possibilities of medieval romance: the characters are of noble birth with leisure time for shooting, feasting, dancing, and chatting wittily. The well-mannered young man is literally distraught with love for the beautiful noblewoman, the lovesickness being expected and the attraction to the married woman permitted by the code of courtly love. But there are significant differences from the conventional story.

Ferdinando goes through his totally physical experience without ultimate repentance for his deceit of his host Valasco, for his ingratitude to the virtuous Frances, or for his addiction to carnal pleasures. He does not become the Petrarchan lover who realizes finally that true love is a meeting of minds and that Frances is the epitome of the Beauty at which true love should aspire. Frances's goodness is not rewarded, and Leonora's departure from the established code is not punished.

In Gascoigne's tone, however, lies the nostalgic acceptance of the ideality of Frances as against the actuality of her foil, Leonora; the implied lament is that the myth of Frances does not function in any real environment. Similarly, in THE STEEL GLASS, a poem mirroring contemporary abuses, Gascoigne presented women as having "angel's face[s]" (the ideality of Frances) and "harmful hellish hearts" (the actuality of Leonora), but assured his readers that they would "espy, / some sunny summer's day, / To look again, and see some seemly sights," presumably the return of the ideal. Yet in Gascoigne's presentation of a specific and real situation rather than an ideal one lies his chief contribution to the beginnings of the novel. Though Gascoigne remains primarily on the level of straightforward description of action, which of course includes speech, he convinces his readers that Ferdinando's disturbed emotional state is something more than conformity to the medieval role of spurned lover. Even the admission on paper that people of noble birth and upbringing such as Leonora and her secretary can behave as they do is a step toward freeing the concept of character from the confines of feudal pretenses. The dialogue may conform to the demands of clever courtship, but it is nevertheless fast-moving repartee. Frances' apparently inconsistent motivation can best be understood by her complete conformity to the rules of courtly love, which allow a maiden both sophistication and innocence; in her characterization, Gascoigne has achieved the difficult combination of a significant symbol of ideals and an impressive individuality.

Lyly's EUPHUES: THE ANATOMY OF WIT (1578) illustrates

much more clearly than Gascoigne's story the conservative attachments of the humanists. Lyly has written a story that is scarcely a story. Euphues, a young Athenian of good birth and breeding (as his name literally suggests), disregards the admonition of an old man and starts out to encounter the society of dissolute Naples in the company of a local gallant, Philautus. Euphues quite willingly falls in love with Philautus' fiancée Lucilla, the daughter of a wealthy and important gentleman, and temporarily breaks off his friendship with Philautus so that he may be with her. But Lucilla soon rejects Euphues for another young man about town and leaves him to find comfort in common misery with Philautus.

Even the bit of action related in this summary serves in the story only as transition between the long discourses on youth, age, friendship, love, and the like. At first there appears to be nothing but a series of short essays on moral values, often classical in their source, such as the early humanist might have written for the serious edification of his readers. Yet it is not the logical development of ideas to which the reader pays attention, but the style in which these ideas are presented. This style, now referred to as *euphuism*, although Lyly was preceded by others in its use, is composed of parallel constructions, often with sounds repeated at corresponding points; of sound-devices such as alliteration and assonance; and of frequent metaphors and classical allusions. The complicated style is in effect a series of conscious and repeated rhythms which finally force the reader's attention away from content and toward sound but at the same time require careful attention on the part of the reader because he naturally expects content.

EUPHUES was exceedingly popular with the sophisticated members of the court and the educated gentry. They were the very persons conditioned to accept feudal values in a world changing so fast economically that a substructure for action according to these values was disappearing. The ideal knight of the medieval romances revealed his ascendant position by fighting for the lord to whom he was loyal or the lady whom he admired, but the members of the remnant feudal aristocracy of the sixteenth century could show that they "belonged" only by the complexity of their talk and the refinement of their manners and tastes. The artificial involvement of Lyly's style not only appealed to sophisticated tastes but also reflected the nonproductive pursuits of the sophisticated. As in their own lives, the aristocratic readers could discover in EUPHUES the replacement of action by style. Perhaps unintentionally Lyly had written a kind of comedy of manners which allowed his public to see itself in caricature. The style and the implicit content are repetitious, monotonous, dull only as far as the society reflected by the style is dull. For Lyly's contemporary readers to be bored with EUPHUES was for them to be bored with themselves.

Nevertheless, a point often neglected by Lyly's modern readers is the tone of his prose. Athens, which produced the shallow Euphues, was obviously Oxford, which produced Lyly; and Naples, which ensnared him in its dissoluteness, was obviously London, which Lyly faced as a young man in his twenties. The high-born ladies and gentlemen of the Naples-London society, with the possible exception of Livia, Lucilla's confidante, are portrayed as superficial, fickle, emptily witty. They are what is left of the feudal milieu, and though Lyly struggled to establish himself in that milieu, he laughs mockingly at a proclaimed morality which is really only clever verbosity. Humanistically, he has presented his society as he sees it and ridiculed it for not being what it is supposed to be: in this very tone he pointed a way to the use of irony and satire as realistic approaches to individual behavior.

EUPHUES AND HIS ENGLAND, Lyly's sequel, is in part a recantation of the first section, not in the surface evidences of the style but in the choice and tone of material. Some attempt is made to repair the damage done to women, young gentlemen, and love. Philautus, the center of Part II, meets a woman as decadent as Lucilla, but he is at least allowed a happy marriage to an upright lady at the end, and Euphues, this time a loyal friend and an open admirer of England, returns to the ivory tower of now restful Athens. Those at court sensitive about recognizing themselves in EUPHUES were appeased, and the more sophisticated continued to accentuate the manners mocked by Lyly with consciously "talking euphues."

The strongest criticism of Lyly and the strongest apology for the feudal aristocracy came from Sir Philip Sidney. In his DEFENSE OF POESY (*ca.* 1580) Sidney had protested against the elaborateness of contemporary style, and a few years later he wrote his ARCADIA in part as a reaction against euphuism. The long story centers around two princes, Musidorus of Thessaly and Pyrocles of Macedonia, who brave innumerable adventures in the ancient land of Arcadia and its surroundings. They are separated by shipwreck; they discover each other when they are fighting on the opposite sides of a battle between the Arcadians and the Helots; they follow the princesses Pamela and Philoclea into the forest, where their father has led them to avoid the consequences of an obscure oracle; they disguise themselves as a shepherd and an Amazon so that they may court the princesses; they battle beasts, fight in a tourney, face death on false charges: *ad infinitum* until everything ends happily. Whereas in Lyly the simplicity of the narrative takes on the complexity of the style, in Sidney the involvement of the action overwhelms whatever attempt at simple diction and sentence construction the author started out to achieve. Compared with the sentences of EUPHUES, those of ARCADIA often go their natural way free of conscious rhetorical balance and figurative decoration. But this is not always true, and occasionally even when Sidney attains his goal of natural writing, ARCADIA is cluttered by diction too lush for the requirements of the occasion.

The only simplicity consistently present is the apparent simplicity of pastoral settings and pastoral inhabitants, paradoxically less realistic than Lyly's complex talk, which was at least related to the manners of the upper class. Sidney's settings, created perhaps as prose poems to celebrate the estate of his sister, the Countess of Pembroke, gave his characters new dimensions in which to move, but most of the settings, whether houses or gardens, seashores or forests, were in Sidney's own words "not fairer in natural ornaments than [in] artificial inventions." Nor are the shepherds on which Sidney prided himself any more realistic than the courtiers whom he condemned for having forgotten the simple virtues of early chivalry. His rural inhabitants are the wise and articulate shepherds who rescue the princes in the early pages of the book; or they are Renaissance clowns such as Dametas and his family, guardians of the princess Pamela; or they are country gentlemen of wealth and refinement like the host Kalander. The most appealing shepherd is Musidorus in disguise as Dorus, a role which he enjoyed quite as much as Marie Antoinette later delighted in carrying the shepherdess's crook. It soon becomes clear that pastoral trappings attracted Sidney and his contemporaries as surcease from the intrigue of court and anxiety over the state of their dying feudal society.

But, as usual, the intended peaceful vacation in the country has its complications: Cecropia, Queen of Argos, claims King Basilius's throne for her own and goes to all ends to harass him, innocent persons are wounded or killed, well-intentioned love is unrequited, the entire countryside is upset before all problems are solved. The complexities are often overwritten, but they offer Sidney his chance for the delineation of individual emotions, and he is frequently successful. Too, the settings and the moods of the characters occasionally are made complementary, an accomplishment which is at least a beginning of the effective handling of atmosphere in fiction. Even Arcadia, which Sidney created as an ideal setting for the chivalric values no longer at home in sixteenth-century England, changes with the emotions of man and therefore provides room for individuals who are more than the symbols of ideals.

Thomas Nashe's THE UNFORTUNATE TRAVELLER, OR THE LIFE OF JACK WILTON (1594) has neither the sophisticated intentions of Lyly's EUPHUES nor the dignified intentions of Sidney's ARCADIA. It is strongly in the tradition of LAZARILLO DE TORMES, the Spanish picaresque novel written about 1554 and translated into English in 1576. The center of the usual picaresque story is the *picaro* or rogue, a fellow of low birth or at least of temporary low position; his lack of status allows him the advantage of having nothing to lose and therefore considerable freedom of insight and of comment, an advantage often enjoyed by the jesters of Renaissance drama and the servants of modern movies. Armed with this freedom from vested interests, he is exposed to the world and soon taught that professed morals and actual behavior have little to do with each other; then, with this additional weapon of knowledge from experience, he proceeds on adventures of his own.

The picaresque form has tremendous advantage as a vehicle of social comment because it covers considerable territory; indeed, it looks at society on every level. Nashe gives Wilton the field of all Europe and at least two decades from which to choose his geography and his history. Nashe has little respect for dates, and unhesitatingly puts events in the wrong order; he is quite willing to describe places he has not seen, but his mingling of fact and fiction gives his story an air of reality enhanced by the breezy first-person narration of the hero. Nashe sends Wilton to the siege of Thérouanne and Tournay in Henry VIII's army in 1513, to the battle of Marignano in 1515, to the Münsterian uprising of the Protestant sect of Anabaptists in 1534, to a celebration and disputation at Wittenberg University, to a variety of experiences in Italy in the train of Henry Howard, Earl of Surrey, and back to Henry VIII's retinue at the Field of the Cloth of Gold in France in 1520, at least fourteen years before one of the incidents which preceded it. He sprinkles Wilton's travels with such famous personages as Sir Thomas More, Erasmus, Luther, Carlstadt, Cornelius Agrippa, Pietro Aretino, and Surrey himself; whether these persons were ever at the places in question is not Nashe's concern. He lets Jack dupe a tavern keeper who sells cider to the army, rail at Anabaptists as villainous "puritans," laugh at the drunken and pompous German burghers, muck the serious discussions of Luther and Carl-stadt, and finally condemn with a kind of moral smugness a courtesan, a Jewish physician to the Pope, and several Italian cutthroats with whom he has been melodramatically involved. He allows him to praise Surrey as a distinguished nobleman, a talented poet, and an ideal lover; Cornelius Agrippa as the entertainer of kings, a philosopher, and a magician; and Pietro Aretino, to whom Nashe himself was compared, as the terror and pride of princes and the friend of writers.

Nashe consistently satirizes the pretentious bourgeoisie and the Protestant reformers. He vehemently expressed his atti-tude in his stand against the Puritans in the Martin Marprelate controversy of the 1590's. His approval is reserved for noble-men and for artists patronized by noblemen, but he cannot resist occasional satire of even the aristocracy. One of the dullest passages of THE UNFORTUNATE TRAVELLER is a tourna-ment which Surrey holds to challenge all Italians who deny the beauties and virtues of his mistress Geraldine. Nashe describes in detail the ornamentation of innumerable knights of the joust, burlesquing by his exaggeration the unrestrained attention of Sidney and the medieval romancers to the super-ficial decorations of chivalry. Indeed, Nashe's tone of satire and burlesque unifies and controls the entire book. When Nashe moves, for example, from ridiculing the Anabaptists to praising Surrey, he does so as if he has not been able to put on the brakes and must raucously screech his commendations as well as his condemnations; the reader can hardly be sure that respect is intended in any direction. Institutions are left in shambles and personages in disarray when Jack Wilton takes a look at them; his racy language, better for destruction than for edification, ironically leaves little of the system which Nashe may have intended to defend. Nashe's mainte-nance of tone and point of view and his realistic diction are important contributions to the art of fiction. A potential con-tribution was the literal movement of character, aided by vast settings and rapid language, but Nashe's hero had nowhere to go. This lack of goal for the individual was perhaps the chief hindrance of a backward-looking humanism to the development of character-through-action essential to prose fiction.

If Deloney as a writer of fiction was less skilled in conscious techniques than were Gascoigne, Lyly, Sidney, and Nashe, all men of some education, he had the advantage of believing in a goal for his protagonists. Deloney, a silk weaver before he became a ballad maker and teller of tales, was in all his activities, literary and otherwise, very much a part of the bourgeois climate of opinion ignored by Gascoigne, Lyly, and Sidney and attacked head-on by Nashe. Probably by way of rationalizing patterns of economic behavior already established and freeing this behavior from the sense of guilt which medieval mores imposed upon it, the bourgeois myth emphasized the potentialities of the individual rather than the obligation of the individual in the social organism. Each man, it was contended, was endowed with the capacity to work and obligated to use this capacity in the manipulation of resources about him. All men, therefore, were equal in the sight of God and presented with equal opportunity on God's earth. Exercising his natural industry and the accompanying virtues of diligence, thrift, and morality, a man might reach the goal at which he aimed without fear of class limitations; his sense of bourgeois morality would protect him from seeking the vain goals which characterized the decadent feudal aristocracy. The community and the state, furthermore, existed only by the consent and for the convenience of the individual, not as a means of controlling him. Economic success, since it was considered evidence of man's virtue, was equated with religious salvation; though the source of potential salvation was described variously by different Protestant sects, it was generally agreed that salvation had to be earned. These new ways of thinking condoned as just and natural the economic revolution of the middle class and the concomitant Protestant Reformation and gave the condemned *avarice* of the Middle Ages the admirable name of *ambition*.

Here was a social philosophy suggesting the entire structure of a prose tale. The medieval concept of each man moving within his assigned sphere encouraged the episodic structure of the romance in which the hero moved from episode to episode always within his particular class; each episode served to prove another feudal virtue, but the order of the episodes was rarely climactic since the conclusion of the incidents was arbitrary. This charge of lack of structure is applicable to Sidney in his romance (despite his tying all threads together at the end) and to Nashe in his anti-romance (perhaps a conscious burlesque of the lack of organization in the Arthurian romance, though one hardly knows what structure Nashe was capable of substituting). As we have pointed out, Lyly replaced the structure of action by the construction of sentences. Gascoigne attained some tightness of structure from the narrow scope of his story, which, in its restriction to a single incident, is more like the modern novelette than the novel.

Deloney's first and most important story, THE PLEASANT HISTORY OF JOHN WINCHCOMBE, IN HIS YOUNGER YEARS CALLED JACK OF NEWBURY, THE FAMOUS AND WORTHY CLOTHIER OF ENGLAND (1597), is based on the life and times of an actual person who lived during the reigns of Henry VII and Henry VIII and died in 1519. Jack's career is the prototype of the Horatio Alger story. He starts at the bottom as an apprentice to a clothier, attracts the attention of his master's widow through his admirable person and especially his diligence as a worker, becomes the head of the business through marriage to her, and develops the enterprise into an important and sizable factory. He protects and respects his workers: just as he has been raised in status by the widow, after her death he chooses one of his working maidens to be his wife. He outfits and sends a group of men to Flodden Field to fight for the King, and in return he is visited by Henry VIII himself. He becomes the spokesman for free enterprise on behalf of his fellow tradesmen, attacking Cardinal Wolsey, Henry's advisor, as the feudal representative, and praising Henry for his middle-class sympathies. He condones the duping of the jester Will Summers and an Italian merchant by the native workers, and he himself tricks an English lord into marrying one of his working maidens, bearing out the familiar pattern of folk stories about city slickers who are outwitted by the unsophisticated and innocent laborers. He helps a bankrupt draper to rise to the position of alderman of London. The height of Jack's own rise is his refusal to accept the King's offer of knighthood: his rejection of a title shows his contempt for feudal social stratification and his satisfaction with individual merit.

The incidents in the career of Jack of Newbury are related simply and directly, but with lively dialogue, earthy humor, and a clear sense of direction. The main characters evolve as individuals, though they may have set the pattern for stock figures in subsequent fiction. The minor characters, on the other hand, are often the stereotypes found in Renaissance *fabliaux*, but as a part of popular lore they help to form the background of a bourgeois climate of opinion. Jack's story is not only about the people but also for the people to read. In this regard Deloney attains the ideal at which the proletarian novels of the 1930's aimed, though, significantly, in the Renaissance the bourgeoisie was presented as the economic group seeking expression and in the 1930's as the group denying expression to a new class of workers. In other words, Deloney's story of a tradesman's rise in the world, which in the sixteenth century had radical implications, has become the conservative myth of private success.

Deloney's other stories, THE GENTLE CRAFT and THOMAS OF READING, are really collections of stories about the shoemakers and the clothiers, respectively. Some of the tales achieve the unity of action and of tone found in JACK OF NEWBURY, but they are complicated by Deloney's later interest in interweaving subplots, which succeeded variously in enriching or in distracting from the main line of action. Deloney became somewhat more venturesome in handling serious situations such as the moving story of the murder of Thomas Cole in his last novel, but occasionally what he intended to be emotional turned out to be tritely sentimental.

Deloney may not have been a specific influence on the subsequent development of the novel, but the prose tale continued to move along similar lines to those which he employed, no doubt partly because the climate reflected by his works was strengthened in the Revolution of 1642 and legalized as the dominant mores in the Bloodless Revolution of 1688. Bunyan's PILGRIM'S PROGRESS (1678), Defoe's ROBINSON CRUSOE (1719), and Richardson's PAMELA (1740) would hardly have been possible without the positive contribution of bourgeois individualism. And, paradoxically, Defoe's MOLL FLANDERS (1721) and the novels of Fielding, Sterne, and Smollett needed the bourgeois values to mock and the techniques of, say, Lyly and Nashe for mocking them. Even in the eighteenth century the middle-class climate, just formulated, was beginning to change, and new attitudes were affecting the basic form of the novel, just arrived at. But that is another story.

Out of different climates of opinion come different concepts. The writer of fiction, a part of his climate, imposes these concepts upon nature, and nature, redefined, helps to create a new climate. The novel as a form remains dynamic, and critics and readers remain interested.

West Point, New York   ROBERT ASHLEY
Washington, Pa.   EDWIN M. MOSELEY
January, 1953

BIBLIOGRAPHICAL NOTE

An invaluable work on the novel is Ernest A. Baker's HISTORY OF THE ENGLISH NOVEL (London: H. F. & G. Witherby, Ltd., 1924–1939), 10 vols. More concise studies are Wilbur L. Cross's THE DEVELOPMENT OF THE ENGLISH NOVEL (New York: The Macmillan Company, 1899); R. M. Lovett and H. S. Hughes's THE HISTORY OF THE NOVEL IN ENGLAND (Boston: Houghton Mifflin Company, 1932); Walter Raleigh's THE ENGLISH NOVEL (London: Charles Scribner's Sons, 1894); George Saintsbury's THE ENGLISH NOVEL (New York: E. P. Dutton & Co., Inc., 1913); and Edward Wagenknecht's CAVALCADE OF THE ENGLISH NOVEL (New York: Henry Holt & Company, Inc., 1943, 1954). Baker and Wagenknecht contain useful bibliographical lists. J. J. Jusserand's THE ENGLISH NOVEL IN THE TIME OF SHAKESPEARE (London: Unwin, 1890) is concerned with a single period of fiction, and Charlotte E. Morgan's THE RISE OF THE NOVEL OF MANNERS (New York: Columbia University Press, 1911), with a single type. Louis B. Wright's MIDDLE-CLASS CULTURE IN ELIZABETHAN FICTION (Chapel Hill: University of North Carolina Press, 1935), a comprehensive study of the social background, makes frequent references to fiction.

TEXTUAL NOTE

The editors of this anthology have attempted to provide a readable text for the average college student who is neither a linguist nor a specialist in Renaissance literature, and at the same time to retain as much as possible of the flavor of the originals. To accomplish this double purpose, the editors have *partially* modernized the texts.

In general, spelling has been modernized, but certain coined, quaint, or archaic words have been retained in their original form if they are readily identifiable with their modern equivalents. British spellings found in the originals have been retained. WEBSTER'S NEW COLLEGIATE DICTIONARY has been the authority for the spelling of modern words, THE OXFORD ENGLISH DICTIONARY for obsolete words.

The use of apostrophes, hyphens, italics, and quotation marks and the capitalization of nouns have been modernized. Dialogue has been punctuated as in modern usage. Otherwise, the punctuation has not been changed. Departures from the basic texts, other than those mentioned above, have been listed in the notes.

In order to keep notes at a minimum, the editors have explained only those words and allusions which the student cannot find for himself in a modern one-volume dictionary.

The editors have aimed at consistency within the policies stated above. Readers should recognize that much of the apparent inconsistency of the texts results from inconsistency in the originals.

TABLE OF CONTENTS

GEORGE GASCOIGNE

THE ADVENTURES OF MASTER F. J.

1573, 1575

George Gascoigne (1539?–1577)

In an age notable for versatility and originality, no writer pioneered more widely than George Gascoigne. The first English treatise on prosody, the first English prose comedy, the first original English poem in blank verse, and the first English novel all came from his pen.

According to his most recent biographer, Charles T. Prouty, Gascoigne was born in 1539, although earlier estimates of his birth date ranged from 1525 to 1542. On both sides he came of substantial and prosperous stock. His father, a justice of the peace and thrice MP from Bedford, was a hot-tempered, quarrelsome man with a penchant for bringing unsuccessful lawsuits. His mother, who was related to a Bishop of London and to Martin Frobisher, the explorer, was equally fond of litigation. George inherited the family weakness.

After attending Cambridge University without earning a degree, Gascoigne was admitted to Gray's Inn. But he never studied the law seriously and never practised. In 1558 he served as MP from Bedford and represented his father, who was ill, at the coronation of Queen Elizabeth. He attempted to make his way at court, but, succeeding only in running himself heavily into debt, he retired to the country to escape his creditors.

On November 23, 1561, he married Elizabeth Bacon, widow of William Bretton and also, it seems, wife of Edward Boyes. Since Elizabeth had neglected to secure a divorce, Boyes felt that he still had some claim to her. Gascoigne disagreed, the two came to blows in the street one night, the matter went to court, and the authorities forbade both Gascoigne and Boyes to "have access . . . unto the said Eliza-

beth, nor she to any of them" until it should be decided to
whom she and her property belonged. Some time between
1563 and 1566 Elizabeth was legally divorced from Boyes and
given permission "to marry again at her election and disposition." Apparently she and Gascoigne legitimized their marriage by a second ceremony, but legal suits arising from this
anomalous union plagued Gascoigne for the rest of his life.

In 1564 or 1565 Gascoigne decided to try the law again
and once more took residence at Gray's Inn. For the second
time, he made little progress toward a legal career. But his
literary talent bore fruit in two plays acted by his fellow
students in 1566. One of these, SUPPOSES, based on an Italian
original, is described by Prouty as the "first real prose comedy
. . . [and] the first really well-constructed vernacular comedy that appeared on the English stage." The other, JOCASTA,
translated from an Italian version of Euripedes' THE PHOENIS-
SAE, was the first attempt at Greek tragedy in the English
theater. Taken together, the two dramas make Gascoigne one
of the most important figures in the pre-Shakespearean theater.

In 1568 Gascoigne's father died. The deathbed was the
scene of a violent quarrel between George and his father,
with the elder Gascoigne berating his son and threatening dis-
inheritance. Shortly after his father's death, Gascoigne began
to quarrel with his mother and brother and was soon involved
in legal disputes over the estate. Eventually they ceased speaking to one another.

By 1570 Gascoigne was destitute; his constant lawsuits,
which he almost always lost, led to his ruin and, finally, to
his being jailed for debt. After his release, Gascoigne saw only
one way out—soldiering, and in the spring of 1572 he was in
Holland fighting the Spaniards. The following October, thoroughly disgusted with the incompetence and chicanery of
both armies, he was back in England. Encouraged by a patron, he decided to publish his poems. But before the volume
appeared and before he could assume the seat in Parliament to
which he had been elected by the district of Midhurst, he

suddenly fled England in March, 1573. Once again he joined the English volunteers in the Netherlands. Gascoigne's hasty flight may have been precipitated by an anonymous letter to the Privy Council listing "Certeyne objections why George Gascoigne oughte not to be admitted to be a Burgesse of the Parliament." Among others, the objections were that Gascoigne was a debtor, "a defamed person . . . a common Rymer . . . a notorious Ruffianne . . . a spie; an Atheist and godlesse personne."

A year and a half in Holland merely served to confirm Gascoigne's distaste for military life, and he returned to England in October, 1574. In the meantime, his A HUNDRETH SUNDRIE FLOWRES, which contained the original version of THE ADVENTURES OF MASTER F. J., had appeared anonymously. Severely criticized because of its alleged levity and immorality, the book was not a success. This failure, on top of his bitter disappointments as a lawyer, a courtier, and a soldier, marked a belated turning point in Gascoigne's career. From now on he worked hard to establish himself as a writer and to win the favor of the Queen and of lesser patrons. Furthermore, all his subsequent writings had a strong didactic bias; Gascoigne's biographers attribute this bias more to a sincere moral reformation than to a desire to placate the reading public.

The first product of the new Gascoigne was DULCE BELLUM INEXPERTIS, a satiric verse narrative of his martial experiences. The bitter sarcastic tone of this poem is in striking contrast to the usual attitude toward war expressed by most Elizabethan writers. In the summer of 1575 Gascoigne was commissioned by the Earl of Leicester to help prepare a pageant for the entertainment of the Queen at Kenilworth. Gascoigne also performed a similar task for the reception of Elizabeth at Woodstock later in the summer. In 1576 he published THE STEEL GLASS, one of the few examples of Elizabethan satire and the first original blank verse poem in English. At about the same time he issued a second edition of A HUNDRETH SUNDRIE FLOWRES under the title of THE POSIES. THE POSIES contained the revised version of MASTER F. J., with much of the allegedly improper material expurgated and the setting shifted from northern England to Italy. The latter change is often cited as evidence that MASTER F. J. was based on an incident in Gascoigne's life and that he was fearful of scandal or a possible libel suit. THE POSIES also contained CERTAIN NOTES OF INSTRUCTION, the first English treatise on versification.

In the fall of 1576, Gascoigne was sent by the English government to France and Belgium to report on the conflict between Spain and the Low Countries. During this mission he witnessed the sack of Antwerp, which he described vividly in THE SPOIL OF ANTWERP, perhaps the outstanding bit of journalistic writing in the Elizabethan period. Except for THE GRIEF OF JOYS, a series of elegies presented to the Queen as a New Year's gift, THE SPOIL OF ANTWERP was Gascoigne's last literary work. He died on October 7, 1577.

Gascoigne's pioneering work in poetry, drama, and fiction has assured him a place in English literary history. While not a major author, he was the outstanding writer of Elizabeth's early reign, and more than any contemporary he prepared the way for the great writers who followed.

The standard edition of Gascoigne is J. W. Cunliffe's THE WORKS OF GEORGE GASCOIGNE, 2 vols., Cambridge University Press, 1907–1910; volume one, THE POSIES, contains the revised MASTER F. J. The original version is reprinted in C. T. Prouty's A HUNDRETH SUNDRIE FLOWRES, University of Missouri, 1942; Professor Prouty's reprint has been invaluable to the editors of this anthology, and many of his critical notes have been paraphrased, with his permission, in the notes which follow. The biographies are F. E. Schelling's THE LIFE AND WRITINGS OF GEORGE GASCOIGNE, Publications of the University of Pennsylvania, Series in Philology, Literature, and Archaeology, II, 4, and C. T. Prouty's GEORGE GASCOIGNE: ELIZABETHAN COURTIER, SOLDIER, AND POET, Columbia University Press, 1942.

The text is taken from Cunliffe's edition of THE POSIES.

THE PLEASANT FABLE OF FERDINANDO JERONIMI AND LEONORA DE VALASCO, *TRANSLATED OUT OF THE ITALIAN RIDING TALES OF BARTELLO*

❦

IN THE pleasant country of Lombardy, (and not far from the city of Florence) there was dwelling sometimes a lord of many rich seignories and dominions, who nevertheless bore his name of the Castle of Valasco: this lord had one only son and two daughters: his son was called (during the life of his father) the heir of Valasco, who married a fair gentlewoman of the House of Bellavista named Leonora: the elder daughter of the Lord of Valasco was called Francischina, a young woman very toward, both in capacity and other active qualities. Now the Lord of Valasco having already married his son & heir, and himself drawing in age, was desirous to see his daughters also bestowed before his death, and especially the eldest, who both for beauty and ripeness of age might often put him in remembrance that she was a collop of his own flesh: and therefore sought means to draw unto his house Ferdinando Jeronimi a young gentleman of Venice, who delighting more in hawking, hunting, and such other pastimes than he did in study, had left his own house in Venice, and was come into Lombardy to take the pleasures of the country. So that the Lord of Valasco knowing him to be of a very good parentage, and therewithal not only rich but adorned with sundry good qualities, was desirous (as is said) to draw him home to his house (under pretence of hunting and hawking) to the end he might behold his fair daughter Francischina: who both for parentage and other worldly respects, might no less content his mind, than her beauty was

7

likely to have allured his liking. But it fell out far contrary to his desire, for Ferdinando Jeronimi beholding the Lady Leonora, who was indeed very fair, and of a very courtlike behaviour, became enamoured of her, and forgetting the courtesy that the Lord of Valasco had shewed him in entertaining him and his servants, with their horses, by the space of .iiii. months (which is a rare courtesy nowadays, and especially in such a country) he sought all means possible to make the heir of Valasco a becco.[1] And to the end that all men may perceive what fruits grow on such trees, and what issues come of such intents, I will set down in English the fable as it is written in Italian by Bartello. And because I do suppose that Leonora is the same name which we call Elinor in English, and that Francischina also doth import none other than Frances, I will so entitle them as to our own countrymen may be most perspicuous. Understand you then, that Ferdinando having now a hot affection unto the said Dame Elinor, and thinking it meeter to utter his first conceits in writing than in speech, did write unto her as followeth.

"Fair lady I pray you understand that (being altogether a stranger in this country) my good hap hath been to behold you to my no small contentation. And my evil hap accompanies the same with such imperfection of my deserts, as that I find always a ready repulse in mine own forwardness: So that considering the natural climate of the country, I must say that I have found fire in frost.[2] And yet comparing the inequality of my deserts, with the least part of your worthiness, I feel a continual frost, in my most fervent fire. Such is then the extremity of my passions, the which I could never have been content to commit unto this telltale paper, were it not that I am destitute of all other help. Accept therefore I beseech you, the earnest good will of a more trusty (than worthy) servant, who being thereby encouraged, may supply the defects of his ability with ready trial of dutiful loyalty. And let this poor paper (besprent with salt tears, and blown over with scalding sighs) be saved of you as a safeguard[3] for your sampler, or a bottom[4] to wind your sewing silk, that

when your last needleful is wrought, you may return to reading thereof and consider the care of him who is

More yours than his own.

F. J."

This letter by her received, her answer was this: She took
occasion one day, at his request to dance with him: the which
doing, she bashfully began to declare unto him, that she had
read over the writing which he delivered unto her: with like
protestation, that (as at delivery thereof, she understood not
for what cause he thrust the same into her bosom,) so now
she could not perceive thereby any part of his meaning:
nevertheless at last seemed to take upon her the matter, and
though she disabled herself, yet gave him thanks as &c.
Whereupon he broke the brawl,[5] and walking abroad, devised
immediately these few verses following.

Fair Beersheba the bright once bathing in a well,
With dew bedimmed King David's eyes that ruled Israel.
And Solomon himself, the source of sapience,
Against the force of such assaults could make but small defence:
To it the stoutest yield, and strongest feel like woe,
Bold Hercules and Sampson both, did prove it to be so.
What wonder seemeth then? when stars stand thick in skies,
If such a blazing star have power to dim my dazzled eyes?

L'envoi.

To you these few suffice, your wits be quick and good,
You can conject by change of hue, what humors feed my blood.

F. J.

Before he could put these verses in legible writing, it
pleased M. Elinor of her courtesy thus to deal with him.
Walking in a garden among divers other gentlemen & gentlewomen, with a little frowning smile in passing by him, she
delivered unto him a paper, with these words. "For that I understand not," quoth she, "the intent of your letters, I pray
you take them here again, and bestow them at your pleasure."
The which done and said, she passed by without change
either of pace or countenance. Ferdinando somewhat trou-

bled with her angry look, did suddenly leave the company, and walking into a park near adjoining, in great rage began to wreak his malice on this poor paper, and the same did rend and tear in pieces. When suddenly at a glance he perceived it was not of his own handwriting, and therewithal abashed, upon better regard he perceived in one piece thereof written in Roman[6] these letters *Colei:* which in English betokeneth *She:* wherefor placing all the pieces thereof, as orderly as he could, he found therein written, these few lines hereafter following.

"Your sudden departure, from our pastime yesterday, did enforce me for lack of chosen company to return unto my work, wherein I did so long continue, till at the last the bare bottom did draw unto my remembrance your strange request. And although I found therein no just cause to credit your coloured words, yet have I thought good hereby to requite you with like courtesy, so that at least you shall not condemn me for ungrateful. But as to the matter therein contained: if I could persuade myself, that there were in me any coals to kindle such sparks of fire, I might yet peradventure be drawn to believe that your mind were frozen with like fear. But as no smoke ariseth, where no coal is kindled, so without cause of affection the passion is easy to be cured. This is all that I understand of your dark letters: and as much as I mean to answer.

Colei: in English: *she*."

Ferdinando immediately upon receipt hereof, grew in jealousy that the same was not her own device. And therein I have no less allowed his judgment, than commended his invention of the verses, and letters before rehearsed. For as by the style this letter of hers bewrayeth that it was not penned by a woman's capacity, so the sequel of her doings may decipher, that she had more ready clerks than trusty servants in store. Well yet as the perfect hound, when he hath chased the hurt deer, amid the whole herd, will never give over till he have singled it again. Even so Ferdinando though somewhat abashed with this doubtful shew, yet still constant in his former intention, ceased not by all possible means, to bring this deer yet once again to the bows, whereby she might be the more surely stricken: and so in the end enforced to yield. Wherefore he thought not best to commit the said verses willingly into her custody, but privily lost them in her chamber, written in counterfeit. And after on the next day thought better to reply, either upon her, or upon her secretary in this wise as here followeth.

"The much that you have answered is very much, and much more than I am able to reply unto: nevertheless in mine own defense, thus much I allege: that if my sudden departure pleased not you, I cannot myself therewith be pleased, as one that seeketh not to please many, and more desirous to please you than any. The cause of mine affection, I suppose you behold daily. For (self-love avoided) every wight may judge of themselves as much as reason persuadeth: the which if it be in your good nature suppressed with bashfulness, then mighty Jove grant, you may once behold my wan cheeks washed in woe, that therein my salt tears may be a mirror to represent your own shadow, and that like unto Narcissus you may be constrained to kiss the cold waves, wherein your counterfeit is so lively portrayed. For if abundance of other matters failed to draw my gazing eyes in contemplation of so rare excellency, yet might these your letters both frame in me an admiration of such divine esprit, and a confusion to my dull understanding, which so rashly presumed to wander in this endless labyrinth. Such I esteem you, and thereby am become such, and even

HE. F. J."

This letter finished and fair written over, his chance was to meet her alone in a gallery of the same house: (where his manhood in this kind of combat was first tried:) and therein I can compare him to a valiant prince, who distressed with power of enemies had committed the safeguard of his person to treaty of ambassade,[7] and suddenly (surprised with a *camassado*[8] in his own trenches) was enforced to yield as prisoner. Even so Ferdinando Jeronimi lately overcome by the beautiful beams of this Dame Elinor, and having now committed his most secret intent to these late rehearsed letters, was at unawares encountered with his friendly foe, and constrained either to prepare some new defence, or else like a recreant to yield himself as already vanquished. Wherefore (as in a trance) he lifted up his dazzled eyes, and so continued in a certain kind of admiration, not unlike the astronomer, who (having after a whole night's travail, in the grey morning found his desired star) has fixed his hungry eyes to behold the comet long looked for: whereat this gracious dame (as one that could discern the sun before her chamber windows were wide open) did deign to embolden the fainting knight with these or like words.

"I perceive now," quoth she, "how mishap doth follow me, that having chosen this walk for a simple solace, I am here disquieted by the man that meaneth my destruction:" and therewithal, as half angry, began to turn her back, when Ferdinando (now awaked) gan thus salute her.

"Mistress," quoth he, "and I perceive now, that good hap haunts me, for being by lack of opportunity constrained to commit my welfare unto these blabbing leaves of bewraying paper," shewing that in his hand, "I am here recomforted with happy view of my desired joy:" and therewithal reverently kissing his hand, did softly distrain her slender arm, and so stayed her departure. The first blow thus proffered and defended, they walked and talked traversing divers ways, wherein I doubt not but that the Venetian could quit himself reasonably well. For after long talk she was contented to accept his proffered service, but yet still disabling herself, and seeming to marvel what cause had moved him to subject his liberty so wilfully, or at least in a prison (as she termed it) so unworthy. Whereunto I need not rehearse his answer, but suppose now, that thus they departed: saving I had forgotten this: she required of him the last rehearsed letter, saying that his first was lost, and now she lacked a new bottom for her silk, the which I warrant you, he granted: and so proffering to take a humble *congé* by *bezo las manos*,[9] she graciously

gave him the *zuccado dez labros:* [10] and so for then departed.
And thereupon recounting her words, he compiled these fol-
lowing, which he termed *terza sequenza,*[11] to sweet Mistress
SHE.

Of thee dear dame, three lessons would I learn:
What reason first persuades the foolish fly
(As soon as she a candle can discern)
To play with flame, till she be burnt thereby?
Or what may move the mouse to bite the bait
Which strikes the trap, that stops her hungry breath?
What calls the bird, where snares of deep deceit
Are closely couch'd to draw her to her death?
Consider well, what is the cause of this,
And though percase thou wilt not so confess,
Yet deep desire, to gain a heavenly bliss,
May drown the mind in dole and dark distress:
Oft is it seen (whereat my heart may bleed)
Fools play so long till they be caught indeed.
         And then

It is a heaven to see them hop and skip,
And seek all shifts to shake their shackles off:
It is a world, to see them hang the lip,
Who (erst) at love, were wont to scorn and scoff.
But as the mouse, once caught in crafty trap,
May bounce and beat against the boarden[12] wall,
Till she have brought her head in such mishap,
That down to death her fainting limbs must fall:
And as the fly once singed in the flame,
Cannot command her wings to wave away:
But by the heel, she hangeth in the same
Till cruel death her hasty journey stay:
So they that seek to break the links of love
Strive with the stream, and this by pain I prove.
         For when

I first beheld that heavenly hue of thine,
Thy stately stature, and thy comely grace,
I must confess these dazzled eyes of mine
Did wink for fear, when I first view'd thy face:
But bold desire did open them again,
And bad me look till I had look'd too long,

I pitied them that did procure my pain,
And lov'd the looks that wrought me all the wrong:
And as the bird once caught (but works her woe)
That strives to leave the limed twigs behind:
Even so the more I strove to part thee fro,
The greater grief did grow within my mind:
Remediless then must I yield to thee,
And crave no more, thy servant but to be.
                    Till then and ever. HE. F. J.

When he had well sorted this sequence, he sought opportunity to leave it where she might find it before it were lost. And now the coals began to kindle, whereof (but erewhile) she feigned herself altogether ignorant. The flames began to break out on every side: and she to quench them, shut up herself in her chamber solitarily. But as the smithy gathers greater heat by casting on of water, even so the more she absented herself from company, the fresher was the grief which galled her remembrance: so that at last the report was spread through the house, that Mistress Elinor was sick. At which news Ferdinando took small comfort; nevertheless Dame Venus with good aspect did yet thus much further his enterprise. The dame (whether it were by sudden change, or of wonted custom) fell one day into a great bleeding at the nose. For which accident the said Venetian, amongst other pretty conceits, had a present remedy: Whereby he took occasion (when they of the house had all in vain sought many ways to stop her bleeding) to work his feat in this wise: First he pleaded ignorance, as though he knew not her name, and therefore demanded the same of Mistress Frances, who when she had to him declared that her name was Elinor, he said these words or very like in effect: "If I thought I should not offend Mistress Elinor, I would not doubt to stop her bleeding, without either pain or difficulty." This gentlewoman somewhat tickled with his words, did incontinent make relation thereof to the said Mistress Elinor: who immediately (declaring that Ferdinando was her late received servant) returned the said messenger unto him with especial charge, that he should employ his devoir towards the recovery of her health: with whom the same Ferdinando repaired to the chamber of his desired: and finding her set in a chair, leaning on the one side over a silver basin: After his due reverence, he laid his hand on her temples, and privily rounding her in her ear, desired her to command a hazel stick and a knife: the which being brought, he delivered unto her, saying on this wise. "Mistress I will speak certain words in secret to myself, and do require no more: but when you hear me say openly this word *Amen*, that you with this knife will make a nick upon this hazel stick: and when you have made five nicks, command me also to cease." The dame partly of good will to the knight, and partly to be stanched of her bleeding, commanded her maid, and required the other gentles, somewhat to stand aside: which done, he began his orisons, wherein he had not long muttered before he pronounced *Amen*, wherewith the lady made a nick on the stick with her knife. The said Ferdinando continued to another *Amen*, when the lady having made another nick, felt her bleeding began to stanch: & so by the third *Amen* thoroughly stanched. Ferdinando then changing his prayers into private talk, said softly unto her: "Mistress, I am glad that I am hereby enabled to do you some service, and as the stanching of your own blood may some way recomfort you, so if the shedding of my blood may any way content you, I beseech you command it, for it shall be evermore readily employed in your service:" and therewithal with a loud voice pronounced *Amen:* wherewith the good lady making a nick, did secretly answer thus: "Good servant," quoth she, "I must needs think myself right happy to have gained your service and good will, and be you sure, that although there be in me so such desert as may draw you into this depth of affection: yet such as I am, I shall be always glad to shew myself thankful unto you. And now, if you think yourself assured that I shall bleed no more, do then pronounce your fifth *Amen:*" the which pronounced, she made also her fifth nick, and held up her head, calling the company unto her, and declaring unto them, that her bleeding was thoroughly stanched. And Ferdinando tarrying awhile in the chamber, found opportunity to lose his sequence near to his desired mistress: And after *congé* taken, departed. After whose departure the lady arose out of her chair, and her maid going about to remove the same, espied, and took up the writing: the which her mistress perceiving, gan suddenly conjecture that the same had in it some like matter to the verses once before left in like manner, and made semblant to mistrust that the same should be some words of conjuration: and taking it from her maid, did peruse it, and immediately said to the company, that she would not forgo the same for a great treasure. But to be plain, I think that (Ferdinando excepted) she was glad to be rid of all company, until she had with sufficient leisure turned over and retossed every card in this sequence. And not long after being now tickled through all the veins with an unknown humour, adventured of herself to commit unto a like ambassador the deciphering of that which hitherto she had kept more secret: and thereupon wrote with her own hand and head in this wise.

"Good servant, I am out of all doubt much beholding unto you, and I have great comfort by your means in the stanching of my blood, and I take great comfort to read your letters, and I have found in my chamber divers songs which I think to be of your making, and I promise you, they are excellently made: and I assure you that I will be ready to do for you any pleasure that I can, during my life: wherefore I pray you come to my chamber once in a day, till I come abroad again, and I will be glad of your company: and for because that you have promised to be my HE: I will take upon me this name, your SHE."

This letter was doubtless of her own handwriting: and as therein the reader may find great difference of style, from her former letter, so may you now understand the cause. She had in the same house a friend, a servant, a secretary: what should I name him? such one as she esteemed in time past more than was cause in time present. And to make my tale good, I will (by the same words that Bartello useth) describe him unto you. He was in height the proportion of two Pigmies, in breadth the thickness of two bacon hogs, of presumption a giant, of power a gnat, apishly witted, knavishly mannered, and crabbedly favored. What was there in him then to draw a fair lady's liking? Marry sir even all in all, a well-lined purse, wherewith he could at every call, provide such pretty conceits as pleased her peevish fantasy: and by that means he had thoroughly (long before) insinuated himself with this amorous dame. This manling, this minion, this slave, this secretary, was now by occasion ridden to Florence forsooth: and though his absence were unto her a disfurnishing of eloquence: it was yet unto Ferdinando Jeronimi an opportunity of good advantage: for when he perceived the change of her style, and thereby grew in some suspicion that the same proceeded by absence of her chief chancellor, he thought good now to smite while the iron was hot, and to lend his mistress such a pen in her secretary's absence, as he should never be able (at his return) to amend the well writing thereof. Wherefore according to her command he repaired once every day to her chamber, at the least whereas he guided himself so well, and could devise such store of sundry pleasures and pastimes, that he grew in favour not only with his desired, but also with the rest of the gentlewomen. And one day passing the time amongst them, their play grew to this end, that his mistress, being queen, demanded of him these three questions. "Servant," quoth she, "I charge you, as well upon your allegiance being now my subject, as also upon your fidelity, having vowed your service unto me, that you answer me these three questions, by the very truth of your secret thought. First, what thing in this universal world doth most rejoice and comfort you?" Ferdinando Jeronimi abasing his eyes towards the ground, took good advisement in his answer, when a fair gentlewoman of the company clapped him on the shoulder, saying, "How now sir, is your hand on your halfpenny?" [13] To whom he answered, "No fair lady, my hand is on my heart, and yet my heart is not in mine own hands:" wherewithal abashed, turning towards Dame Elinor he said: "My sovereign and mistress, according to the charge of your command, and the duty that I owe you, my tongue shall bewray unto you the truth of mine intent. At this present a reward given me without desert, doth so rejoice me with continual remembrance, that though my mind be so occupied to think thereon, as that day nor night I can be quiet from that thought, yet the joy and pleasure which I conceive in the same is such, that I can neither be cloyed with continuance thereof, nor yet afraid, that any mishap can countervail so great a treasure. This is to me such a heaven to dwell in, as that I feed by day, and repose by night upon the fresh record of this reward." This (as Bartello sayeth) he meant by the kiss that she lent him in the gallery, and by the profession of her last letters and words. Well, though this answer be somewhat misty, yet let his excuse be: that taken upon the sudden, he thought better to answer darkly, than to be mistrusted openly. Her second question was, what thing in this life did most grieve his heart, and disquiet his mind, whereunto he answered. That although his late rehearsed joy were incomparable, yet the greatest enemy that disturbed the same, was the privy worm of his own guilty conscience, which accused him evermore with great unworthiness: and that this was his greatest grief. The lady biting upon the bit[14] at his cunning answers made unto these two questions, gan thus reply. "Servant, I had thought to have touched you yet nearer with my third question, but I will refrain to attempt your patience: and now for my third demand, answer me directly in what manner this passion doth handle you? and how these contraries may hang together by any possibility of concord? for your words are strange." Ferdinando now rousing himself boldly, took occasion thus to handle his answer. "Mistress," quoth he, "my words indeed are strange, but yet my passion is much stranger: and thereupon this other day to content mine own fantasy I devised a sonnet, which although it be a piece of cockerel's music,[15] and such as I might be ashamed to publish in this company, yet because my truth in this answer may the better appear unto you, I pray you vouchsafe to receive the same in writing:" and drawing a paper out of his pocket, presented it to her, wherein was written this sonnet.

> Love, hope, and death, do stir in me such strife,
> As never man but I led such a life.
> First burning love doth wound my heart to death,
> And when death comes at call of inward grief,
> Cold lingering hope doth feed my fainting breath
> Against my will, and yields my wound relief:
> So that I live, but yet my life is such,
> As death would never grieve me half so much.
> No comfort then but only this I taste,
> To salve such sore, such hope will never want,
> And with such hope, such life will ever last,
> And with such life, such sorrows are not scant.
> Oh strange desire, O life with torments toss'd
> Through too much hope, mine only hope is lost.
>   Even HE F. J.

This sonnet was highly commended, and in my judgement it deserveth no less. His duty thus performed, their pastimes ended, and at their departure for a watchword he counseled his mistress by little and little to walk abroad: saying, that the gallery near adjoining was so pleasant, as if he were half dead he thought that by walking therein he might be half & more revived. "Think you so servant?" quoth she, "and the last time that I walked there, I suppose I took the cause of my malady:[16] but by your advice (for that you have so clerkly stanched my bleeding) I will assay to walk there tomorrow." "Mistress," quoth he, "and in more full accomplishment of my duty towards you, and in sure hope that you will use the same only to your own private commodity, I will there await upon you, and between you and me will teach you the full order how to stanch the bleeding of any creature, whereby you shall be as cunning as myself." "Gramercy good servant," quoth she, "I think you lost the same in writing here yesterday, but I cannot understand it: & therefore tomorrow (if I feel myself anything amended) I will send for you thither to instruct me thoroughly:" thus they departed. And at supper time, the Lord of Valasco finding fault that his guest's stomach served him no better, began to accuse the grossness of his viands, to whom one of the gentlewomen which had passed the afternoon in his company, answered. "Nay sir," quoth she, "this gentleman hath a passion, the which once in a day at the least doth kill his appetite." "Are you so well acquainted with the disposition of his body?" quoth the lord of the house. "By his own saying," quoth she, "& not otherwise." "Fair lady," quoth Ferdinando, "you either mistook me or overheard me then: for I told of a comfortable humor which so fed me with continual remembrance of joy, as that my stomach being full thereof doth desire in manner none other victuals." "Why sir," quoth the host, "do you then live by love?" "God forbid sir," quoth Ferdinando, "for then my cheeks would be much thinner than they be: but there are divers other greater causes of joy, than the doubtful lots of love: & for mine own part, to be plain, I cannot love, & I dare not hate." "I would I thought so," quoth the gentlewoman. And thus with pretty nips, they passed over their supper: which ended, the lord of the house required Ferdinando Jeronimi to dance and pass the time with the gentlewomen, which he refused not to do. But suddenly, before the music was well tuned, came out Dame Elinor in her night attire, and said to the lord, that (supposing the solitariness of her chamber had increased her malady) she came out for her better recreation to see them dance. "Well done daughter," quoth the lord. "And I mistress," quoth Ferdinando, "would gladly bestow the leading of you about this great chamber, to drive away the faintness of your fever." "No good servant," quoth the lady, "but in my stead, I pray you dance with this fair gentlewoman," pointing him to the lady that had so taken him up at supper. Ferdinando to avoid mistrust, did agree to her request without further entreaty. The dance begun, this knight marched on with the image of S. Frances in his hand, and S. Elinor in his heart. The violands[17] at end of the pavane[18] stayed awhile: in which time this dame said to Ferdinando Jeronimi on this wise: "I am right sorry for you in two respects, although the familiarity have hitherto had no great continuance between us: and as I do lament your case, so do I rejoice (for mine own contentation) that I shall now see a due trial of the experiment which I have long desired." This said, she kept silence: When Ferdinando (somewhat astonied with her strange speech) thus answered: "Mistress although I cannot conceive the meaning of your words, yet by courtesy I am constrained to yield you thanks for your good will, the which appeareth no less in lamenting of mishaps, than in rejoicing at good fortune. What experiment you mean to try by me, I know not, but I dare assure you, that my skill in experiments is very simple." Herewith the instruments sounded a new measure, and they passed forthwards, leaving to talk, until the noise ceased: which done, the gentlewoman replied. "I am sorry sir, that you did erewhile, deny love and all his laws, and that in so open audience." "Not so," quoth Ferdinando, "but as the word was roundly taken, so can I readily answer it by good reason." "Well," quoth she, "how if the hearers will admit no reasonable answer?" "My reasons yet be nevertheless," quoth he, "in reasonable judgement." Herewith she smiled, and he cast a glance towards Dame Elinor, askances[19] art thou pleased? Again the viols called them forthwards, and again at the end of the brawl said Ferdinando Jeronimi to this gentlewoman: "I pray you mistress, and what may be the second cause of your sorrow sustained in my behalf?" "Nay soft," quoth she, "percase I have not yet told you the first, but content yourself, for the second cause you shall never know at my hands, until I see due trial of the experiment which I have long desired." "Why then," quoth he, "I can but wish a present occasion to bring the same to effect, to the end that I might also understand the mystery of your meaning." "And so might you fail of your purpose," quoth she, "for I mean to be better assured of him that shall know the depth of my intent in such a secret, than I do suppose that any creature (one except) may be of you." "Gentlewoman," quoth he, "you speak Greek, the which I have now forgotten, and mine instructors are too far from me at this present to expound your words." "Or else too near," quoth she and so smiling stayed her talk, when the music called them to another dance. Which ended, Ferdinando half afraid of false suspect, and more amazed at this strange talk, gave over, and bringing Mistress Frances to her place, was thus saluted by his mistress. "Servant," quoth she, "I had done you great wrong to have danced with you, considering that this gentlewoman and you had former occasion of so weighty conference." "Mistress," said Ferdinando, "you had done me great pleasure, for by our conference I have but brought my brains in a busy conjecture." "I doubt not," said his mistress, "but you will end that business easily." "It is hard," said he, "to end the thing, whereof yet I have found no beginning." His mistress with change of countenance kept silence whereat Dame Frances rejoicing, cast out this bone to gnaw on. "I perceive," quoth she, "it is evil to halt[20] before a cripple." Ferdinando perceiving now that his mistress waxed angry, thought good on her behalf thus to answer: "And it is evil to hop before them that run for the bell:" [21] his mistress replied, "And it is evil to hang the bell at their heels which are always running." The lord of the castle overhearing these proper quips, rose out of his chair, & coming towards Ferdinando required him to dance a galliard. "Sir," said he, "I have hitherto at your appointment but walked about the house, now if you be desirous to see one tumble a turn or twain, it is like enough that I might provoke you to laugh at me, but in good faith my dancing days are almost done, and therefore sir," quoth he, "I pray you speak to them that are more nimble at tripping on the toe." Whilst he was thus saying Dame Elinor had made her *congé*, and was now entering the door of her chamber when Ferdinando all amazed at her sudden departure followed to take leave of his mistress: but she more than angry, refused to hear his good night, and entering her chamber caused her maid to clap to the door. Ferdinando with heavy cheer returned to his company, and Mistress Frances to touch his sore with a corrosive, said to him softly in this wise. "Sir you may now perceive that this

our country cannot allow the French manner of dancing, for
they (as I have heard tell) do more commonly dance to talk,
than entreat to dance." Ferdinando hoping to drive out one
nail with another and thinking this a mean most convenient to
suppress all jealous supposes, took Mistress Frances by the
hand and with a heavy smile answered. "Mistress and I (because I have seen the French manner of dancing) will eftsoons entreat you to dance a bargynet:" [22] "What mean you
by this?" quoth Mistress Frances. "If it please you to follow,"
quoth he, "you shall see that I can jest without joy, and laugh
without lust," and calling the musicians, caused them softly
to sound the tinternell,[23] when he clearing his voice did *alla
Napolitana*[24] apply these verses following, unto the measure.

In prime of lusty years, when Cupid caught me in,
And nature taught the way to love, how I might best begin:
To please my wandering eye, in beauty's tickle trade,
To gaze on each that passed by, a careless sport I made.

With sweet enticing bait, I fish'd for many a dame,
And warmed me by many a fire, yet felt I not the flame:
But when at last I spied, that face that pleas'd me most,
The coals were quick, the wood was dry, & I began to toast.

And smiling yet full oft, I have beheld that face,
When in my heart I might bewail mine own unlucky case:
And oft again with looks that might bewray my grief,
I pleaded hard for just reward, and sought to find relief.

What will you more? so oft my gazing eyes did seek,
To see the rose and lily strive upon that lively cheek:
Till at the last I spied, and by good proof I found,
That in that face was painted plain, the piercer of my wound.

Then (all too late) aghast, I did my foot retire,
And sought with secret sighs to quench my greedy scalding fire
But lo, I did prevail as much to guide my will,
As he that seeks with halting heel, to hop against the hill.

Or as the feeble sight, would search the sunny beam,
Even so I found but labour lost, to strive against the stream.

Then gan I thus resolve, since liking forced love.
Should I mislike my happy choice, before I did it prove?

And since none other joy I had but her to see,
Should I retire my deep desire? no no it would not be:
Though great the duty were, that she did well deserve,
And I poor man, unworthy am so worthy a wight to serve.

Yet hope my comfort stay'd, that she would have regard,
To my good will that nothing crav'd, but like for just reward:
I see the falcon gent sometime will take delight
To seek the solace of her wing, and dally with a kite.

The fairest wolf will choose the foulest for her make,
And why? because he doth endure most sorrow for her sake:
Even so had [I like] hope, when doleful days were spent
When weary words were wasted well, to open true intent.

When floods of flowing tears, had washt my weeping eyes,
When trembling tongue had troubled her, with loud lamenting
cries:
At last her worthy will would pity this my plaint,
And comfort me her own poor slave, whom fear had made so
faint.
Wherefore I made a vow, the stony rock should start,
Ere I presume, to let her slip out of my faithful heart.

L'envoi.
And when she saw by proof, the pith of my good will,
She took in worth this simple song, for want of better skill:
And as my just deserts, her gentle heart did move,
She was content to answer thus: I am content to love.
F. J.

By these verses he meant in clouds to decipher unto Mistress Frances such matter as she would snatch at, and yet could take no good hold of the same. Furthermore, it answered very aptly to the note which the music sounded, as the skillful reader by due trial may approve. This singing dance, or dancing song ended, Mistress Frances giving due thanks, seemed weary also of the company and proffering to depart, gave yet this farewell to Ferdinando not vexed by

choler, but pleased with contentation, & called away by heavy
sleep: "I am constrained," quoth she, "to bid you good
night," and so turning to the rest of the company, took her
leave. Then the master of the house commanded a torch to
light Ferdinando to his lodging, where the sudden change of
his mistress' countenance, together with the strangeness of
Mistress Frances' talk, made such an encounter in his mind,
that he could take no rest that night: wherefore in the morning rising very early (although it were far before his mistress'
hour), he cooled his choler by walking in the gallery near to
her lodging, and there in this passion compiled these verses
following.

> A cloud of care hath cover'd all my coast,
> And storms of strife do threaten to appear:
> The waves of woe, which I mistrusted most,
> Have broke the banks wherein my life lay clear:
> Chips of ill chance, are fallen amid my choice,
> To mar the mind, that meant for to rejoice.
>
> Before I sought, I found the haven of hap,
> Wherein (once found) I sought to shroud my ship,
> But low'ring love hath lift me from her lap,
> And crabbed lot begins to hang the lip:
> The props of dark mistrust do fall so thick,
> They pierce my coat, and touch my skin at quick.
>
> What may be said, where truth cannot prevail?
> What plea may serve, where will itself is judge?
> What reason rules, where right and reason fail?
> Remediless then must the guiltless trudge:
> And seek out care, to be the carving knife,
> To cut the thread that ling'reth such a life.

F. J.

This is but a rough meter, and reason, for it was devised in
great disquiet of mind, and written in rage, but to the matter.
When he had long (and all in vain) looked for the coming of
his mistress into her appointed walk: he wandered into the
park near adjoining to the castle wall, where his chance was
to meet Mistress Frances, accompanied with one other gentle-

woman, by whom he passed with a reverence of courtesy: and so walking on, came into the side of a thicket, where he sat down under a tree to allay his sadness with solitariness. Mistress Frances, partly of courtesy and affection, and partly to content her mind by continuance of such talk as they had commenced overnight, entreated her companion to go with her unto this tree of reformation, whereas they found the knight with his arms folded in a heavy kind of contemplation, unto whom Mistress Frances stepped apace (right softly) and at unawares gave this salutation. "I little thought Sir Knight," quoth she, "by your evensong yesternight, to have found you presently at such a morrow mass, but I perceive you serve your saint with double devotion: and I pray God grant you treble meed for your true intent." He being taken thus upon the sudden, could none otherwise answer but thus: "I told you mistress," quoth he, "that I could laugh without lust, and jest without joy:" and therewithal starting up, with a more bold countenance came towards the dames, proffering unto them his service, to wait upon them homewards. "I have heard say ofttimes," quoth Mistress Frances, "that it is hard to serve two masters at one time, but we will be right glad of your company." "I thank you," quoth he, and so walking on with them, fell into sundry discourses, still refusing to touch any part of their former communication, until Mistress Frances said unto him: "By my troth," quoth she, "I would be your debtor these two days, to answer me truly but unto one question that I will propound:" "Fair gentlewoman," quoth he, "you shall not need to become my debtor, but if it please you to quit question by question, I will be more ready to gratify you in this request, than either reason requireth, or than you would be willing to work my contentation." "Master Ferdinando Jeronimi," quoth she, & that sadly, "peradventure you know but a little how willing I would be to procure your contentation, but you know that hitherto familiarity hath taken no deep root betwixt us twain. And though I find in you no manner of cause whereby I might doubt to commit this or greater matter unto you, yet have I stayed hitherto so to do, in doubt lest you might thereby justly condemn me both of arrogancy and lack of discretion, wherewith I must yet foolishly affirm, that I have with great pain bridled my tongue from disclosing the same unto you. Such is then the good will that I bear towards you, the which if you rather judge to be impudency, than a friendly meaning, I may then curse the hour that I first concluded thus to deal with you:" herewithal being now red for chaste bashfulness, she abased her eyes, and stayed her talk: to whom Ferdinando thus answered. "Mistress Frances, if I should with so exceeding villainy requite such and so exceeding great courtesy, I might not only seem to degenerate from all gentry, but also to differ in behaviour from all the rest of my life spent: wherefore to be plain with you in few words I think myself so much bound unto you for diverse respects, as if ability do not fail me, you shall find me mindful in requital of the same, and for disclosing your mind to me, you may if so it please you adventure it without adventure, for by this sun," quoth he, "I will not deceive such trust as you shall lay upon me, and furthermore, so far forth as I may, I will be yours in any respect: wherefore I beseech you accept me for your faithful friend, and so shall you surely find me." "Not so," quoth she, "but you shall be my Trust, if you vouchsafe the name, and I will be to you as you shall please to term me:" "My Hope," quoth he, "if you be so pleased:" and thus agreed, they two walked apart from the other gentlewoman, and fell into sad talk, wherein Mistress Frances did very courteously declare unto him, that indeed, one cause of her sorrow sustained in his behalf, was that he had said so openly overnight, that he could not love, for she perceived very well the affection between him and Madame Elinor, and she was also advertised that Dame Elinor stood in the portal of her chamber, harkening to the talk that they had at supper that night, wherefore she seemed to be sorry that such a word (rashly escaped) might become great hindrance unto his desire: but a greater cause of her grief was (as she declared) that his hap was to bestow his liking so unworthily, for she seemed to accuse Dame Elinor, for the most unconstant woman living: In full proof whereof, she bewrayed unto him, how she the same Dame Elinor, had long time been yielded to the minion secretary, whom I have before described: "In whom though there be," quoth she, "no one point of worthiness, yet shameth she not to use him as her dearest friend, or rather her holiest idol" and that this not withstanding Dame Elinor had been also sundry times won to choice of change, as she named unto Ferdinando two gentlemen whereof the one was named Hercule Donaty, and the other Hannibal de Cosmis, by whom she was during sundry times of their several abode in those countries, entreated to like courtesy: for these causes the Dame Frances seemed to mislike his choice, and to lament that she doubted in process of time to see him abused.

The experiment she meant was this, for that she thought Ferdinando (I use Bartello's words) a man in every respect very worthy to have the several use of a more commodious common, she hoped now to see if his inclosure thereof might be defensible against her said secretary, and such like. These things and divers other of great importance, this courteous Lady Frances did friendly disclose unto him, and furthermore, did both instruct and advise him to proceed in his enterprise. Now to make my talk good, and lest the reader might be drawn in a jealous suppose of this Lady Frances, I must let you understand that she was a virgin of rare chastity, singular capacity, notable modesty, & excellent beauty: and though Ferdinando Jeronimi had cast his affection on the other (being a married woman) yet was there in their beauties no great difference: but in all other good gifts a wonderful diversity, as much as might between constancy & flitting fantasy, between womanly countenance and girlish garishness, between hot dissimulation & temperate fidelity. Now if any man will curiously ask the question why he should choose the one and leave the other, over & besides the common proverb, "So many men so many minds," thus may be answered we see by common experience, that the highest flying falcon, doth more commonly prey upon the corn-fed crow & the simple shiftless dove, than on the mounting kite: & why? because the one is overcome with less difficulty than that other. Thus much in defence of this Lady Frances, & to excuse the choice of Ferdinando who thought himself now no less beholding to good fortune, to have found such a trusty friend, than bounden to Dame Venus, to have won such a mistress. And to return unto my pretence, understand you, that he (being now with these two fair ladies come very near the castle) grew in some jealous doubt (as on his own behalf) whether he were best to break company or not. When his assured Hope, perceiving the same, gan thus recomfort him: "Good sir," quoth she, "if you trusted your trusty friends, you should not need thus cowardly to stand in dread of your friendly enemies." "Well said in faith," quoth Ferdinando, "& I must confess, you were in my bosom before I wist: but yet I have heard said often, that in trust is treason." "Well spoken for yourself," quoth his Hope. Ferdinando now remembering that he had but erewhile taken upon him the name of her Trust, came home *per misericordiam,*[25] when his Hope entering the castle gate, caught hold of his lap, & half by force led him by the gallery unto his mistress' chamber: whereas after a little dissembling disdain, he was at last by the good help of his Hope, right thankfully received: & for his mistress was now ready to dine, he was therefore for that time arrested there, & a supersedeas[26] sent into the great chamber unto the lord of the house, who expected his coming out of the park. The dinner ended, & he thoroughly contented both with welfare & welcome, they fell into sundry devices of pastime: at last Ferdinando taking into his hand a lute that lay on his mistress' bed, did unto the note of the Venetian galliard apply the Italian ditty written by the worthy Bradamant unto the noble Rugier, as Ariosto hath it. "Rugier *qual semper fui,* &c." but his mistress could not be quiet until she heard him repeat the tinternell which he used overnight, the which he refused not, at end whereof his mistress thinking how she had shewed herself too earnest to use any further dissimulation, especially perceiving the toward inclination of her servant's hope, fell to flat and plain dealing & walked to the window, calling her servant apart unto her, of whom she demanded secretly and in sad earnest, "Who devised this tinternell?" "My father's sister's brother's son," quoth he. His mistress laughing right heartily, demanded yet again, by whom the same was figured: "By a niece of an aunt of yours, mistress," quoth he. "Well then servant," quoth she, "I swear unto you by my father's soul, that my mother's youngest daughter, doth love your father's eldest son above any creature living." Ferdinando hereby recomforted gan thus reply. "Mistress, though my father's eldest son be far unworthy of so noble a match, yet since it pleaseth her so well to accept him, I would thus much say behind his back, that your mother's daughter hath done him some wrong:" "And wherein servant?" quoth she: "By my troth mistress," quoth he, "it is not yet xx. hours, since without touch of breast, she gave him such a nip by the heart, as did altogether bereave him his night's rest with the bruise thereof." "Well servant," quoth she, "content yourself, for your sake, I will speak to her to provide him a plaster, the which I myself will apply to his hurt: And to the end it may work the better with him, I will purvey a lodging for him, where hereafter he may sleep at more quiet."

This said: the rosy hew distained her sickly cheeks, and she returned to the company, leaving Ferdinando ravished between hope and dread, as one that could neither conjecture the meaning of her mystical words, nor assuredly trust unto the knot of her sliding affections. When the Lady Frances, coming to him, demanded, "What dream you sir?" "Yea marry do I fair lady," quoth he. "And what was your dream, sir?" quoth she. "I dreamt," quoth he, "that walking in a pleasant garden garnished with sundry delights, my hap was to espy hanging in the air, a hope wherein I might well behold the aspects and face of the heavens, and calling to remembrance the day and hour of my nativity, I did thereby (according to my small skill in astronomy) try the conclusion of mine adventures." "And what found you therein," quoth Dame Frances. "You awaked me out of my dream," quoth he, "or else peradventure you should not have known." "I believe you well," quoth the Lady Frances and laughing at his quick answer brought him by the hand unto the rest of his company: where he tarried not long before his gracious mistress bade him to farewell, and to keep his hour there again when he should by her be summoned. Hereby he passed the rest of that day in hope awaiting the happy time when his mistress should send for him. Supper time came, and passed over, and not long after came the handmaid of the Lady Elinor into the great chamber desiring him to repair unto their mistress, the which he willingly accomplished: and being now entered into her chamber, he might perceive his mistress in her night's attire, preparing herself towards bed, to whom Ferdinando said, "Why how now mistress? I had thought this night to have seen you dance (at least or at last) amongst us?" "By my troth good servant," quoth she, "I adventured so soon unto the great chamber yesternight, that I find myself somewhat sickly disposed, and therefore do strain courtesy (as you see) to go the sooner to my bed this night: but before I sleep," quoth she, "I am to charge you with a matter of weight," and taking him apart from the rest, declared that (as that present night) she would talk with him more at large in the gallery near adjoining to her chamber. Hereupon Ferdinando discreetly dissimuling his joy, took his leave & returned into the great chamber, where he had not long continued before the lord of the castle commanded a torch to light him unto his lodging, whereas he prepared himself and went to bed, commanding his servant also to go to his rest. And when he thought as well his servant, as the rest of the household to be safe, he arose again, & taking his nightgown, did under the same convey his naked sword, and so walked to the gallery, where he found his good mistress walking in her nightgown and attending his coming. The moon was now at the full, the skies clear, and the weather temperate, by reason whereof he might the more plainly and with the greater contentation behold his long desired joys: and spreading his arms abroad to embrace his loving mistress, he said, "Oh my dear lady when shall I be able with any desert to countervail the least part of this your bountiful goodness?" The dame (whether it were of fear indeed, or that the wiliness of womanhood had taught her to cover her conceits with some fine dissimulation) started back from the knight, and shrieking (but softly) said unto him. "Alas servant what have I deserved, that you come against me with naked sword as against an open enemy?" Ferdinando perceiving her intent excused himself, declaring that he brought the same for their defense, and not to offend her in any wise.

The lady being therewith somewhat appeased they began with more comfortable gesture to expel the dread of the said late affright, and sithence[27] to become bolder of behaviour, more familiar in speech, and most kind in accomplishing of common comfort. But why hold I so long discourse in describing the joys which (for lack of like experience) I cannot set out to the full? Well, remedy was there none, but Dame Elinor must return unto her chamber, and he must also convey himself (as closely as might be) into his chamber, the which was hard to do, the day being so far sprung, and he having a large base court to pass over before he could recover his stairfoot door. And though he were not much perceived, yet the Lady Frances being no less desirous to see an issue of these enterprises, than he was willing to cover them in secrecy, laid watch, & even at the entering of his chamber door, perceived the point of his naked sword glistering under the skirt of his nightgown: whereat she smiled & said to herself, "This gear goeth well about." Well Ferdinando having now recovered his chamber he went to bed, there let him sleep, as his mistress did on the other side. Although the Lady Frances being throughly tickled now in all the veins, could not enjoy such quiet rest, but arising took another gentlewoman of the house with her, and walked into the park to take the fresh air of the morning. They had not long walked there, but they returned, and though Ferdinando Jeronimi had not yet slept sufficiently, for one which had so far traveled in the night past, yet they went into his chamber to raise him, and coming to his bedside, found him fast on sleep. "Alas," quoth that other gentlewoman, "it were pity to awake him:" "Even so it were," quoth Dame Frances, "but we will take away somewhat of his, whereby he may perceive that we were here," and looking about the chamber, his naked sword presented itself to the hands of Dame Frances, who took it with her, and softly shutting his chamber door again, went down the stairs and recovered her own lodging, in good order and unperceived of anybody, saving only that other gentlewoman which accompanied with her. At the last Ferdinando awaked, and apparelling himself, walked out also to take the air, and being thoroughly recomforted as well with remembrance of his joys forepassed, as well with the pleasant harmony which the birds made on every side, and the fragrant smell of the redolent flowers and blossoms which budded on every branch: he did in these delights compile these verses following called "A Moonshine Banquet."

Dame Cynthia herself (that shines so bright,
And deigneth not to leave her lofty place:
But only then, when Phoebus shews his face.
Which is her brother born and lends her light,)
Disdain'd not yet to do my lady right:
To prove that in such heavenly wights as she,
It fitteth best that right and reason be.
For when she spied my lady's golden rays,
Into the clouds,
Her head she shrouds,
And shamed to shine where she her beams displays.

Good reason yet, that to my simple skill,
I should the name of Cynthia adore:
By whose high help, I might behold the more,
My lady's lovely looks at mine own will,
With deep content, to gaze, and gaze my fill:
Of courtesie and not of dark disdain,
Dame Cynthia disclos'd my lady plain.
She did but lend her light (as for a light)

With friendly grace,
To shew her face,
That else would shew and shine in her despight.

Dan Phoebus he with many a low'ring look,
Had her beheld of yore in angry wise:
And when he could none other mean devise
To stain her name, this deep deceit he took,
To be the bait that best might hide his hook:
Into her eyes his parching beams he cast,
To scorch their skins, that gaz'd on her full fast:
Whereby when many a man was sunburnt so
They thought my queen,
The son had been,
With scalding flames, which wrought them all that wo,

So that when many a look had look'd so long,
As that their eyes were dim and dazzled both:
Some fainting hearts that were both lewd [28] and loth
To look again from whence that error sprung,
Gan close their eye for fear of farther wrong:
And some again once drawn into the maze,
Gan lewdly blame the beams of beauty's blaze:
But I with deep foresight did soon espy,
How Phoebus meant,
By false intent,
To slander so her name with cruelty.

Wherefore at better leisure thought I best,
To try the treason of his treachery:
And to exalt my lady's dignity
When Phoebus fled and drew him down to rest.
Amid the waves that walter [29] in the west,
I gan behold this lovely lady's face,
Whereon Dame Nature spent her gifts of grace:
And found therein no parching heat at all,
But such bright hew,
As might renew,
An angel's joys in reign celestial.

The courteous moon that wish'd to do me good,
Did shine to shew my dame more perfectly,

But when she saw her passing jollity,
The moon for shame, did blush as red as blood,
And shrunk aside and kept her horns in hood:
So that now when Dame Cynthia was gone,
I might enjoy my lady's looks alone,
Yet honoured still the moon with true intent:
Who taught us skill,
To work our will,
And gave us place, till all the night was spent.

F. J.

And now to return to my tale, by that time, that he returned out of the park, it was dinner time, and at dinner they all met, I mean both Dame Elinor, Dame Frances, & Ferdinando. I leave to describe that the Lady Frances was gorgeously attired, and set forth with very brave apparel, and Madame Elinor only in her nightgown girt to her, with a coif trimmed *alla Piedmonteze*,[30] on the which she wore a little cap crossed over the crown with two bands of yellow sarcenet or cypress, in the midst whereof she had placed (of her own handwriting) in paper this word, "Contented." This attire pleased her then to use, and could not have displeased Mistress Frances, had she not been more privy to the cause, than to the thing itself: at least the lord of the castle, of ignorance, and Dame Frances, of great temperance, let it pass without offence. At dinner, because the one was pleased with all former reckonings, and the other party privy to the account, there passed no word of taunt or grudged, but *omnia bene*.[31] After dinner Dame Elinor being no less desirous to have Ferdinando's company, than Dame Frances was to take him in some pretty trip, they began to question how they might best pass the day: the Lady Elinor seemed desirous to keep her chamber, but Mistress Frances (for another purpose) seemed desirous to ride abroad, thereby to take the open air: they agreed to ride a mile or twain for solace, and requested Ferdinando to accompany them, the which willingly granted. Each one parted from other, to prepare themselves & now began the sport, for when he was booted, his horses saddled, and he ready to ride, he gan to miss his rapier, whereat all astonied he began to blame his man, but blame whom he would, found it could not be. At last the ladies going towards the horseback called for him in the base court, and demanded if he were ready: to whom he answered, "Madam, I am more than ready, and yet not so ready as I would be," and immediately taking himself in trip, he thought best to utter no more of his conceit, but in haste more than good speed mounted his horse, & coming toward the dames presented himself, turning, bounding, & taking up his courser to the uttermost of his power in bravery: after suffering his horse to breathe himself, he gan also allay his own choler, & to the dames he said. "Fair ladies I am ready when it pleaseth you to ride where so you command." "How ready soever you be servant," quoth Dame Elinor, "it seemeth your horse is readier at your command than at ours." "If he be at my command mistress," quoth he, "he shall be at yours." "Gramercy good servant," quoth she, "but my meaning is, that I fear he be too stirring for our company." "If he prove so mistress," quoth he, "I have here a soberer palfrey to serve you on." The dames being mounted they rode forthwards by the space of a mile or very near, & Ferdinando (whether it were of his horse's courage or his own choler came not so near them as they wished) at last the Lady Frances said unto him, "Master Jeronimi you said that you had a sober horse, which if it be so, we would be glad of your company but I believe by your countenance your horse and you are agreed." Ferdinando alighting called his servant, changed horses with him, and overtaking the dames, said to Mistress Frances: "And why do you think fair lady that my horse and I are agreed?" "Because by your countenance," quoth she, "it seemeth your patience is stirred." "In good faith," quoth he, "you have guessed aright, but not with any of you." "Then we care the less servant," quoth Dame Elinor. "By my troth mistress," quoth he (looking well about him that none might hear but they too), "it is with my servant, who hath lost my sword out of my cham-

ber." Dame Elinor little remembering the occasion, replied,
"It is no matter servant," quoth she, "you shall hear of it
again, I warrant you, and presently we ride in God's peace,
and I trust shall have no need of it:" "Yet mistress," quoth
he, "a weapon serveth both uses, as well to defend, as to offend." "Now by my troth," quoth Dame Frances, "I have
now my dream, for I dreamt this night that I was in a pleasant
meadow alone, where I met with a tall gentleman, apparelled
in a nightgown of silk, all embroidered about with a guard [32]
of naked swords, and when he came towards me I seemed to
be afraid of him, but he recomforted me saying, 'Be not
afraid fair lady, for I use this garment only for mine own defence:' and in this sort went that warlike god Mars, what
time he taught Dame Venus to make Vulcan a hammer of
the new fashion. Notwithstanding these comfortable words,
the fright of the dream awakened me, and sithens unto this
hour I have not slept at all." "And what time of the night
dreamt you this?" quoth Ferdinando. "In the grey morning
about dawning of the day, but why ask you?" quoth Dame
Frances. Ferdinando with a great sigh answered, "Because
that dreams are to be marked more at some hour of the night,
than at some other?" "Why are you so cunning at the interpretation of dreams servant?" quoth the Lady Elinor: "Not
very cunning mistress," quoth he, "but guess like a young
scholar." The dames continued in these and like pleasant talks:
but Jeronimi could not be merry, as one that esteemed the
preservation of his mistress' honour, no less than the obtaining of his own delights, and yet to avoid further suspicion,
he repressed his passions, as much as he could. The Lady
Elinor (more careless than considerative of her own case)
pricking forwards said softly to him, "I had thought you had
received small cause servant to be thus dumpish, when I
would be merry." "Alas dear mistress," quoth he, "it is altogether for your sake, that I am pensive." Dame Frances
of courtesy withdrew herself and gave them leave, whenas
Ferdinando declared unto his mistress, that his sword was
taken out of his chamber, and that he dreaded much by the

words of the Lady Frances, that she had some understanding
of the matter. Dame Elinor now calling to remembrance
what had passed the same night, at the first was abashed, but
immediately (for these women be readily witted) cheered her
servant, and willed him to commit unto her the salving of
that sore. Thus they passed the rest of the way in pleasant
talk with Dame Frances, and so returned towards the castle
where Jeronimi suffered the two dames to go together, and
he alone unto his chamber to bewail his own misgovernment.
But Dame Elinor (whether it were according to old custom,
or by wily policy) found mean that night, that the sword
was conveyed out of Mistress Frances' chamber, and brought
unto hers: and after redelivery of it unto her servant, she
warned him to be more wary from that time forthwards:
afterward when he grew more bold and better acquainted
with his mistress' disposition, he adventured one Friday in
the morning to go unto her chamber, and thereupon wrote
as follows: which he termed "A Friday's Breakfast."

> That selfsame day, and of that day that hour,
> When she doth reign, that mock'd Vulcan the smith,
> And thought it meet to harbor in her bower,
> Some gallant guest for her to dally with,
> That blessed hour, that blest and happy day,
> I thought it meet, with hasty steps to go
> Unto the lodge, wherein my lady lay,
> To laugh for joy, or else to weep for woe.
> And lo, my lady of her wonted grace,
> First lent her lips to me (as for a kiss)
> And after that her body to embrace,
> Wherein Dame Nature wrought nothing amiss.
> What followed next, guess you that know the trade,
> For in this sort, my Friday's feast I made.
>   F. J.

Many days passed these two lovers with great delight, their
affairs being no less politicly governed, than happily achieved.
And surely it should seem in sad earnest, that he did not
only love her, but was furthermore so ravished in ecstasies

with continual remembrance of his delights, that he made an idol of her in his inward conceit. So seemeth it by this challenge to beauty, which he wrote in her praise and upon her name.

Beauty shut up thy shop, and truss up all thy trash,
My Nell hath stol'n thy finest stuff, and left thee in the lash[33]
Thy market now is marred, thy gains are gone God wot,
Thou hast no ware, that may compare, with this that I have got
As for thy painted pale, and wrinkles surfled [34] up:
Are dear enough, for such as lust to drink of every cup:
Thy bodies bolstered out, with bumbact[35] and with bags,
Thy rolls,[36] thy ruffs, thy cauls,[37] thy coifs, thy jerkins & thy
 jags.[38]
Thy curling, and thy cost, thy frisling[39] and thy fair,[40]
To court to court with all those toys & there set forth such ware
Before their hungry eyes, that gaze on every guest,
And choose the cheapest chaffer still, to please their fancy best.
But I whose steadfast eyes, could never cast a glance,
With wand'ring look, amid the press, to take my choice by chance
Have won by due desert, a piece that hath no peer,
And left the rest as refuse all, to serve the market there:
There let him choose that list, there catch the best who can:
A painted blazing bait may serve, to choke a gazing man.
But I have slipp'd thy flower, that freshest is of hue:
I have thy corn, go sell thy chaff, I list to seek no new,
The windows of mine eyes, are glaz'd with such delight,
As each new face seems full of faults, that blazeth in my sight:
And not without just cause, I can compare her so,
Lo here my glove I challenge him, that can, or dare say no.
Let Theseus come with club, or Paris brag with brand,
To prove how fair their Helen was, that scourg'd the Grecian
 land:
Let mighty Mars himself, come armed to the field:
And vaunt dame Venus to defend, with helmet, spear, & shield.
This hand that had good hap, my Helen to embrace,
Shall have like luck to foil her foes, & daunt them with disgrace.
And cause them to confess by verdict and by oath,
How far her lovely looks do stain, the beauties of them both.
And that my Helen is more fair than Paris' wife,
And doth deserve more famous praise, than Venus for her life.

Which if I not perform, my life then let me leese,[40a]
Or else be bound in chains of change, to beg for beauty's fees.

By this challenge I guess, that either he was then in an ecstasy, or else, sure I am now in a lunacy, for it is a proud challenge made to Beauty herself, and all her companions: and imagining that Beauty having a shop where she uttered her wares of all sundry sorts, his lady had stolen the finest away, leaving none behind her, but painting, bolstering, forcing and such like, the which in his rage he judgeth good enough to serve the court: and thereupon grew a great quarrel. When these verses were by the negligence of his mistress dispersed into sundry hands, and so at last to the reading of a courtier. Well Ferdinando had his desire, if his mistress liked them, but as Bartello writeth she grew in jealousy, that the same were not written by[41] her, because her name was Elinor and not Helen. And about this point have been divers and sundry opinions among the Venetians, for this & divers other of his most notable poems, have come to view of the world. And some have attributed this praise unto a Helen, who deserved not so well as this Dame Elinor should seem to deserve, and yet never a barrel of good herring between them both: But that other Helen, because she was sayeth Bartello, of so base conditions, as may deserve no manner commendation in any honest judgement, therefore he thinketh that he would never bestow verse of[41a] so mean a subject. And yet some of his acquaintance knowing also that he was sometimes acquainted with Helen, have stood in argument, that it was written by Helen, & not by Elinor. Well mine author affirmeth that it was written by this Dame Elinor, and that unto her he thus alleged, that he took it all for one name, or at least he never read of any Elinor such matter as might sound worthy like commendation, for beauty. And indeed considering all circumstances of histories, and comparing also the time that such reports do spread of his acquaintance with Helen, it cannot be written less than six or seven years before he knew Helen: marry peradventure if there were any acquaintance between him and that Helen afterwards, he might adapt it to her name, and so make it serve both their turns, as elder lovers have done before, and still do, and will do world without end. Well by whom he wrote it I know not, and to return to the purpose, he sought more certainly to please his Mistress Elinor with this sonnet written in her praise as followeth.

> The stately dames of Rome, their pearls did wear,
> About their necks to beautify their name:
> But she (whom I do serve) her pearls doth bear,
> Close in her mouth, and smiling shew, the same.
> No wonder then, though ev'ry word she speaks,
> A jewel seem in judgement of the wise,
> Since that her sugar'd tongue the passage breaks,
> Between two rocks, bedeck'd with pearls of price.
> Her hair of gold, her front of ivory,
> (A bloody heart within so white a breast)
> Her teeth of pearl lips ruby, crystal eye,
> Needs must I honour her above the rest:
> Since she is formed of none other mould,
> But ruby, crystal, ivory, pearl, and gold.
> Ferdinando Jeronimi.

Of this sonnet, were it not a little too much praise (as the Italians do most commonly offend in the superlative) I could the more commend it: but I hope the party to whom it was dedicated had rather it were much more, than anything less. Well, thus these two lovers passed many days in exceeding contentation, & more than speakable pleasures, in which time Ferdinando did compile very many verses according to sundry occasions proffered, and they were for the most part sauced with a taste of glory, as you know that in such cases a lover being charged with inexprimable[42] joys, and therewith enjoined both by duty and discretion to keep the same covert, can by no means devise a greater consolation, than to commit it into some ciphered words, and figured speeches, in verse, whereby he feeleth his heart half (or more than half) eased of swelling. For as sighs are some present ease to the pensive mind, even so we find by experience, that such secret intercommoning[43] of joys doeth increase delight. I would not have you construe my words to this effect, that

I think a man cannot sufficiently rejoice in the lucky lots of love, unless he impart the same to others: God forbid that ever I should enter into such an heresy, for I have always been of this opinion, that as to be fortunate in love, is one of the most inward contentations to man's mind of all earthly joys: even so if he do but once bewray the same to any living creature, immediately either dread of discovering doth bruise his breast with an intolerable burden, or else he leeseth the principal virtue which gave effect to his gladness, not unlike to a pothecary's pot, which being filled with sweet ointments or perfumes, doth retain in itself some scent of the same, and being poured out doeth return to the former state, hard, harsh, and of small savour: So the mind being fraught with delights, as long as it can keep them secretly enclosed, may continually feed upon the pleasant record thereof, as the well-willing and ready horse biteth on the bridle, but having once disclosed them to any other, straightway we lose the hidden treasure of the same, and are oppressed with sundry doubtful opinions ...d dreadful conceits. And yet for a man to record unto himself in the inward contemplation of his mind, the often remembrance of his late received joys, doth as it were ease the heart of burden, and add unto the mind a fresh supply of delight, yea, and in verse principally (as I conceive) a man may best contrive his way of comfort in himself. Therefore as I have said Ferdinando swimming now in delights did nothing but write such verse as might accumulate his joys, to the extremity of pleasure, the which for that purpose he kept from sight of the world, as one more desirous to seem obscure & defective, than overmuch to glory in his adventures, especially for that in the end his hap was as heavy, as hitherto he had been fortunate. And here I will surcease to rehearse any more of his verses until I have expressed how that his joys being exalted to the highest degree began to bend towards declination. For now the unhappy secretary whom I have before remembered, was returned from Florence, on whom Ferdinando had no sooner cast his eyes, but immediately he fell into a great passion of mind,

which might be compared unto a fever. This fruit grew of
the good instructions that his Hope had planted in his mind,
whereby I might take just occasion to forewarn every lover,
how they suffer this venomous serpent jealousy to creep into
their conceits: for surely, of all other diseases in love, I suppose that to be uncurable, and would hold longer discourse
therein, were it not that both this tale & the verses of Ferdinando himself hereafter to be recited, shall be sufficient to
speak for me in this behalf. The lover (as I say upon the
sudden) was driven into such a malady, as no meat might
nourish his body, no delights please his mind, no remembrance of joys forepassed content him, nor any hope of the
like to come might recomfort him: hereat (some unto whom
I have imparted this tale) have taken occasion to discommend
his fainting heart, yet surely the cause inwardly & deeply
considered, I cannot so lightly condemn him: for an old
saying is, that every man can give counsel better than follow
it: and needs must the conflicts of his thoughts be strange:
between the remembrance of his forepassed pleasure, and the
present sight of this monster, whom before (for lack of like
instruction) he had not so thoroughly marked and beheld.
Well, such was the grief unto him, that he became sickly
and kept his chamber. The ladies having received the news
thereof, gan all at once lament his misfortune, & of common
consent agreed to visit him: they marched thither in good
equipage, I warrant you, and found Ferdinando lying upon
his bed languishing, whom they all saluted generally, and
sought to recomfort: but especially his mistress, having in
her hand a branch of willow, wherewith she defended her
from the hot air, gan thus say unto him: "Servant," quoth she,
"for that I suppose your malady to proceed of none other
cause but only slothfulness, I have brought this pretty rod to
beat you a little: nothing doubting, but when you feel the
smart of a twig or twain, you will like a tractable young
scholar, pluck up your quickened spirits, & cast this drowsi-
ness apart." Ferdinando with a great sigh answered: "Alas
good mistress," quoth he, "if any like chastisement might

quicken me, how much more might the presence of all you lovely dames recomfort my dulled mind? whom to behold, were sufficient to revive an eye now dazzled with the dread of death: & that not only for the heavenly aspects which you represent, but also much the more for your exceeding courtesy, in that you have deigned to visit me so unworthy a servant. But good mistress," quoth he, "as it were shame for me to confess that ever my heart could yield for fear, so I assure you that my mind cannot be content to induce infirmity by sluggish conceit: But in truth mistress I am sick," quoth he, and therewithal the trembling of his heart had sent up such throbbing into his throat, as that his voice (now deprived of breath) commanded the tongue to be still. When Dame Elinor for compassion distilled into tears, and drew towards the window, leaving the other gentlewomen about his bed, who being no less sorry for his grief, yet for that they were none of them so touched in their secret thoughts, they had bolder spirits and freer speech to recomfort him, amongst the rest the Lady Frances, (who indeed loved him deeply, and could best conjecture the cause of his conceits) said unto him: "Good Trust," quoth she, "if any help of physic may cure your malady, I would not have you hurt yourself with these doubts which you seem to retain: If choice of diet may help, behold us here (your cooks) ready to minister all things needful: if company may drive away your annoy, we mean not to leave you solitary, if grief of mind be cause of your infirmity, we all here will offer our devoir to turn it into joy: if mishap have given you cause to fear or dread anything, remember Hope, which never faileth to recomfort an afflicted mind. And good Trust," quoth she (distraining his hand right heartily), "let this simple proof of our poor good wills be so accepted of you, as that it may work thereby the effect of our desires." Ferdinando (as one in a trance) had marked very little of her courteous talk, & yet gave her thanks, and so held his peace whereat the ladies (being all amazed) there became a silence in the chamber on all sides. Dame Elinor fearing thereby that she might the more easily be espied, and having now dried up her tears, returned to her servant, recomforting him by all possible means of common courtesy, promising that since in her sickness he had not only stanched her bleeding, but also by his gentle company and sundry devices of honest pastime, had driven away the pensiveness of her mind, she thought herself bound with like willingness to do her best in anything that might restore his health, & taking him by the hand said further. "Good servant, if thou bear indeed any true affection to thy poor mistress, start upon thy feet again, and let her enjoy thine accustomed service to her comfort, for sure," quoth she, "I will never leave to visit this chamber once in a day, until I may have thee down with me." Ferdinando hearing the hearty words of his mistress, and perceiving the earnest manner of her pronunciation, began to receive unspeakable comfort in the same, and said: "Mistress, your exceeding courtesy were able to revive a man half dead, and to me it is both great comfort, and it doeth also glad my remembrance, with a continual smart of mine own unworthiness: but as I would desire no longer life, than till I might be able to deserve some part of your bounty, so I will endeavor myself to live, were it but only unto that end, that I might merit some part of your favour with acceptable service, and requite somedeal the courtesy of all these other fair ladies, who have so far (above my deserts) deigned to do me good." Thus said, the ladies tarried not long before they were called to evensong, when his mistress taking his hand, kissed it saying: "Farewell good servant, and I pray thee suffer not the malice of thy sickness to overcome the gentleness of thy good heart." Ferdinando ravished with joy, suffered them all to depart, and was not able to pronounce one word. After their departure, he gan cast in his mind the exceeding courtesy used towards him by them all, but above all other the bounty of his mistress: and therewithal took a sound & firm opinion, that it was not possible for her to counterfeit so deeply (as indeed I believe that she then did not) whereby he suddenly felt his heart greatly eased, and began in himself thus to reason. "Was

ever man of so wretched a heart? I am the most bounden
to love," quoth he, "of all them that ever professed his service, I enjoy one of the fairest that ever was found, and I
find her the kindest that ever was heard of: yet in mine own
wicked heart, I could villainously conceive that of her, which
being compared with the rest of her virtues, is not possible
to harbour in so noble a mind. Hereby I have brought myself without cause into this feebleness: and good reason that
for so high an offense, I should be punished with great infirmity: what shall I then do? yield to the same? no, but
according to my late protestation, I will recomfort this
languishing mind of mine, to the end I may live but only to
do penance for this so notable a crime so rashly committed:"
and thus saying, he start from his bed, and gan to walk towards the window: but the venomous serpent which (as
before I rehearsed) had stung him, could not be content that
these medicines applied by the mouth of his gentle mistress,
should so soon restorte[44] him to guerison.[45] And although
indeed they were such mithridate to him as that they had now
expelled the rancour of the poison yet that ugly hellish monster had left behind her in the most secret of his bosom, (even
between the mind and the man) one of her familiars named
Suspect, which gan work in the weak spirits of Ferdinando
effects of no less peril than before he had received, his head
swelling with these troublesome toys, and his heart swimming
in the tempests of tossing fantasy: he felt his legs so feeble,
that he was constrained to lie down on his bed again, and
repeating in his own remembrance every word that his mistress had spoken unto him, he gan to dread, that she had
brought the willow branch to beat him with, in token that
he was of her forsaken: for so lovers do most commonly
expound the willow garland, and this to think, did cut his
heart in twain. A wonderful change: and here a little to
stay you, I will describe as I find it in Bartello the beginning,
the fall, the return, and the being of this hellish bird, who
indeed may well be counted a very limb of the Devil. Many
years since, one of the most dreadful dastards in the world,

and one of them that first devised to wear his beard at length, lest the barber might do him a good turn sooner than he looked for it, and yet not so soon as he deserved, had builded for his security a pile on the highest and most inaccessible mount of all his territories: the which being fortified with strong walls, and environed with deep ditches, had no place of entry, but one only door so straight and narrow, as might by any possibility receive the body of one living man: from which he ascended up a ladder, and so creeping through a marvelous straight hole, attained to his lodging, the which was so dark and obscure, as scarcely either sun or air could enter into it: thus he devised to lodge in safety, and for the more surety gan trust none other letting down this ladder but only his wife: and at the foot thereof kept always by daylight, a fierce mastif close enkenneled which never saw nor heard the face or voice of any other creature but only of them two: him by night he trusted with the scout of this pretty passage, having nevertheless between him & this dog, a double door with treble locks, quadruple bars, and before all a port coulez[46] of iron: neither yet could he be so hardy as to sleep, until he had caused a guard of servants (whom he kept abroad for that purpose) to search all the corners adjoining to all his fortress, and then between fearful sweat and shivering cold, with one eye opened & the other closed, he stole sometimes a broken sleep, divided with many terrible dreams. In this sort the wretch lived all too long, until at last his wife being not able any longer to support this hellish life, grew so hardy, as with his own knife to dispatch his carcass out of this earthly purgatory: the which being done, his soul (and good reason) was quickly conveyed by Charon unto hell: there Rhadamanthus judge of that bench, commanded him quickly to be thrust into a boiling pool: and being therein plunged very often, he never shrieked or cried, "I scald," as his other companions there cried, but seemed so lightly to esteem it, that the judge thought meet to condemn him unto the most terrible place, where are such torments, as neither pen can write, tongue express, or thought conceive: but the miser (even there) seemed to smile and to make small account of his punishment. Rhadamanthus hereof informed, sent for him, and demanded the cause why he made so light of his durance? he answered that whiles he lived on earth, he was so continually afflicted and oppressed with suspicion, as that now (only to think that he was out of those meditations) was sufficient armour to defend him from all other torments. Rhadamanthus astonied hereat, gan call together the senators of that kingdom, and propounded this question, how & by what punishment they might devise to touch him according to his deserts? & hereupon fell great disputation: at last being considered, that he had already him plunged in the most unspeakable torments, & thereat little or nothing had changed countenance, therewithal that no soul was sent unto them to be relieved of his smart, but rather to be punished for his former delights: it was concluded by the general counsel, that he should be eftsoons sent into ye world & restored to the same body wherein he first had his resiance,[47] so to remain for perpetuity, and never to depart nor to perish. Thus this body and soul being once again united, and now eftsoons with the same pestilence infected, he became of a suspicious man, Suspicion itself: and now the wretch remembering the treason of his wife, who had so willingly dispatched him once before, gan utterly abhor her, and fled her company, searching in all countries some place of better assurance, and when he had in vain trod over the most part of the earth, he embarked himself to find some unknown island, wherein he might frame some new habitation: and finding none so commodious as he desired, he fortuned (sailing alone by the shore) to espy a rock, more than six hundred cubits high, which hung so suspiciously over the seas, as though it would threaten to fall at every little blast: this did Suspicion imagine to be a fit foundation whereon he might build his second bower: he forsook his boat, and traveled by land to espy what entry or access might be made unto the same, and found from land no manner of entry or access, unless it were that some courteous bird of the air would be ambassador, or convey some engines, as whilom the eagle did carry Ganymede into heaven. He then returned to seas, and approaching near to this rock, found a small stream of fresh water issuing out of the same into the seas: the which, although it were so little and so straight, as might uneaths[48] receive a boat of bigness to carry one living creature at once, yet in his conceit he thought it more large and spacious than that broad way called of our forefathers *Via Appia,* or than that other named *Flaminia,* he abandoned his bark, and putting off his clothes adventured (for he was now assured not to drown) to wade and swim against the stream of this unknown brook, the which (a wondrous thing to tell, and scarcely to be believed) came down from the very top and height of this rock: and by the wave he found six straits & dangerous places, where the water seemed to stay his course, passing under six straight and low bridges, and hard by every of those places, a pile raised up in manner of a bulwark, the which were hollow, in such sort as lodgings and other places necessary might in them commodiously be devised, by such one as could endure the hellishness of the place. Passing by these he attained with much pain unto the top of the rock, the which he found hollowed as the rest, and far more fit for his security, than otherwise apt for any commodity. There gan Suspicion determine to nestle himself, and having now placed six chosen porters, to wit, (Dread, Mistrust, Wrath, Desperation, Frenzy, and Fury:) at these six strong bulwarks, he lodged himself in that vii. all alone, for he trusted no company, but ever mistrusting that his wife should eftsoons find him out therein, he shrieketh continually like to a screech owl to keep the watch waking, never content to sleep by day nor by night. But to be sure that he should not oversleep himself, gan stuff his couch with porpentine's[49] quills, to the end that when heavy sleep overcame him, and he thereby should be constrained to charge his pallet with more heavy burden, those plumes might then prick through and so awake him. His garments were steel upon iron, and that iron upon iron, and iron again, and the more he was armed, the less he trusted to be out of danger. He chopped and changed continually now this, now that, now keys, now locks, ditches new scoured, and walls newly fortified, and thus always uncontented liveth this wretched hell-hound Suspicion, in this hellish dungeon of habitation: from whence he never removeth his foot, but only in the dead & silent nights, when he may be assured that all creatures (but himself) are whelmed in sound sleep. And then with stealing steps he stalketh about the earth, infecting, tormenting, & vexing all kinds of people with some part of his afflictions: but especially such as either do sit in chair of greatest dignity and estimation, or else such as have achieved some dear and rare emprise. Those above all others he continually galleth with fresh wounds of dread, lest they might lose and forgo the rooms whereunto with such long travail and good haps they had attained, and by this means percase he had crept into the bosom of Ferdinando, who (as is before declared) did erst swim in the deepest seas of earthly delights. Now then I must think it high time to return unto him, who (being now through feebleness eftsoons cast down upon his bed) gan cast in his inward meditations all things passed, and as one thoroughly puffed up and filled with one peevish conceit, could think upon nothing else, and yet accusing his own guilty conscience to be infected with jealousy, did compile this as followeth.

What state to man, so sweet and pleasant were,
As to be tied, in links of worthy love?
What life so blest and happy might appear,
As for to serve Cupid that god above?
If that our minds were not sometimes infect,
With dread, with fear, with care, with cold suspect:
With deep despair, with furious frenzy,
Handmaids to her, whom we call jealousy.

For ev'ry other sop of sour chance,
Which lovers taste amid their sweet delight:
Increaseth joy, and doth their love advance,

In pleasure's place, to have more perfect plight.
The thirsty mouth thinks water hath good taste,
The hungry jaws, are pleas'd, with each repast:
Who hath not prov'd what dearth by wars doth grow,
Cannot of peace the pleasant plenties know.

And though with eye, we see not ev'ry joy,
Yet may the mind, full well support the same,
An absent life long led in great annoy
(When presence comes) doth turn from grief to game,
To serve without reward is thought great pain,
But if despair do not therewith remain,
It may be borne for right rewards at last,
Follow true service, though they come not fast.

Disdains, repulses, finally each ill,
Each smart, each pain, of love each bitter taste,
To think on them gan frame the lover's will,
To like each joy, the more that comes at last:
But this infernal plague if once it touch,
Or venom once the lover's mind with grutch,[50]
All feasts and joys that afterwards befall,
The lover counts them light or nought at all.

This is that sore, this is that poison'd wound,
The which to heal, nor salve, nor ointments serve,
Nor charm of words, nor image can be found,
Nor observance of stars can it preserve,
Nor all the art of magic can prevail,
Which Zoroactes[50a] found for our avail,
Oh cruel plague, above all sorrow's smart,
With desperate death thou slay'st the lover's heart.

And me even now, thy gall hath so infect,
As all the joys which ever lover found,
And all good haps, that ever Troilus' sect,[51]
Achieved yet above the luckless ground:
Can never sweeten once my mouth with mel,
Nor bring my thoughts, again in rest to dwell.
Of thy mad moods, and of naught else I think,
In such like seas, fair Bradamant[52] did sink

    Ferdinando. Jeronimi.

Thus Ferdinando continued on his bed, until his bountiful mistress with the company of the other courteous dames returned after supper to his chamber. At their first entry: "Why how now servant," quoth Dame Elinor, "we hoped to have found you on foot?" "Mistress," quoth he, "I have assayed my feet since your departure, but I find them yet unable to support my heavy body, and therefore am constrained as you see, to acquaint myself with these pillows." "Servant," said she, "I am right sorry thereof, but since it is of necessity to bear sickness, I will employ my endeavor to allay some part of your pains, and to refresh your weary limbs with some comfortable matter:" and therewithal calling her handmaid, delivered unto her a bunch of pretty little keys, and whispering in her ear, dispatched her towards her chamber: The maid tarried not long, but returned with a little casket, the which her mistress took, opened and drew out of the same much fine linen, amongst the which she took a pillow-bere[53] very fine and sweet, which although it were of itself as sweet as might be (being of long time kept in that odoriferous chest) yet did she with damask water[54] and that of the best that might be (I warrant you) all to sprinkle it with her own hands, which in my conceit might much amend the matter. Then calling for a fresh pillow, sent her maid to air the same and at her return put on this, thus perfumed pillow-bere. In meantime also she had with her own hands attired her servant's head in a fair wrought kerchief taken out of the same casket: then laid him down upon this fresh and pleasant place, and prettily as it were in sport, bedewed his temples with sweet water which she had ready in a casting bottle of gold, kissing his cheek and saying: "Good servant be whole, for I might not long endure thus to attend thee, and yet the love that I bear toward thee, cannot be content to see thee languish." "Mistress," said Ferdinando (and that with a trembling voice), "assure yourself, that if there remain in me any spark of life or possibility of recovery, then may this excellent bounty of yours be sufficient to revive me without any further travail or pain unto your person: for whom I am highly to blame, in that I do not spare to put you unto this trouble, & better it were that such a wretch as I had died unknown, than that by your exceeding courtesy, you should fall into any malady, either by resorting unto me, or by these your pains taken about me." "Servant," quoth she, "all pleasures seem painful to them that take no delight therein, and likewise all toil seemeth pleasant to such as set their felicity in the same: but for me be you sure, I do it with so good a will that I can take no hurt thereby, unless I shall perceive that it be rejected or neglected, as unprofitable or uncomfortable unto you." "To me mistress," quoth Ferdinando, "it is such pleasure, as neither my feeble tongue can express, nor my troubled mind conceive." "Why? are you troubled in mind, then servant?" quoth Dame Elinor. Ferdinando now blushing answered, "But even as all sick men be mistress." Herewith they stayed their talk awhile, and the first that broke silence was the Lady Frances: who said, "And to drive away the troubles of your mind, good Trust, I would be glad if we could devise some pastime amongst us to keep you company: for I remember that with such devices you did greatly recomfort this fair lady when she languished in like sort." "She languished indeed gentle Hope," quoth he, "but God forbid that she had languished in like sort." "Everybody thinketh their own grief greatest," quoth Dame Elinor, "but indeed whether my grief were the more or the less, I am right sorry that yours is such as it is: And to say whether our passions proceeded of like cause or not, I would we could (according to this lady's saying) devise some like pastimes to try if your malady would be cured with like medicines." A gentlewoman of the company whom I have not hitherto named, gan thus propound. "We have accustomed," quoth she, "heretofore in most of our games to choose a king or queen, and he or she during their government, have charged every of us, either with commandments or questions, as best seemed to their majesty. Wherein (to speak mine opinion) we have given overlarge a scope, neither seemeth it reasonable that one should have the power to discover the thoughts, or at least to bridle the affects of all the rest. And though indeed in questioning (which doth of the twain more nearly touch the mind) every one is at free liberty to answer what they list: yet oft have I heard a question demanded in such sort, and upon such sudden, that it hath been hardly answered without moving matter of contention. And in commands also, sometimes it happeneth one to be commanded unto such service, as either they are unfit to accomplish (and then the party's weakness is thereby detected) or else to do something that they would not, whereof ensueth more grutch than game. Wherefore in mine opinion, we shall do well to choose by lot amongst us a governor, who (for that it shall be sufficient pre-eminence to use the chair of majesty,) shall be bound to give sentence upon all such arguments and questions as we shall orderly propound unto them: and from him or her (as from an oracle) we will receive answer, and deciding of our litigious causes." This dame had stuff in her, an old courtier, & a wily wench, named Pergo. Well this proportion[54a] of Pergo pleased them well, and by lot it happened that Ferdinando must be moderator of these matters, and collector of these causes. The which being so constituted, the Lady Elinor said unto this dame Pergo. "You have devised this pastime," quoth she, "& because we think you to be most expert in the handling thereof, do you propound the first question, & we shall be both the more ready and able to follow your example:" the Lady Pergo refused not, but began on this wise. "Noble governor," quoth she, "amongst the adventures that have befallen me, I remember especially this one, that in youth it was my chance to be beloved of a very courtlike young gentleman, who abode near the place wherein my parents had their resiance. This gentleman (whether it were for beauty, or for any other respect that he saw in me, I know not) but he was enamoured of me, & that with an exceeding vehement passion, & of such force were his affects, that notwithstanding many repulses which he had received at my hands, he seemed daily to grow in the renewing of his desires. I on the other side, although I could by no means mislike of him by any good reason (considering that he was of birth no way inferior unto me, of possessions not to be disdained, of person right comely, of behaviour courtly, of manners modest, of mind liberal, and of virtuous disposition) yet such was the gaiety of my mind, as that I could not be content to lend him overlarge thongs of my love: but always dangerously[55] behaved myself towards him, and in such sort, as he could neither take comfort of mine answers, nor yet once find himself requited with one good look for all his travail. This notwithstanding, the worthy knight continued his suit with no less vehement affection than erst he had begun it, even by the space of seven years. At the last, whether discomfited by my dealings, or tried by long travail, or that he had percase light upon the lake that is in the forest of Ardena,[56] and so in haste and all thirsty, had drunk some drops of disdain, whereby his hot flames were quenched, or that he had undertaken to serve no longer, but his just term of apprenticehood, or that the teeth of time had gnawed and tired his dulled spirits in such sort, as that all benumbed he was constrained to use some other artificial balm for the quickening of his senses, or by what cause moved I know not he did not only leave his long continued suit, but (as I have since perceived) grew to hate me more deadly than before I had disdained him. At the first beginning of his retire I perceived not his hatred, but imagined that being over-wearied, he had withdrawn himself for a time. And considering his worthiness, therewithal his constancy of long time proved, I thought that I could not in the whole world find out a fitter match to bestow myself, than on so worthy a person. Wherefore I did by all possible means procure that he might eftsoons use his accustomed repair unto my parents: And further, in all places where I happened to meet him, I used all the courtesies towards him that might be contained within the bonds of modesty. But all was in vain, for he was now become more dangerous[57] to be won, than the haggard falcon. Our lots being thus unluckily changed, I grew to burn in desire, and the more dangerous that he shewed him-

self unto me, the more earnest I was by all means to procure
his consent of love. At the last I might perceive that not only
he disdained me, but (as methought) boiled in hatred against
me. And the time that I thus continued tormented with these
thoughts, was also just the space of seven years. Finally when
I perceived no remedy for my perplexities, I assayed by absence to wear away this malady, and therefore utterly refused
to come in his presence, yea or almost in any other company.
Whereby I have consumed in lost time the flower of my
youth, & am become as you see (what with years, and what
with the tormenting passions of love) pale, wan, and full of
wrinkles. Nevertheless, I have thereby gained thus much,
that at last I have wound myself clear out of Cupid's chains,
and remain careless at liberty. Now mark to what end I tell
you this: first vii. years passed in the which I could never be
content to yield unto his just desires: next other vii. years
I spent in seeking to recover his lost love: and sithens both
those vii. years, there are even now on Saint Valentine's Day
last, other vii. years passed, in the which (neither I have desired to see him) nor he hath coveted to hear of me. My
parents now perceiving how the crow's-foot is crept under
mine eye, and remembering the long suit that this gentleman
had in youth spent on me, considering therewithal that green
youth is well mellowed in us both, have of late sought to
persuade a marriage between us, the which the knight hath
not refused to hear of, and I have not disdained to think on.
By their mediation we have been eftsoons brought to parley,
wherein over and besides the ripping up of many old griefs,
this hath been chiefly rehearsed & objected between us, what
wrong and injury each of us hath done to other. And here-
abouts we have fallen to sharp contention. He alleged, that
much greater is the wrong which I have done unto him,
than that repulse which he hath sithens used to me, and I
have affirmed the contrary. The matter yet hangeth in variance. Now, of you worthy governor I would be most glad
to hear this question decided, remembering that there was no
difference in the times between us. And surely, unless your

judgment help me, I am afraid my marriage will be marred, and I may go to lead apes in hell." [58] Ferdinando answered, "Good Pergo, I am sorry to hear so lamentable a discourse of your luckless love, and much the sorrier, in that I must needs give sentence against you. For surely great was the wrong that either of you have done to other, and greater was the needless grief which causeless each of you hath conceived in this long time, but greatest in my judgment hath been both the wrong and the grief of the knight. In that notwithstanding his deserts (which yourself confess) he never enjoyed any guerdon of love at your hands. And you (as you allege) did enjoy his love of long time together. So that by the reckoning, it will fall out (although being blinded in your own conceit, you see it not) that of the one & twenty years you enjoyed his love vii. at the least, but that ever he enjoyed yours we cannot perceive. And much greater is the wrong that rewardeth evil for good, than that which requireth tip for tap. Further, it seemeth that whereas you went about in time to try him, you did altogether lose time which can never be recovered. And not only lost your own time, whereof you would seem now to lament, but also compelled him to leese his time, which he might (be it spoken without offence to you) have bestowed in some other worthy place, and therefore, as that grief is much greater which hath no kind of comfort to allay it, so much more is that wrong which altogether without cause is offered." "And I," said Pergo, "must needs think, that much easier is it for them to endure grief which never tasted of joy, and much less is that wrong which is so willingly proffered to be by recompense restored. For if this knight will confess that he never had cause to rejoice in all the time of his service, then with better contentation might he abide grief than I, who having tasted of the delight which I did secretly conceive of his deserts, do think each grief a present death by the remembrance of those forepassed thoughts: & less wrong seemeth it to be destitute of the thing which were never obtained, than to be deprived of a jewel whereof we have been already possessed, so that under your correction I might conclude, that greater hath been my grief and injury sustained, than that of the knight." To whom Jeronimi replied, as touching delight, "It may not be denied but that every lover doth take delight in the inward contemplation of his mind, to think of the worthiness of his beloved: & therefore you may not allege that the knight had never cause to rejoice, unless you will altogether condemn yourself of worthiness.[59] Marry if you will say that he tasted not the delights that lovers seek, then mark, who was the cause but yourself? And if you would accuse him of like ingratitude, for that he disdained you in the later vii. years (whenas he might by accepting your love, have recompensed himself of all former wrongs) you must remember therewithal, that the cruelty by you shewed towards him was such, that he could by no means perceive that your change proceeded of good will, but rather eftsoons to hold him enchained in unknown links of subtle dealings, & therefore not without cause he doubted you: & yet without cause you rejected him. He had often sought occasion, but by your refusals he could never find him, you having occasion fast by the foretop, did dally with him so long, till at the last he slipped his head from you, & then catching at the bald noddle, you found yourself the cause, & yet you would accuse another. To conclude, greater is the grief that is sustained without desert, & much more is the wrong that is offered without cause." Thus Ferdinando Jeronimi decided the question propounded by Pergo, and expected that some other dame should propound another? But his mistress (having her hand on another halfpenny) gan thus say unto him. "Servant this pastime is good, and such as I must needs like of, to drive away your pensive thoughts: but sleeping time approacheth & I fear we disquiet you: wherefore the rest of this time we will (if so like you) bestow in trimming up your bed, and tomorrow we shall meet here and renew this new begun game with Madame Pergo." "Mistress," quoth he, "I must obey your will, and most humbly thank you of your great goodness, and all these ladies for their courtesy. Even so requiring you that you will no further trouble yourselves about me, but let my servant alone with conducting me to bed." "Yes servant," quoth she, "I will see if you can sleep any better in my sheets:" and wherewith commanded her handmaid to fetch a pair of clean sheets, the which being brought (marvelous fine and sweet) the Ladies Frances and Elinor did courteously unfold them, and laid them on the bed, which done, they also entreated him to unclothe him and go to bed, being laid, his mistress dressed and couched the clothes about him, sithens moistened his temples with rosewater, gave him handkerchiefs and other fresh linen about him, in doing whereof, she whispered in his ear, saying: "Servant, this night I will be with thee," and after with the rest of the dames gave him goodnight and departed, leaving him in a trance between hope and despair, trust and mistrust. Thus he lay ravished, commanding his servant to go to bed, and feigning that himself would assay if he could sleep. About ten or eleven of the clock came his mistress in her nightgown: who knowing all privy ways in that house very perfectly, had conveyed herself into his chamber, unseen and unperceived: and being now come unto his bedside kneeled down, and laying her arm over him said these or like words: "My good servant, if thou knewest what perplexities I suffer in beholding of thine infirmities, it might then suffice, either utterly to drive away the malady, or much more to augment thy griefs: for I know thou lovest me: and I think also that thou hast had sufficient proof of mine unfeigned good will: in remembrance whereof, I fall into sundry passions: First, I count the happy lots of our first acquaintance, and therein I call to mind the equality of our affections, for I think that there were never two lovers conjoined with freer consent on both parties: and (if my overhasty delivery of yielding words be not wrested hereafter to my condemnation) I can then assure myself to escape forever without desert of any reproof. Herewithal I cannot forget the sundry adventures happened since we became one heart divided in two bodies, all which have been both happily achieved, and delectable enjoyed. What resteth then to consider but this thy present state? The first corrosive that I have felt, and the last cordial that I look for, the end of my joys, and the beginning of my torments." And here her salt tears gan bathe the dying lips of her servant: who (hearing these words, and well considering her demeanor) began now to accuse himself of such and so heinous treason, as that his guilty heart was constrained to yield unto a just scourge for the same. He swooned under her arm: the which when she perceived, it were hard to tell what fears did most affright her.

And it were hard now to rehearse how he was revived, since there were none present but he dying, (who could not declare) and she living, who would not disclose so much as I mean to bewray. For mine author dreameth that Ferdinando returning to life, the first thing which he felt, was that his good mistress lay pressing his breast with the whole weight of her body, & biting his lips with her friendly teeth. And peradventure she refrained (either of courtesy towards him, or for womanish fear, to hurt her tender hand) to strike him on the cheeks in such sort, as they do that strive to call again a dying creature: and therefore thought this the aptest mean to reduce him unto remembrance. Ferdinando now awaked, could no less do, than of his courteous nature receive his mistress into his bed: Who (as one that knew that way better, than how to help his swooning,) gan gently strip off her clothes, and lovingly embracing him, gan demand of him in this sort. "Alas good servant," quoth she, "what kind of malady is this that so extremely doth torment thee?" Jeronimi with fainting speech answered: "Mistress as for my malady, it hath been easily cured by your bountiful medicines applied. But I must confess, that in receiving that guerison[60] at your hands, I have been constrained to fall into an ecstasy, through the galling remembrance of mine own unworthiness. Nevertheless good mistress, since I perceive such fidelity remaining between us, as that few words will persuade such trust as lovers ought to embrace, let these few words suffice to crave your pardon: and do eftsoons pour upon me (your unworthy servant) the abundant waves of your accustomed clemency, for I must confess, that I have so highly offended you, as (but your goodness surpass the malice of my conceits) I must remain (and that right worthily) to the severe punishment of my deserts: and so should you but lose him who hath cast away himself, and neither can accuse you, nor dare to excuse himself of the crime." Dame Elinor (who had rather have found her servant perfectly revived, than thus with strange conceits encumbered: and musing much at his dark speech,) became importunate to know the certainty of his thoughts. And Ferdinando as one not master of himself, gan at the last plainly confess how he had mistrusted the change of her vowed affections: Yea and (that more was) he plainly expressed with whom, of whom, by whom, and to whom she bent her better liking.

Now, here I would demand of such as are expert: Is there any greater impediment to the fruition of a lover's delights, than to be mistrusted? or rather, is it not the ready way to rase all love and former good will out of remembrance, to tell a guilty mind that you do mistrust it? It should seem yes, by Dame Elinor, who began now to take the matter hotly: and of such vehemency were her fancies, that she now fell into flat defiance with Ferdinando, who although he sought by many fair words to temper her choleric passions, and by yielding himself to get the conquest of another, yet could he by no means determine the quarrel. The soft pillows being present at all these hot speeches, put forth themselves as mediators for a truce between these enemies, and desired that (if they would needs fight) it might be in their presence but one only blow, & so from thence forth to become friends again forever. But the dame denied flatly, alleging that she found no cause at all to use such courtesy unto such a recreant: adding further many words of great reproach: the which did so enrage Ferdinando, as that having forgotten all former courtesies, he assaileth his enemies by force. At last she rose suddenly and determined to save herself by flight, leaving him in bed, with many despiteful words, and swearing that he should never (eftsoons) take her at the like advantage, the which oath she kept better than her former professed good will: and having now recovered her chamber (because she found her hurt to be nothing dangerous) I doubt not, but she slept quietly the rest of the night. As Ferdinando also (persuading himself that he should with convenient leisure recover her from this haggard conceit) took some better rest towards the morning, than he had done in many nights forepast. So let them both sleep whiles I turn my pen unto the before-named secretary, who being (as I say) come lately from Florence, had made many proffers to renew his accustomed consultations: but the sorrow which his mistress had conceived in Jeronimi his sickness together with her continual repair to him during the same, had been such lets unto his attempts, as it was long time before he could obtain audience.

At the last these new accidents fell so favourably for the furtherance of his cause, that he came to his mistress' presence and there pleaded for himself. Now, if I should at large write his allegations, together with her subtle answers, I should but cumber your ears with unpleasant rehearsal of feminine frailty. To be short, the late disdainful mood which she had conceived against Ferdinando together with a scruple which lay in her conscience, touching the xi. article of her belief,[61] moved her presently with better will to consult with this secretary, as well upon the speedy revenge of her late received wrongs as also upon the reformation of her religion.[62] And in very deed, it fell out that the secretary (having been of long time absent, & there his quills and pens not worn so near as they were wont to be,) did now prick such fair large notes, that his mistress liked better to sing fa-burden[63] under him, than to descant any longer upon Ferdinando's plain song, and thus they continued in good accord, until it fortuned that Dame Frances came into her chamber upon such sudden as she had like to have marred all the music, well they conveyed their clefs as closely as they could, but yet not altogether without some suspicion given to the said Dame Frances, who although she could have been content to take any pain in Jeronimi's behalf, yet otherwise she could never have bestowed the watching about so worthless a prize. After womanly salutations they fell into sundry discourses, the secretary still abiding in the chamber with them. At last two or three other gentlewomen of the castle came into Madame Elinor's chamber, who after their *bon jour* did all (*una voce*)[64] seem to lament the sickness of Ferdinando and called upon the Dames Elinor and Frances, to go visit him again.

The Lady Frances courteously consented, but Madame Elinor first alleged that she herself was also sickly, the which she attributed to her late pains taken about him and said, that only for that cause she was constrained to keep her bed longer than her accustomed hour. The dames (but specially the Lady Frances) gan straightways conjecture some great cause of sudden change, and so leaving Dame Elinor, walked all together into the park to take the air in the morning: And as they thus walked it chanced that Dame Pergo heard a cuckoo chant, who (because the pride of the spring was now past) cried, "Cuck, cuck, cuckoo," in her stammering voice. "A ha," quoth Pergo, "this foul bird begins to fly the country, and yet before her departure, see how spitefully she can devise to salute us." "Not so," quoth Dame Frances, "but some other whom she hath espied," wherewith Dame Pergo looking round about her, and espying none other company said. "Why here is nobody but we few women," quoth she. "Thanks be to God the house is not far from us," quoth Dame Frances. Hereat the wily Pergo partly perceiving Dame Frances' meaning, replied on this sort: "I understand you not," quoth she, "but to leap out of this matter, shall we go visit Master Jeronimi and see how he doth this morning." "Why," quoth Dame Frances, "do you suppose that the cuckoo called unto him?" "Nay marry," quoth Pergo, "for (as far as I know) he is not married." "As who should say," quoth Dame Frances, "that the cuckoo envieth none but married folks." "I take it so," said Pergo, the Lady Frances answered. "Yes sure I have noted as evil luck in love (after the cuckoo's call) to have happened unto divers unmarried folks, as ever I did unto the married, but I can be well content that we go unto him, for I promised on the behalf of us all, that we would use our best devoir to recomfort him until he had recovered health: and I do much marvel that the Lady Elinor is now become so unwilling to take any travail in his behalf, especially remembering that but yesternight she was so diligent to bring him to bed. But I perceive that all earthly things are subject unto change." "Even so they be," quoth Pergo, "for you may behold the trees which but even this other day were clad in gladsome green, and now their leaves begin to fade and change colour." Thus they passed talking and walking until they returned unto the castle, whereas they went straight unto Ferdinando's chamber, and found him in bed. "Why how now Trust," quoth Dame Frances, "will it be no better?" "Yes shortly I hope," quoth he. The ladies all saluted him: and he gave them the gramercy: at the last Pergo popped this question unto him: "And how have you slept in your mistress' sheets Master Jeronimi?" quoth she. "Reasonably well," quoth he, "but I pray you where is my mistress this morning?" "Marry," said Pergo, "we left her in bed scarce well at ease." "I am the more sorry," quoth he. "Why Trust," said Mistress Frances, "be of good comfort, & assure yourself that here are others who would be as glad of your well-doing, as your mistress in any respect." "I ought not to doubt thereof," quoth Ferdinando, "having the proof that I have had of your great courtesies, but I thought it my duty to ask for my mistress being absent." Thus they passed some time with him until they were called away unto prayers, and that being finished they went to dinner, where they met Dame Elinor attired in a night kerchief after the sullenest (the solemnest fashion I should have said,) who looked very drowsily upon all folks, unless it were her secretary, unto whom she deigned sometime to lend a friendly glance. The lord of the castle demanded of her how Master Jeronimi did this morning. She answered that she knew not for she had not

seen him that day. "You may do well then daughter," quoth
the lord, "to go now unto him, and to assay if he will eat
anything, and if here be no meats that like him, I pray you
command (for him) anything that is in my house." "You
must pardon me sir," quoth she, "I am sickly disposed, and
would be loth to take the air," "Why then go you Mistress
Frances," quoth he, "and take somebody with you: and I
charge you see that he lack nothing." Mistress Frances was
glad of the ambassage, and arising from the table with one
other gentlewoman, took with her a dish of chickens boiled
in white broth, saying to her father: "I think this meat meetest for Master Jeronimi of any that is here." "It is so," quoth
he, "daughter, and if he like not that, cause somewhat else to
be dressed for him according to his appetite." Thus she departed and came to Ferdinando, who being plunged in sundry
woes and thrilled with restless thoughts, was now beginning
to rise. But seeing the dames, couched down again, and said
unto them. "Alas fair ladies you put yourselves to more pains
than either I do desire, or can deserve." "Good Trust," quoth
Dame Frances, "our pains are no greater than duty requireth,
nor yet so great as we could vouchsafe in your behalf."

"And presently my father hath sent us unto you," quoth
she, "with this pittance, and if your appetite desire any one
thing more than other, we are to desire likewise that you will
not refrain to call for it." "Oh my good Hope," quoth he,
"I perceive that I shall not die as long as you may make me
live." And (being now somedeal recomforted with the remembrance of his mistress' words which she had used overnight at her first coming, and also thinking that although she
parted in choler, it was but justly provoked by himself, and
that at leisure he should find some salve for that sore also) he
determined to take the comfort of his assured Hope, and so
to expel all venoms of mistrust before received. Wherefore
raising himself in his bed, he cast a nightgown about his
shoulders saying: "It shall never be said that my fainting heart
can reject the comfortable cordials of so friendly physicians."
"Now by my troth well said gentle Trust," quoth Dame

Frances, "and in so doing, assure yourself guerison with speed." This thus said, the courteous dame become his carver, & he with a bold spirit gan taste of her cookery. But the late conflicts of his conceits had so disacquainted his stomach from repasts, that he could not well away with meat: and yet nevertheless by little & little received some nurture. When his Hope had crammed him as long as she could make him feed, they delivered the rest to the other gentlewoman who having not dined, fell to her provender. In which meanwhile the Lady Frances had much comfortable speech with Signor Jeronimi and declared that she perceived very well the malady, "But my Trust," quoth she, "be all whole, and remember what I foretold you in the beginning: nevertheless you must think that there are remedies for all mischiefs and if you will be ruled by mine advice, we will soon find the mean to ease you of this mishap." Ferdinando took comfort in her discretion, & friendly kissed her hand, gave her a cartload of thanks for her great good will, promising to put to his uttermost force, and evermore to be ruled by her advice. Thus they passed the dinner while, the Lady Frances always refusing to declare her conceit of the late change which she perceived in his mistress, for she thought best first to win his will unto conformity, by little and little, and then in the end to persuade him with necessity. When the other gentlewoman had victualed her, they departed, requiring him to rise and boldly to resist the faintness of his fever. The which he promised and so bade them *a Dio*.[65] The ladies at their return found the court in Dame Elinor's chamber, who had there assembled her secretary, Dame Pergo & the rest: there they passed an hour or twain in sundry discourses, wherein Dame Pergo did always cast out some bone for Mistress Frances to gnaw upon, for that indeed she perceived her hearty affection towards Ferdinando whereat Mistress Frances changed no countenance, but reserved her revenge until a better opportunity. "At last," quoth Dame Frances unto Mistress Elinor, "and when will you go unto your servant fair lady?" "When he is sick and I am whole," quoth Dame Elinor. "That is even now," quoth the other, "for how sick he is yourself can witness: and how well you are we must bear record." "You may as well be deceived in my disposition," quoth Dame Elinor, "as I was overseen[66] in his sudden alteration: and if he be sick, you are meet to be his physician: for you saw yesterday that my pains did little profit towards his recomfort." "Yes surely," said the other, "not only I but all the rest had occasion to judge that your courtesy was his chief comfort." "Well," quoth Dame Elinor, "you know not what I know." "Nor you what I think," quoth Dame Frances. "Think what you list," quoth Elinor. "Indeed," quoth Frances, "I may not think that you care, neither will I die for your displeasure:" & so half angry she departed. At supper they met again, and the master of the house demanded of his daughter Frances how Ferdinando did? "Sir," quoth she, "he did eat somewhat at dinner, and sithens I saw him not." "The more to blame," quoth he, "and now I would have all you gentlewomen take of the best meats and go sup with him, for company driveth away carefulness, and leave you me here with your leavings alone." "Nay sir," quoth Mistress Elinor, "I pray you give me leave to bear you company, for I dare not adventure thither." The lord of the castle was contented & dispatched away the rest: who taking with them such viands as they thought meetest, went unto Jeronimi's chamber, finding him up, and walking about to recover strength: whereat Dame Frances rejoiced, and declared how her father had sent that company to attend him at supper. Ferdinando gave great thanks, & missing now nothing but his mistress, thought not good yet to ask for her, but because he partly guessed the cause of her absence, he contented himself, hoping that when his lure was new garnished, he should easily reclaim her from those coy conceits. They passed over their supper all in quiet, and soon after Mistress Frances, being desirous to requite Dame Pergo's quips, requested that they might continue the pastime which Dame Pergo had begun overnight: whereunto they all consented, and the lot fell unto Dame Frances to propound the second question who addressing her speech

unto Ferdinando said in this wise, "Noble governor, I will rehearse unto you a strange history, not feigned, neither borrowed out of any old authority, but a thing done indeed of
late days, and not far distant from this place where we now
remain. It chanced that a gentleman our neighbour being
married to a very fair gentlewoman, lived with her by the
space of four or five years in great contentation, trusting her
no less than he loved her, and yet loving her as much as any
man could love a woman. On that other side the gentlewoman
had won (unto her beauty) a singular commendation for her
chaste and modest behaviour. Yet it happened in time that a
lusty young gentleman (who very often resorted to them)
obtained that at her hands, which never any man could before
him attain: and to be plain, he won so much in her affections,
that forgetting both her own duty, and her husband's kindness, she yielded her body at the commandment of this lover,
in which pastime they passed long time by their politic government. At last the friends of this lady (and especially three
sisters which she had) espied overmuch familiarity between
the two lovers, and dreading lest it might break out to their
common reproach took their sister apart, and declared that
the world did judge scarce well of the repair of that gentleman unto her house: and that if she did not foresee it in time,
she should not only leese the good credit which she herself
had hitherto possessed, but furthermore should distain their
whole race with common obloquy & reproach. These and
sundry other godly admonitions of these sisters, could not
sink in the mind of this gentlewoman, for she did not only
stand in defiance what any man could think of her, but also
seemed to accuse them, that (because they saw her estimation
(being their younger) to grow above their own) they had
therefore devised this mean to set variance between her husband and her. The sisters seeing their wholesome counsel so
rejected, and her continue still in her obstinate opinion, addressed their speech unto her husband, declaring that the
world judged not the best, neither they themselves did very
well like of the familiarity between their sister and that gen-

tleman, and therefore advised him to forecast all perils, and in time to forbid him his house. The husband (on the other side) had also conceived such a good opinion of his guest, & had grown into such a strict familiarity with him, that you might with more ease have removed a stone wall, than once to make him think amiss, either of his wife, or of her lover. Yea, and immediately after this conference, he would not stick thus to say unto his wife. 'Lamia (for so indeed was her name) thou hast three such busy-brained sisters, as I think shortly their heads will break: they would have me to be jealous of thee, no no Lamia. &c.,' so that he was not only far from any such belief, but furthermore did every day increase his courtesies towards the lover. The sisters being thus on all sides rejected, and yet perceiving more & more an unseemly behaviour between their sister and her minion, began to melt in their own grease: and such was their enraged pretence of revenge, that they suborned divers servants in the house to watch so diligently, as that this treason might be discovered. Amongst the rest, one maid of subtile spirit had so long watched them, that at last she spied them go into the chamber together, and locked the door to them: whereupon she ran with all haste possible to her master, and told him that if he would come with her, she would shew him a very strange sight. The gentleman (suspecting nothing) went with her, until he came into a chamber near unto that wherein they had shut themselves. And she pointing her master to the keyhole, bade him look through, where he saw the thing which most might mislike him to behold. Whereat he suddenly drew his dagger, and turned towards the maid, who fled from him for fear of mischief. But when he could not overtake her in the heat of his choler, he commanded that she should forthwith truss up that little which she had, and to depart his service. And before her departure, he found means to talk with her, threatening that if ever she spoke any word of this mystery in any place where she should come, it should cost her life. The maid for fear departed in silence, and the master never changed countenance to either his wife or to her paramour, but feigned unto his wife that he had turned away the maid upon that sudden, for that she had thrown a kitchen knife at him, whiles he went about to correct a fault in her. &c. Thus the good gentleman drank up his own sweat unseen everyday, increasing courtesy to the lover, and never changing countenance to his wife in anything, but only that he refrained to have such knowledge of her carnally, as he in time past had, and other men have of their wives. In this sort he continued by the space almost of half a year, nevertheless lamenting his mishap in solitary places. At last (what moved him I know not) he fell again to company with his wife as other men do, and (as I have heard it said) he used this policy. Every time that he had knowledge of her, he would leave either in the bed, or in her cushioncloth, or by her lookingglass, or in some place where she must needs find it, a piece of money which then was in Italy called a caroline. Thus he dealt with her continually by the space of four or five months, using her nevertheless very kindly in all other respects, and providing for her all things necessary at the first call. But unto his guest he still augmented his courtesy, in such sort, that you would have thought them to be sworn brothers. All this notwithstanding his wife much musing at these small pieces which she found in this sort, and furthermore, having sundry times found her husband in solitary places making great lamentation, she grew inquisitive, what should be the secret cause of these alterations, unto whom he would none otherwise answer, but that any man should find occasion to be more pensive at one time than at another. The wife notwithstanding increasing her suspect, imparted the same unto her lover, alleging therewithal that she doubted very much lest her husband had some vehement suspicion of their affairs. The lover encouraged her, & likewise declared, that if she would be importunate to enquire the cause, her husband would not be able to keep it from her: and having now thoroughly instructed her, she dealt with her husband in this sort. One day when she knew him to be in his study alone, she came in to him, and having fast locked the door after her, & conveyed the key into her pocket, she began first with earnest entreaty, and then with tears to crave that he would no longer keep from her the cause of his sudden alteration. The husband dissimuled the matter still: at last she was so earnest to know for what cause he left money in such sort at sundry times: That he answered on this wise: 'Wife,' quoth he, 'thou knowest how long we have been married together, and how long I made so dear account of thee as ever man made of his wife: since which days, thou knowest also how long I refrained thy company, and how long again I have used thy company, leaving the money in this sort, and the cause is this. So long as thou didst behave thyself faithfully towards me, I never lothed thy company: but sithens I have perceived thee to be a harlot, and therefore did I for a time refrain and forbear to lie with thee, and now I can no longer forbear it, I give thee every time that I lie with thee, a caroline, which is to make thee understand thine own whoredom: and this reward is sufficient for a whore.'

"The wife began stoutly to stand at defiance, but the husband cut off her speech, and declared when, where, and how he had seen it: hereat the woman being abashed, and finding her conscience guilty of as much as he had alleged, fell down on her knees, & with most bitter tears craved pardon, confessing her offence: whereat her husband (moved with pity) & melting likewise in floods of lamentation, recomforted her, promising that if from that day forwards she would be true unto him, he would not only forgive all that was past, but become more tender and loving unto her than ever he was. What do I tarry so long? they became of accord: and in full accomplishment thereof, the gentlewoman did altogether eschew the company, the speech, and (as much as in her lay) the sight of her lover: although her husband did continue his courtesy towards him, and often charged his wife to make him fair resemblant.[66a] The lover was now only left in perplexity, who knew nothing what might be the cause of all these changes, and that most grieved him, he could by no means obtain again the speech of his desired: he watched all opportunities, he suborned messengers, he wrote letters, but all in vain. In the end she caused to be declared unto him a time and place where she would meet him and speak with him. Being met, she put him in remembrance of all that had passed between them: she laid also before him how trusty she had been unto him in all professions: she confessed also how faithfully he had discharged the duty of a friend in all respects, and therewithal she declared that her late alteration and pensiveness of mind was not without great cause, for that she had of late such a mishap, as might change the disposition of any living creature: Yea, and that the case was such, as unless she found present remedy, her death must needs ensue, and that speedily, for the preventing whereof, she alleged that she had beaten her brains with all devices possible, and that in the end she could think of no redress but one, the which lay only in him to accomplish. Wherefore she besought him for all the love and good will which had ever passed between them, now to shew the fruits of true friendship, and to gratify her with a free grant to this request. The lover who had always been desirous to pleasure her in anything, but now especially to recover her wonted kindness, gan frankly promise to accomplish anything that might be to him possible, yea, though it were to his great detriment, and therewithal, did deeply blame her in that she would so long torment herself with any grief, considering that it lay in him to help it. The lady answered, that she had so long kept it from his knowledge, because she doubted whether he would be content to perform it or not, although it was such a thing as he might easily grant without any manner of hurt to himself, & yet now in the end she was forced to adventure upon his courtesy, being no longer able to bear the burden of her grief: the lover solicited her most earnestly to disclose it: and she (as fast) seemed to mistrust that he would not accomplish it. In the end she took out a book (which she had brought for the nonce) & bound him by oath to accomplish it. The lover mistrusting nothing less than that ensued, took the oath willingly, which done, she declared all that had passed between her & her husband: his grief, her repentance, his pardon, her vow, and in the end of her tale enjoined the lover, that from thenceforwards, he should never attempt to break her constant determination, the lover replied that this was unpossible. But she plainly assured him, that if he granted her that request, she would be his friend in all honest & goodly wise: if not, she put him out of doubt that she would eschew his company and flee from his sight as from a scorpion. The lover considering that her request was but just, accusing his own guilty conscience, remembering the great courtesies always used by her husband, and therewithal seeing the case now brought to such an issue, as that by no other means than by this it could be concealed from the knowledge of the world: but most of all, being urged by his oath, did at last give an unwilling consent, and yet a faithful promise to yield unto her will in all things, and thus being become of one assent, he remaineth the dearest friend & most welcome guest that may be, both to the lady and her husband: and the man and the wife so kind (each to other) as if there never had been such a breach between them. Now, of you noble governor I would feign learn, whether the perplexity of the husband when he looked in at the keyhole, or of the wife when she knew the cause why the carolines were so scattered, or of the lover when he knew what was his mistress' charge, was greater of the three? I might have put in also the troubled thoughts of the sisters & the maid, when they saw their good will rejected, but let these three suffice." "Gentle Hope," quoth Ferdinando, "you have rehearsed (& that right eloquently) a notable tale, or rather a notable history, because you seem to affirm, that it was done indeed of late & not far hence. Wherein I note five especial points: that is a marvelous patience in the husband, no less repentance in the wife, no small boldness of the maid, but much more rashness in the sisters, & last of all, a rare tractability in the lover. Nevertheless to return unto your question. I think the husband's perplexity greatest, because his losses abounded above the rest, & his injuries were uncomparable." The Lady Frances did not seem to contrary him but rather smiled in her sleeve at Dame Pergo, who had no less patience to hear the tale recited, than the Lady Frances had pleasure in telling of it. By this time the sleeping hour approached, & the ladies prepared their departure, whenas Mistress Frances said unto the Venetian: "Although percase I shall not do it so handsomely as your mistress, yet good Trust," quoth she, "if you vouchsafe it, I can be content to trim up your bed in the best manner that I may, as one who would be as glad as she to procure your quiet rest." Ferdinando gave her great thanks desiring her not to trouble herself, but to let his man alone with that charge. Thus they departed, & how all parties took rest that night I know not: but in the morning Ferdinando began to consider with himself that he might lie long enough in his bed before his mistress would be appeased in her peevish conceits: wherefore he arose, & being appareled in his nightgown, took occasion to walk in the gallery near adjoining unto his mistress' chamber: but there might he walk long enough ere his mistress would come to walk with him. When dinner time came he went into the great chamber whereas the lord of the castle saluted him, being joyful of his recovery: Jeronimi giving due thanks, declared that his friendly entertainment together with the great courtesy of the gentlewomen was such, as might revive a man although he were half dead. "I would be loath," quoth the host, "that any gentleman coming to me for good will, should want any courtesy of entertainment that lieth in my power." When the meat was served to the table, the gentlewomen came in all but Dame Elinor and Mistress Pergo, the which Ferdinando marked very well, and it did somewhat abate his appetite. After dinner, his Hope came unto him and demanded of him how he would pass the day for his recreation? to whom he answered even as it best pleased her. She devised to walk into the park, and so by little and little to acquaint himself with the air: he agreed, and they walked together being accompanied with one or two other gentlewomen. And although there were now more cause that he should mistrust his mistress than ever he had before received, yet the vehement passions which he saw in her when she first came to visit him, and moreover the earnest words which she pronounced in his extremity, were such a refreshing to his mind, as that he determined no more to trouble himself with like conceits: concluding further, that if his mistress were not faulty, then had he committed a foul offence in needless jealousy, and that if she were faulty (especially with the secretary) then no persuasion could amend her, nor any passion help him: and this was the cause that enabled him after such passing pangs to abide the doubtful conclusion: And thus manfully and valiantly to repress faintness of his mind: nothing doubting but that he should have won his mistress to pardon his presumption, & lovingly to embrace his service in wonted manner: but he was far deceived, for she was now in another tune, the which Mistress Frances began partly to discover unto him as they walked together: for she burdened him that his malady proceeded only of a disquiet mind. "And if it did so my gentle Hope," quoth he, "what remedy?" "My good Trust," quoth she, "none other but to plant quiet where disquiet began to grow." "I have determined," quoth he, "but I must crave the help of your assured friendship." "Thereof you may make account," quoth she, "but wherein?" Ferdinando walking apart with her, began to declare that there was some contention happened between his mistress and him: the lady told him that she was not ignorant thereof. Then he desired her to treat so much in the cause, as they might eftsoons come to parley: "Thereof I dare assure you," quoth Mistress Frances, and at their return she led him into his mistress' chamber, whom they found lying on her bed, whether galled with any grief, or weary of the thing (which you wot of) I know not, but there she lay: unto whom Ferdinando gave two or three salutations before she seemed to mark him. At last said the Lady Frances unto her, "Your servant hearing of your sickness, hath adventured thus far into the air to see you." "I thank him," quoth Dame Elinor & so lay still, refusing to give him any countenance. Whereat he perceiving all the other gentlewomen fall to whispering, thought good, boldly to plead his own case: and approaching the bed began to enforce his unwilling mistress unto courtesy, wherein he used such vehemence as she could not well by any means refuse to talk with him: but what their talk was, I may not take upon me to tell you. Sufficeth this to be known, that in the end she pretended to pass over all old grudges, and thenceforth to pleasure him as occasion might serve, the which occasion was so long in happening, that in the end he being now eftsoons troubled with unquiet fantasies, and forced to use his pen again as an ambassador between them: one day amongst the rest found opportunity to thrust a letter into her bosom, wherein he had earnestly requested another moonshine banquet or Friday's breakfast to recomfort his dulled spirits, whereunto the dame yielded this answer in writing, but of whose enditing judge you.

"I can but smile at your simplicity, who burden your friends with an impossibility. The case so stood as I could not though I would. Wherefore from henceforth either learn to frame your request more reasonably, or else stand content with a flat repulse.

S H E."

Ferdinando liked this letter but a little: & being thereby driven into his accustomed vein, he compiled in verse this answer following, upon these words contained in her letter, "I could not though I would."

"I could not though I would:" good lady say not so,
Since one good word of your good will might soon redress my
　　woe,
Where "would" is free before, there "could" can never fail:
For proof, you see how galleys pass where ships can bear no sail,
The weary mariner where skies are overcast,
By ready will doth guide his skill and wins the haven at last,
The pretty bird that sings with prick against her breast,[67]
Doth make a virtue of her need, to watch when others rest,
And true the proverb is, which you have laid apart,
There is no hap can seem too hard unto a willing heart.
Then lovely lady mine, you say not as you should,

In doubtful terms to answer thus: "I could not though I would."
Yes yes, full well you know, your "can" is quick and good:
And wilful "will" is eke too swift, to shed my guiltless blood.
But if good will were bent as press'd as power is,[68]
Such will would quickly find the skill to mend that is amiss.
Wherefore if you desire to see my true love spilt,
Command and I will slay myself, that yours may be the guilt,
But if you have no power to say your servant nay,
Write thus: "I may not as I would, yet must I as I may."
                    Ferdinando. Jeronimi.

Thus Jeronimi replied upon his mistress' answer, hoping thereby to recover some favour at her hands, but it would not be: so that now he had been as likely (as at the first) to have fretted in fantasies, had not the Lady Frances continually comforted him: and by little & little she drove such reason into his mind, that now he began to subdue his humour with discretion, and to determine that if he might espy evident proof of his mistress' frailty, he would then stand content with patience perforce, & give his mistress the *bezo las manos*. And it happened one day amongst others, that he resorted to his mistress' chamber and found her (*allo solito*)[69] lying upon her bed, and the secretary with Dame Pergo and her handmaid keeping of her company. Whereat Ferdinando somewhat repining, came to her and fell to dalliance, as one that had now rather adventure to be thought presumptious than yield to be accounted bashful, he cast his arm over his mistress, and began to accuse her of sluggishness, using some other bold parts, as well to provoke her, as also to grieve the other. The lady seemed little to delight in his dallying, but cast a glance at her secretary, & therewith smiled, when as the secretary and Dame Pergo burst out into open laughter. The which Ferdinando perceiving, and disdaining her ingratitude, was forced to depart, and in that fantasy compiled this sonnet.

> With her in arms that had my heart in hold,
> I stood of late to plead for pity so:
> And as I did her lovely looks behold,

She cast a glance upon my rival foe.
His fleering face provoked her to smile,
When my salt tears were drowned in disdain:
He glad, I sad, he laugh'd, (alas the while)
I wept for woe: I pin'd for deadly pain.
And when I saw none other boot prevail,
But reason rule must guide my skillful mind:
Why then (quoth I) old proverbs never fail,
For yet was never good cat[70] out of kind.
Nor woman true but even as stories tell,
Won with an egg, and lost again with shell.
Ferdinando. Jeronimi.

This sonnet declareth that he began now to account of her as she deserved, for it hath a sharp conclusion, and it is somewhat too general. Well, as it is he lost it, where his mistress found it, and she immediately imparted the same unto Dame Pergo, and Dame Pergo unto others: so that it quickly became common in the house. Amongst others Mistress Frances having recovered a copy of it, did seem to pardon the generality, and to be well pleased with the particularity thereof, the which she bewrayed one day unto Ferdinando in this wise. "Of all the joys that ever I had my good Trust," quoth she, "there is none wherein I take more comfort than in your conformity.[71] And although your present rage is such that you can be content to condemn a number unknown, for the transgression of one too well known: yet I do rather rejoice that you should judge your pleasure over many, than to be abused by any." "My good Hope," quoth he, "it were not reason that after such manifold proofs of your exceeding courtesies, I should use strange or contentious speech with so dear a friend. And indeed I must confess that the opinion which I have conceived of my mistress, hath stirred my pen to write very hardly against all the feminine gender. But I pray you pardon me," quoth he, "& if it please you I will recant it, as also (percase) I was but cloyed with succudry,[72] and presumed to think more than may be proved." "Yea but how if it were proved?" quoth Dame Frances. "If it were so which God forbid," quoth he, "then could you not blame me to conceive that opinion." "Howsoever I might blame you," quoth she, "I mean not to blame you, but I demand further, if it be as I think & you suspect, what will you then do?" "Surely," quoth he, "I have determined to drink up mine own sorrow secretly, and to bid them both adieu." "I like your farewell better than your fantasy," quoth she, "and whensoever you can be content to take so much pains, as the knight (which had a nightgown guarded with naked swords) did take, I think you may put yourself out of doubt of all these things." By these words and other speech which she uttered unto him, Ferdinando smelt how the world went about, and therefore did one day in the grey morning adventure to pass through the gallery toward his mistress' chamber, hoping to have found the door open, but he found the contrary, and there attending in good devotion, heard the parting of his mistress and her secretary, with many kind words: whereby it appeared that the one was very loth to depart from the other. Poor Jeronimi was enforced to bear this burden, and after he had attended there as long as the light would give him leave, he departed also to his chamber, and apparelling himself, could not be quiet until he had spoken with his mistress, whom he burdened flatly with this despiteful treachery: and she as fast denied it, until at last being still urged with such evident tokens as he alleged, she gave him this bone to gnaw upon. "And if I did so," quoth she, "what then?" Whereunto Ferdinando made none answer, but departed with this farewell. "My loss is mine own, and your gain is none of yours, and sooner can I recover my loss, than you enjoy the gain which you gape after." And when he was in place solitary, he compiled these following for a final end of the matter.

> And if I did what then?
> Are you agriev'd therefore?
> The sea hath fish for every man,
> And what would you have more?
>
> Thus did my mistress once,
> Amaze my mind with doubt:

And popp'd a question for the nonce,
To beat my brains about.

Whereto I thus replied,
Each fisherman can wish,
That all the seas at every tide,
Were his alone to fish.

And so did I (in vain,)
But since it may not be:
Let such fish there as find the gain,
And leave the loss for me.

And with such luck and loss,
I will content myself:
Till tides of turning time may toss,
Such fishers on the shelf.

And when they stick on sands,
That every man may see:
Then will I laugh and clap my hands,
As they do now at me.
        Ferdinando Jeronimi.

Thus Ferdinando being no longer able to bear these extreme despites, resolved to absent himself, as well for his own further quiet, as also to avoid the occasion of greater mischiefs that might ensue: And although the exceeding courtesies and approved fidelity of Dame Frances had been sufficient to allure the fast liking of any man, especially considering that she was reasonably fair, and descended of a worthy father, who now fell flatly to move and solicit the same, yet such sinister conceits had he taken by the frailty of Dame Elinor, as that rejecting all proffers, and contemning all courtesies, he took his leave, & (without pretence of return) departed to his house in Venice: spending there the rest of his days in a dissolute kind of life: & abandoning the worthy lady Francischina, who (daily being galled with the grief of his great ingratitude) did shortly bring herself into a miserable consumption: whereof (after three years languishing) she died: Notwithstanding all which occurrents the Lady Elinor lived

long in the continuance of her accustomed change: & thus
we see that where wicked lust doeth bear the name of love,
it doth not only infect the light-minded, but it may also become confusion to others which are vowed to constancy. And
to that end I have recited this fable which may serve as ensample to warn the youthful reader from attempting the like
worthless enterprise. I know not how my rude translation
thereof will delight the finest judgements: But sure as Bartello
writeth it in Italian, it is both pleasant and profitable: the
which hath made me adventure thus to publish the same in
such simple style as I am able to endite: Desiring the gentle
reader, rather to take example of reformation therein, than to
find fault at the homely handling of the same.

Ever or never.

JOHN LYLY

EUPHUES: THE ANATOMY OF WIT

1578

John Lyly (1554?–1606)

Lyly's statement in EUPHUES, "I have ever thought so super-stitiously of wit, that I fear I have committed idolatry against wisdom," reveals considerable self-insight. By the middle of the sixteenth century, when Lyly was born, the social frame-work of the chivalric code had ceased to function effectively; the feudal aristocracy had turned to showing its superior position not through any productive pattern of economic be-havior, but through such artificial aspects of manners as elab-orate dress and sophisticated talk. Lyly had a ticket of admis-sion to the circle of this aristocracy, and he had a gift for the complex playing with words which interested it. But he was unhappily more a dependent on this class than a member of it: his wit amused those who could afford to be amused, but it created problems which he himself could not afford, often hindering him from the security which he desired.

Lyly's family was not of the aristocracy, but its scholarly and literary pursuits had won the recognition and acquaint-ance of the upper class. His grandfather, William Lyly, was a distinguished grammarian and the friend of Sir Thomas More, Erasmus, and Colet; his uncle, the canon of Canter-bury, was the author of several learned works; his father, an educated and comfortably fixed man, was the registrar of the city and diocese of Canterbury. Lyly followed in the aca-demic footsteps of his forebears, in appearance if not in atti-tude. When he was fifteen or sixteen years old, he entered Magdalen College, Oxford, and completed his course of study in 1573. He was described in the Oxford register of 1571 as *plebeii filius*, son of a commoner; yet in 1574 Lyly called him-self an *alumnus* of Lord Burleigh, the strongest representative of the feudal aristocracy in the court of Elizabeth, suggesting that he had received financial aid through the help of the distinguished courtier. Lyly had written Burleigh requesting a fellowship from the crown, and it was perhaps such a grant that allowed him to continue his studies. He received the M.A. degree from Oxford in 1575 and the same degree from Cambridge four years later. At both schools Lyly had the reputation of a talented and well-to-do young man about the campus, studying little, yet enough to complete his academic courses, expressing himself wittily and facetiously in verse and prose, exploiting to the hilt the role of playboy. Gabriel Harvey, Lyly's friend as early as 1578 and later his severe critic, hinted at Lyly's reputation for "horning, gaming, fooling and knaving," and pigeonholed him as "sometime the fiddlestick of Oxford, now the very bauble of London."

Since to receive his degree at Cambridge Lyly did not necessarily have to reside at the university for any extended period, he spent some time at the court in London even during his early twenties. Harvey probably met him when both of them were living at the Savoy, the former Lancastrian palace converted into a charitable institution for "poor people, sick or lame, or travellers," realistically extended to include struggling writers and students. Through Harvey, Lyly possibly made the acquaintance of such literary figures as Spenser and Sidney, and through Burleigh he certainly met Edward de Vere, the Earl of Oxford, and other courtiers. Lyly's twofold ambition was soon apparent: to become a court-approved writer and to be accepted himself as a member of the leisure-class court, and he worked constantly to attain these ends.

At court Lyly was impressively busy. In 1578 and 1579 he worked on EUPHUES, which was immediately so popular with the sophisticated aristocratic readers that it went through four editions in the first year and twelve in Lyly's lifetime. A year later he had completed EUPHUES AND HIS ENGLAND, in part as an appeasement to the few persons who had been offended by his satire on women in particular and on the society in general. In 1581, possibly through the help of the Earl of Oxford, to whom he had dedicated his second work, he had his first play CAMPASPE presented before Elizabeth, and by the end of the century he had written eight plays and seen all but two of them performed at court by either the St. Paul's or the Royal Chapel boys, companies which the Queen preferred to professional groups of actors. In 1585, he was assistant master of St. Paul's Choir School, tutoring the choirboys in Latin, in logic, and even in music, and probably coaching young actors for performance at court. At the same time he was in charge of royal trappings for hunting, oddly enough in Elizabeth's reign a part of the costuming and properties under the supervision of the Revels Office, the department which handled the selection and the production of court dramatic entertainment.

Yet, despite the popularity of his prose and of his drama and despite, too, the several court appointments related to his literary interests, Lyly frequently made official complaints of a lack of deserved favor at court: in 1595 and in 1598 he wrote to Elizabeth, and in 1597 he wrote to Sir Robert Cecil, Burleigh's son and the Queen's Secretary of State. The first letter to Elizabeth contended that she had promised him the office of Master of Revels, but that "after ten years' tempest" nothing had come of the promise. The tempest to which Lyly referred was made up of a series of minor storms: a disagreement with Harvey, his first literary companion; a falling out with Burleigh, his first patron; a cooling of relations with Oxford, the first sponsor of his drama; and even a criticism from the Queen for his handling of the Revels properties. Furthermore, Lyly may have been aware that his chances for advancement had been affected indirectly by such court conflicts as the opposition between his patron Burleigh and Elizabeth's favorite Leicester, or Elizabeth's temporary disapproval of Oxford. Lyly's troubles with Harvey and with Oxford had not a little to do with his sharp tongue, and his differences with Burleigh and the Queen may have come from his paying more attention to court talk than to court work. Lyly him-

self suspected that he had too much "played the fool" for the
Queen to grant him the responsible position of Master of
Revels. In his first petition he had asked for pastoral retire-
ment in preference to suffering the "shipwreck of my times,
my hopes, and my wits."

Lyly's tempest may also have referred to his participation
in the famous Martin Marprelate controversy, which took its
name from the fictitious sponsor of the Puritan tracts against
government censorship of publications. Already a member of
Elizabeth's censoring agency, Lyly made one or two Nashe-
like contributions on the side of the Queen's bishops, intent
on quelling any further Catholic or Puritan opposition to the
Anglican Church. In 1589 he may have had a hand in A WHIP
FOR AN APE and in PAPPE WITH A HATCHET, which incidentally
drew from Harvey a personal attack on Lyly rather than on
the whole anti-Martin faction. Lyly's other publicly political
activity was his membership in Parliament for four short
terms intermittently between 1588 and 1601, but nothing is
known of his parliamentary service except that his elections
were due in part to the patronage of Edward de la Warre, to
whom EUPHUES had been dedicated.

Lyly's reputation as a court wit who carried his speech and
his manners to an absurd extent was unmodified by his success as a writer or his performance of official duties. He was
the conspicuous butt of Ben Jonson's satire in the figure of
Fastidius Brisk in EVERY MAN OUT OF HIS HUMOR (1599);
Jonson presented him as self-consciously erudite, strainedly
witty, affectedly mannered, and always in bad financial straits.
The last was certainly true. As late as 1602–1603 Lyly was
petitioning the Queen for requitals of promises made but
never fulfilled, and even had his wife, who may have had
court connections, present one request to Elizabeth. But the
Queen died soon thereafter, and no record of Lyly at court
under James I remains. Lyly died in 1606 in his early fifties.

The paradox of Lyly's life is that the wit which lost him
security and status established him as a distinctive Renaissance
man of letters.

The standard edition of Lyly is J. W. Bond's THE COMPLETE WORKS OF JOHN LYLY, 3 vols., The Clarendon Press (Oxford), 1902. Volume one includes an extensive biographical study of Lyly and a comprehensive essay entitled "Euphues and Euphuism." Each of Lyly's works is followed by careful and thorough notes, which the editors of this anthology have found indeed helpful. A concise study is J. Dover Wilson's JOHN LYLY, Macmillan and Bowes, 1905; the most elaborate study is that in French by Albert Feuillerat: JOHN LYLY, Cambridge University Press, 1910. Studies of special interest are S. L. Woolf's "The Humanist as Man of Letters: John Lyly," SEWANEE REVIEW, XXXI, 8-35, and Violet M. Jeffery's JOHN LYLY AND THE ITALIAN RENAISSANCE, Paris, 1929.

The text is taken from Bond's edition of Lyly's WORKS, which collates a 1579 edition of EUPHUES with other early editions.

EUPHUES: THE ANATOMY OF WIT

THERE DWELT in Athens a young gentleman of great patrimony, & of so comely a personage, that it was doubted whether he were more bound to Nature for the lineaments of his person, or to Fortune for the increase of his possessions. But Nature impatient of comparisons, and as it were disdaining a companion, or copartner in her working, added to this comeliness of his body such a sharp capacity of mind, that not only she proved Fortune counterfeit, but was half of that opinion that she herself was only current. This young gallant, of more wit than wealth, and yet of more wealth than wisdom, seeing himself inferior to none in pleasant conceits, thought himself superior to all in honest conditions, insomuch that he deemed himself so apt to all things, that he gave himself almost to nothing, but practicing of those things commonly which are incident to these sharp wits, fine phrases, smooth quipping, merry taunting, using jesting without mean, & abusing mirth without measure. As therefore the sweetest rose hath his prickle, the finest velvet his brack, the fairest flower his bran, so the sharpest wit hath his wanton will, and the holiest head his wicked way. And true it is that some men write and most men believe, that in all perfect shapes, a blemish bringeth rather a liking every way to the eyes, than a loathing any way to the mind. Venus had her mole in her cheek which made her more amiable: Helen her scar on her chin which Paris called *cos amoris*, the whetsone of love. Aristippus his wart, Lycurgus his wen: So likewise in the disposition of the mind, either virtue is overshadowed with some vice, or vice overcast with some virtue. Alexander valiant in war, yet given to wine. Tully eloquent in his glozes, yet vainglorious: Solomon wise, yet too too wanton:

David holy but yet an homicide: none more witty than
Euphues, yet at the first none more wicked. The freshest
colours soonest fade, the teenest[1] razor soonest turneth his
edge, the finest cloth is soonest eaten with moths, and the
cambric sooner stained than the coarse canvas: which appeared well in this Euphues, whose wit being like wax apt to
receive any impression, and having the bridle in his own
hands, either to use the rein or the spur, disdaining counsel,
leaving his country, loathing his old acquaintance, thought
either by wit to obtain some conquest, or by shame to abide
some conflict, and leaving the rule of reason, rashly ran unto
destruction. Who[2] preferring fancy before friends, & his present humor, before honour to come, laid reason in water being
too salt for his taste, and followed unbridled affection, most
pleasant for his tooth. When parents have more care how to
leave their children wealthy than wise, & are more desirous
to have them maintain the name, than the nature of a gentleman: when they put gold into the hands of youth, where they
should put a rod under their girdle, when instead of awe
they make them past grace, & leave them rich executors of
goods, & poor executors of godliness, then is it no marvel,
that the son being left rich by his father's will, become retch-
less[3] by his own will.[4]

It hath been an old said saw, and not of less truth than
antiquity, that wit is the better if it be the dearer bought: as
in the sequel of this history shall most manifestly appear. It
happened this young imp to arrive at Naples (a place of more
pleasure than profit, and yet of more profit than piety) the
very walls and windows whereof shewed it rather to be the
Tabernacle of Venus, than the Temple of Vesta.[5]

There was all things necessary and in readiness that might
either allure the mind to lust, or entice the heart to folly, a
court more meet for an atheist, than for one of Athens, for
Ovid than for Aristotle,[6] for a graceless lover than for a godly
liver: more fitter for Paris than Hector, and meeter for Flora
than Diana.

Here my youth (whether for weariness he could not, or for

wantonness would not go any further) determined to make his abode: whereby it is evidently seen that the fleetest fish swalloweth the delicatest bait, that the highest soaring hawk traineth to the lure, and that the wittiest sconce is inveigled with the sudden view of alluring vanities.

Here he wanted no companions which courted him continually with sundry kinds of devices, whereby they might either soak his purse to reap commodity, or sooth his person to win credit, for he had guests and companions of all sorts.

There frequented to this lodging and mansion house as well the spider to suck poison, of his fine wit, as the bee to gather honey, as well the drone, as the dove, the fox as the lamb, as well Damocles to betray him, as Damon to be true to him:[7] Yet he behaved himself so warily, that he singled his game wisely. He could easily discern Apollo's music, from Pan his pipe, and Venus's beauty from Juno's bravery, and the faith of Laelius, from the flattery of Aristippus,[8] he welcomed all but trusted none, he was merry but yet so wary, that neither the flatterer could take advantage to entrap him in his talk, nor the wisest any assurance of his friendship: who being demanded of one what countryman he was, he answered, "What countryman am I not? if I be in Crete, I can lie, if in Greece I can shift, if in Italy I can court it: if thou ask whose son I am also, I ask thee whose son I am not. I can carouse with Alexander, abstain with Romulus, eat with the Epicure, fast with the Stoic, sleep with Endymion, watch with Chrysippus,"[9] using these speeches & other like. An old gentleman in Naples seeing his pregnant wit, his eloquent tongue somewhat taunting, yet with delight, his mirth without measure, yet not without wit, his sayings vainglorious, yet pithy, began to bewail his nurture: and to muse at his nature, being incensed against the one as most pernicious, and enflamed with the other as most precious: for he well knew that so rare a wit would in time either breed an intolerable trouble, or bring an incomparable treasure to the common weal: at the one he greatly pitied, at the other he rejoiced.

Having therefore gotten opportunity to communicate with

him his mind, with watery eyes, as one lamenting his wanton-ness, and smiling face, as one loving his wittiness, encountered him on this manner.

"Young gentleman, although my acquaintance be small to intreat you, and my authority less to command you, yet my good will in giving you good counsel should induce you to believe me, and my hoary hairs (ambassadors of experience) enforce you to follow me, for by how much the more I am a stranger to you, by so much the more you are beholding to me, having therefore opportunity to utter my mind, I mean to be importunate with you to follow my meaning. As thy birth doth shew the express and lively image of gentle blood, so thy bringing up seemeth to me to be a great blot to the lineage of so noble a brute, so that I am enforced to think that either thou diddest want one to give thee good instruc-tions, or that thy parents made thee a wanton with too much cockering, either they were too foolish in using no discipline, or thou too forward in rejecting their doctrine, either they willing to have thee idle, or thou willful to be ill employed. Did they not remember that which no man ought to forget, that the tender youth of a child is like the tempering of new wax apt to receive any form? He that will carry a bull with Milo,[10] must use to carry him a calf also, he that coveteth to have a straight tree, must not bow him being a twig. The potter fashioneth his clay when it is soft, and the sparrow is taught to come when he is young: As therefore the iron being hot receiveth any form with the stroke of the hammer, and keepeth it being cold forever, so the tender wit of a child if with diligence it be instructed in youth, will with industry use those qualities in his age.

"They might also have taken example of the wise husband-men, who in their fattest and most fertile ground sow hemp before wheat, a grain that dryeth up the superfluous moisture, and maketh the soil more apt for corn: Or of good gardeners who in their curious knots[11] mix hyssop with thyme, as aiders the one to the growth of the other, the one being dry, the other moist: or of cunning painters, who for the whitest work cast the blackest ground, to make the picture more amiable. If therefore thy father had been as wise an husbandman, as he was a fortunate husband, or thy mother as good a huswife as she was a happy wife, if they had been both as good gardeners to keep their knot, as they were grafters to bring forth such fruit, or as cunning painters, as they were happy parents, no doubt they had sowed hemp before wheat, that is discipline before affection, they had set hyssop with thyme, that is manners with wit, the one to aid the other: and to make thy dexterity more, they had cast a black ground for their white work, that is, they had mixed threats with fair looks.

"But things past, are past calling again, it is too late to shut the stable door when the steed is stolen: The Trojans repented too late when their town was spoiled: Yet the remembrance of thy former follies might breed in thee a remorse of conscience, and be a remedy against farther concupiscence. But now to thy present time: The Lacedaemonians were wont to show their children drunken men and other wicked men, that by seeing their filth they might shun the like fault, and avoid such vices when they were at the like state. The Persians to make their youth abhor gluttony would paint an Epicure sleeping with meat in his mouth, & most horribly overladen with wine, that by the view of such monstrous sights, they might eschew the means of the like excess.

"The Parthians to cause their youth to loathe the alluring trains of women's wiles and deceitful enticements, had most curiously carved in their houses a young man blind, besides whom was adjoined a woman so exquisite, that in some men's judgement Pygmalion's image was not half so excellent, having one hand in his pocket as noting their theft, and holding a knife in the other hand to cut his throat: If the sight of such ugly shapes caused a loathing of the like sins, then my good Euphues consider their plight, and beware of thine own peril. Thou art here in Naples a young sojourner, I an old senior; thou a stranger, I a citizen; thou secure doubting no mishap, I sorrowful dreading thy misfortune. Here mayst thou see that which I sigh to see, drunken sots wallowing in every house, in every chamber, yea, in every channel, here mayst thou behold that which I cannot without blushing behold, nor without blubbering utter, those whose bellies be their gods, who offer their goods as sacrifice to their guts: who sleep with meat in their mouths, with sin in their hearts, and with shame in their houses.

"Here, yea, here Euphues, mayst thou see not the carved visard of a lewd woman, but the incarnate visage of a lascivious wanton, not the shadow of love, but the substance of lust: My heart melteth in drops of blood, to see a harlot with the one hand rob so many coffers, and with the other to rip so many corses.

"Thou art here amidst the pikes between Scylla and Charybdis, ready if thou shun Syrtes, to sink into Symplegades.[12] Let the Lacedaemonian, the Persian, the Parthian, yea, the Neapolitan, cause thee rather to detest such villainy, at the sight and view of their vanity.

"Is it not far better to abhor sins by the remembrance of others' faults, than by repentance of thine own follies? Is not he accounted most wise, whom other men's harms do make most wary? But thou wilt happily say, that although there be many things in Naples to be justly condemned, yet there are some things of necessity to be commended; and as thy will doth lean unto the one, so thy wit would also embrace the other.

"Alas Euphues by how much the more I love the high climbing of thy capacity, by so much the more I fear thy fall. The fine crystal is sooner crazed than the hard marble, the greenest beech burneth faster than the driest oak, the fairest silk is soonest soiled, and the sweetest wine turneth to the sharpest vinegar, the pestilence doth most rifest infect the clearest complexion, and the caterpillar cleaveth unto the ripest fruit, the most delicate wit is allured with small enticement unto vice, and most subject to yield unto vanity, if therefore thou do but hearken to the sirens, thou wilt be enamoured, if thou haunt their houses and places, thou shalt be enchanted.

"One drop of poison infecteth the whole tun of wine, one leaf of coloquintida[13] marreth and spoileth the whole pot of porridge, one iron mole[14] defaceth the whole piece of lawn: Descend into thine own conscience, and consider with thyself the great difference between staring and stark blind, wit and wisdom, love and lust. Be merry but with modesty, be sober but not too solemn, be valiant but not too venturous. Let thy attire be comely but not costly, thy diet wholesome but not excessive, use pastime as the word importeth, to pass the time in honest recreation: mistrust no man without cause, neither be thou credulous without proof, be not light to follow every man's opinion, nor obstinate to stand in thine own conceit. Serve God, love God, fear God, and God will so bless thee as either heart can wish or thy friends desire. And so I end my counsel, beseeching thee to begin to follow it." This old gentleman having finished his discourse, Euphues began to shape him an answer in this sort.

"Father and friend (your age showeth the one, your honesty the other) I am neither so suspicious to mistrust your good will, nor so sottish to mislike your good counsel, as I am therefore to thank you for the first, so it stands me upon to think better on the latter: I mean not to cavil with you as one loving sophistry, neither to control you as one having superiority, the one would bring my talk into the suspicion of fraud, the other convince me of folly. Whereas you argue I know not upon what probabilities, but sure I am upon no proof, that my bringing up should be a blemish to my birth. I answer, and swear too that you were not therein a little overshot, either you gave too much credit to the report of others, or too much liberty to your own judgement, you convince my parents of peevishness, in making me a wanton, and me of lewdness in rejecting correction. But so many men so many minds, that may seem in your eye odious, which in another's eye may be gracious. Aristippus a philosopher, yet who more courtly? Diogenes a philosopher, yet who more carterly?[15] Who more popular than Plato, retaining always good company? Who more envious than Timon,[16] denouncing all human society? Who so severe as the Stoics, which like stocks were moved with no melody? Who so secure as the Epicures which wallowed in all kind of licentiousness? Though all men be made of one metal, yet they be not cast all in one mold, there is framed of the selfsame clay as well the title to keep out water as the pot to contain liquor, the sun doth harden the dirt & melt the wax, fire maketh the gold to shine and the straw to smother, perfumes doth refresh the dove & kill the beetle, & the nature of the man disposeth that consent of the manners. Now whereas you seem to love my nature, & loathe my nurture, you bewray your own weakness, in thinking that nature may anyways be altered by education, & as you have ensamples to confirm your pretence, so I have most evident and infallible arguments to serve for my purpose: It is natural for the vine to spread, the more you seek by art to alter it, the more in the end you shall augment it. It is proper for the palm tree to mount, the heavier you load it the higher it sprouteth. Though iron be made soft with fire it returneth to his hardness, though the falcon be reclaimed to the fist she retireth to her haggardness, the whelp of a mastiff will never be taught to retrieve the partridge, education can have no shew, where the excellencey of nature doth bear sway. The silly mouse will by no manner of means be tamed, the subtile fox may well be beaten, but never broken from stealing his prey, if you pound spices they smell the sweeter, season the wood never so well the wine will taste of the cask, plant and transplant the crab tree, where, and whensoever it please you and it will never bear sweet apple, unless you graft by art, which nothing toucheth nature.

"Infinite and innumerable were the examples I could allege and declare to confirm the force of nature, and confute these your vain and false forgeries, were not the repetition of them needless having showed sufficient, or bootless seeing those alleged will not persuade you. And can you be so unnatural, whom Dame Nature hath nourished and brought up so many years, to repine as it were against nature.

"The similitude you rehearse of the wax, argueth your waxing and melting brain, and your example of the hot and hard iron, showeth in you but cold and weak disposition. Do you know that which all men do affirm and know, that black will take no other colour? That the stone abeston[17] being once made hot will never be made cold? That fire cannot be forced downward? That nature will have course after kind? That everything will dispose itself according to nature? Can the Ethiope change or alter his skin? or the leopard his hue? Is it possible to gather grapes of thorns, or figs of thistles? or to cause anything to strive against nature?

"But why go I about to praise nature, the which as yet was never any imp so wicked & barbarous, any Turk so vile and brutish, any beast so dull and senseless, that could, or would, or durst dispraise or contemn? Doth not Cicero conclude and allow, that if we follow and obey nature, we shall never err? Doth not Aristotle allege and confirm, that nature frameth or maketh nothing in any point rude, vain, and unperfect?

"Nature was had in such estimation and admiration among the heathen people, that she was reputed for the only goddess in heaven: If nature then have largely and bountifully endowed me with her gifts, why deem you me so untoward and graceless? If she have dealt hardly with me, why extol you so much my birth? If nature bear no sway, why use you this adulation? If nature work the effect, what booteth any education? If nature be of strength or force, what availeth discipline or nurture? If of none, what helpeth nature? But let these sayings pass as known evidently and granted to be true, which none can or may deny unless he be false, or that he be an enemy to humanity.

"As touching my residence and abiding here in Naples, my youthly and lusty affections, my sports and pleasures, my pastimes, my common dalliance, my delights, my resort and company, and companions, which daily use to visit me, although to you they breed more sorrow and care, than solace and comfort, because of your crabbed age: yet to me they bring more comfort and joy, than care & grief, more bliss than bale, more happiness than heaviness: because of my youthful gentleness. Either you would have all men old as you are, or else you have quite forgotten that you yourself were young, or ever knew young days: either in your youth you were a very vicious and ungodly man, or now being aged very superstitious & devout above measure.

"Put you no difference between the young flourishing bay tree, and the old withered beech? No kind of distinction between the waxing and the waning of the moon? And between the rising and the setting of the sun? Do you measure the hot assaults of youth, by the cold skirmishes of age? whose years are subject to more infirmities than our youth, we merry, you melancholy, we zealous in affection, you jealous in all your doings, you testy without cause, we hasty for no quarrel. You careful, we careless, we bold, you fearful, we in all points contrary unto you, and ye in all points unlike unto us.

"Seeing therefore we be repugnant each to the other in nature, would you have us alike in qualities? Would you have one potion ministered to the burning fever, and to the cold palsy? one plaster to an old issue and a fresh wound? one salve for all sores? one sauce for all meats? No no Eubulus, but I will yield to more, than either I am bound to grant, either thou able to prove: Suppose that which I never will believe, that Naples is a cankered storehouse of all strife, a common stews for all strumpets, the sink of shame, and the very nurse of all sin: shall it therefore follow of necessity that all that are wooed of love, should be wedded to lust, will you conclude as it were *ex consequenti*,[18] that whosoever arriveth here shall be enticed to folly, and being enticed, of force shall be entangled? No, no, it is the disposition of the thought that altereth the nature of the thing. The sun shineth upon the dunghill, and is not corrupted, the diamond lieth in the fire, and is not consumed, the crystal toucheth the toad, and is not poisoned, the bird trochilus liveth by the mouth of the crocodile and is not spoiled, a perfect wit is never bewitched with lewdness, neither enticed with lasciviousness.

"Is it not common that the holm tree springeth amidst the beach? That the ivy spreadeth upon the hard stones? That the soft featherbed breaketh the hard blade? If experience have not taught you this, you have lived long & learned little, or if your moist brain have forgot it, you have learned much and profited nothing. But it may be, that you measure my affections by your own fancies, and knowing yourself either too simple to raise the siege by policy, or too weak to resist the assault by prowess, you deem me of as little wit as yourself, or of less force, either of small capacity, or of no courage. In my judgement Eubulus, you shall as soon catch a hare with a taber, as you shall persuade youth, with your aged & overworn eloquence, to such severity of life, which as yet there was never Stoic so strict, nor Jesuit so superstitious, neither votary so devout, but would rather allow it in words than follow it in works, rather talk of it than try it. Neither were you such a saint in your youth, that abandoning all pleasures, all pastimes, and delights, you would choose rather to sacrifice the first fruits of your life to vain holiness, than to youthly affections. But as to the stomach quatted [19] with dainties, all delicates seem queasy, and as he that surfeiteth with wine useth afterward to allay with water: So these old huddles[20] having overcharged their gorges with fancy, account all honest recreation mere folly, and having taken a surfeit of delight, seem now to savour it with despite. Seeing therefore it is labour lost for me to persuade you, and wind vainly wasted for you to exhort me, here I found you, and here I leave you, having neither bought nor sold with you, but changed ware for ware, if you have taken little pleasure in my reply, sure I am that by your counsel I have reaped less profit. They that use to steal honey, burn hemlock to smoke the bees from their hives, and it may be, that to get some advantage of me, you have used these smoky arguments, thinking thereby to smother me with the conceit of strong imagination:

But as the chameleon though he have most guts, draweth least breath, or as the elder tree though he be fullest of pith, is farthest from strength, so though your reasons seem inwardly to yourself somewhat substantial, and your persuasions pithy in your own conceit, yet being well weighed without, they be shadows without substance, and weak without force. The bird taurus[21] hath a great voice, but a small body, the thunder a great clap, yet but a little stone, the empty vessel giveth a greater sound, than the full barrel. I mean not to apply it, but look into your self and you shall certainly find it, and thus I leave you seeking it, but were it not that my company stay my coming, I would surely help you to look it, but I am called hence by my acquaintance."

Euphues having thus ended his talk departed leaving this old gentleman in a great quandary: who perceiving that he was more inclined to wantonness, than to wisdom, with a deep sigh the tears trickling down his cheeks, said: "Seeing thou wilt not buy counsel at the first hand good cheap, thou shalt buy repentance at the second hand, at such an unreasonable rate, that thou wilt curse thy hard pennyworth, and ban thy hard heart. Ah Euphues little dost thou know that if thy wealth waste, thy wit will give but small warmth, & if thy wit incline to wilfulness, that thy wealth will do thee no great good. If the one had been employed to thrift, the other to learning, it had been hard to conjecture, whether thou shouldest have been more fortunate by riches, or happy by wisdom, whether more esteemed in the common weal for wealth to maintain war, or for counsel to conclude peace. But alas why do I pity that in thee which thou seemest to praise in thyself." And immediately he went to his own house, heavily bewailing the young man's unhappiness.

Here ye may behold gentlemen, how lewdly wit standeth in his own light, how he deemeth no penny good silver but his own, preferring the blossom before the fruit, the bud before the flower, the green blade before the ripe ear of corn, his own wit before all men's wisdoms. Neither is that geason,[22] seeing for the most part it is proper to all those of sharp capacity to esteem of themselves, as most proper: if one be hard in conceiving, they pronounce him a dolt, if given to study, they proclaim him a dunce, if merry a jester, if sad a saint, if full of words, a sot, if without speech, a cipher, if one argue with them boldy, then he is impudent, if coldly an innocent, if there be reasoning of divinity, they cry, *Quae supra nos nihil ad nos,*[23] if of humanity, *Sententias loquitur carnifex.*[24] Hereof cometh such great familiarity between the ripest wits, when they shall see the disposition the one of the other, the sympathia[25] of affections, and as it were but a pair of shears to go between their natures, one flattereth another in his own folly, and layeth cushions under the elbow of his fellow, when he seeth him take a nap with fancy, and as their wit wresteth them to vice, so it forgeth them some feat excuse to cloak their vanity.

Too much study doth intoxicate their brains, for (say they) although iron the more it is used the brighter it is, yet silver with much wearing doth waste to nothing, though the cammock[26] the more it is bowed the better it serveth, yet the bow the more it is bent & occupied, the weaker it waxeth, though the camomile, the more it is trodden and pressed down, the more it spreadeth, yet the violet the oftener it is handled and touched, the sooner it withereth and decayeth. Besides this, a fine wit, a sharp sense, a quick understanding, is able to attain to more in a moment or a very little space, than a dull and blockish head in a month, the scythe cutteth far better and smoother than the saw, the wax yieldeth better and sooner to the seal, than the steel to the stamp or hammer, the smooth & plain beech is easier to be carved and occupied than the knotty box. For neither is there anything, but that hath his contraries: Such is the nature of these novices that think to have learning without labour, and treasure without travail, either not understanding or else not remembering, that the finest edge is made with the blunt whetstone, and the fairest jewel fashioned with the hard hammer. I go not about (gentlemen) to inveigh against wit, for then I were witless, but frankly to confess mine own little wit,

I have ever thought so superstitiously of wit, that I fear I have committed idolatry against wisdom, and if nature had dealt so beneficially with me to have given me any wit, I should have been readier in the defence of it to have made an apology, than anyway to turn to apostasy: But this I note, that for the most part they stand so on their pantoffles[27] that they be secure of perils, obstinate in their own opinions, impatient of labour, apt to conceive wrong, credulous to believe the worst, ready to shake off their old acquaintance without cause, and to condemn them without colour: All which humors are by so much the more easier to be purged, by how much the less they have festered the sinews: But return we again to Euphues.

Euphues having sojourned by the space of two months in Naples, whether he were moved by the courtesy of a young gentleman named Philautus, or enforced by destiny: whether his pregnant wit, or his pleasant conceits wrought the greater liking in the mind of Euphues, I know not for certainty: But Euphues showed such entire love towards him, that he seemed to make small account of any others, determining to enter into such an inviolable league of friendship with him, as neither time by piecemeal should impair, neither fancy utterly dissolve, nor any suspicion infringe. "I have read," saith he, "and well I believe it, that a friend is in prosperity a pleasure, a solace in adversity, in grief a comfort, in joy a merry companion, at all times another I, in all places the express image of mine own person: insomuch that I cannot tell, whether the immortal gods have bestowed any gift upon mortal men, either more noble, or more necessary, than friendship. Is there anything in the world to be reputed (I will not say compared) to friendship? Can any treasure in this transitory pilgrimage be of more value than a friend? in whose bosom thou mayst sleep secure without fear, whom thou mayst make partner of all thy secrets without suspicion of fraud, and partaker of all thy misfortune without mistrust of fleeting, who will account thy bale his bane, thy mishap his misery, the prickling of thy finger, the piercing of his heart. But whither am I carried? Have I not also learned that one should eat a bushel of salt with him, whom he meaneth to make his friend? that trial maketh trust? that there is falsehood in fellowship? and what then? Doth not the sympathy of manners, make the conjunction of minds? Is it not a byword, like will to like? Not so common as commendable it is, to see young gentlemen choose them such friends with whom they may seem being absent to be present, being asunder to be conversant, being dead to be alive. I will therefore have Philautus for my fere, and by so much the more I make myself sure to have Philautus, by how much the more I view in him the lively image of Euphues."

Although there be none so ignorant that doth not know, neither any so impudent that will not confess, friendship to be the jewel of human joy: yet whosoever shall see this amity grounded upon a little affection, will soon conjecture that it shall be dissolved upon a light occasion: as in the sequel of Euphues & Philautus you shall see, whose hot love waxed soon cold. For as the best wine doth make the sharpest vinegar, so the deepest love turneth to the deadliest hate. Who deserved the most blame in mine opinion, it is doubtful, & so difficult, that I dare not presume to give verdict. For love being the cause for which so many mischiefs have been attempted, I am not yet persuaded, whether of them was most to be blamed, but certainly neither of them was blameless. I appeal to your judgement, gentlemen, not that I think any of you of the like disposition able to decide the question, but being of deeper discretion than I am, are more fit to debate the quarrel. Though the discourse of their friendship and falling out be somewhat long, yet being somewhat strange, I hope the delightfulness of the one, will attenuate the tediousness of the other.

Euphues had continual access to the place of Philautus and no little familiarity with him, and finding him at convenient leisure, in these short terms unfolded his mind unto him.

"Gentleman and friend, the trial I have had of thy manners

cutteth off divers terms which to another I would have used in the like matter. And sithence[28] a long discourse argueth folly, and delicate words incur the suspicion of flattery, I am determined to use neither of them, knowing either of them to breed offence. Weighing with myself the force of friendship by the effects, I studied ever since my first coming to Naples to enter league with such a one, as might direct my steps being a stranger, & resemble my manners being a scholar, the which two qualities as I find in you able to satisfy my desire, so I hope I shall find a heart in you willing to accomplish my request. Which if I may obtain, assure yourself that Damon to his Pythias, Pylades to his Orestes, Titus to his Gysippus, Theseus to his Pirithous, Scipio to his Laelius,[29] was never found more faithful than Euphues will be to his Philautus."

Philautus by how much the less he looked for this discourse, by so much the more he liked it, for he saw all qualities both of body & mind in Euphues, unto whom he replied as followeth.

"Friend Euphues (for so your talk warranteth me to term you) I dare neither use a long process, neither a loving speech, lest unwittingly I should cause you to convince me of those things, which you have already condemned. And verily I am bold to presume upon your courtesy, since you yourself have used so little curiosity, persuading myself, that my short answer will work as great an effect in you, as your few words did in me. And seeing we resemble (as you say) each other in qualities, it cannot be that the one should differ from the other in courtesy, seeing the sincere affection of the mind cannot be expressed by the mouth, & that no art can unfold the entire love of the heart, I am earnestly to beseech you not to measure the firmness of my faith, by the fewness of my words, but rather think that the overflowing waves of good will leave no passage for many words. Trial shall prove trust, here is my hand, my heart, my lands and my life at thy commandment: Thou mayst well perceive that I did believe thee, that so soon I did love thee, and I hope thou wilt the rather love me, in that I did believe thee." Either Euphues and Philautus stood in need of friendship, or were ordained to be friends: upon so short warning, to make so soon a conclusion might seem in mine opinion if it continued miraculous, if shaken off, ridiculous.

But after many embracings & protestations one to another, they walked to dinner, where they wanted neither meat, neither music, neither any other pastime, & having banqueted, to digest their sweet confections, they danced all that afternoon, they used not only one board, but one bed, one book (if so be it they thought not one too many.) Their friendship augmented every day, insomuch that the one could not refrain the company of the other one minute, all things went in common between them, which all men accounted commendable. Philautus being a town-born child, both for his own continuance, & the great countenance which his father had while he lived, crept into credit with Don Ferardo one of the chief governors of the city, who although he had a courtly crew of gentlewomen sojourning in his palace, yet his daughter heir to his whole revenues, stained the beauty of them all, whose modest bashfulness caused the other to look wan for envy, whose lily cheeks dyed with a vermilion red made the rest to blush for shame. For as the finest ruby staineth the colour of the rest that be in place, or as the sun dimmeth the moon, that she cannot be discerned, so this gallant girl more fair than fortunate, and yet more fortunate than faithful, eclipsed the beauty of them all, and changed their colours. Unto her had Philautus access, who won her by right of love, and should have worn her by right of law, had not Euphues by strange destiny broken the bonds of marriage, and forbidden the bans[30] of matrimony.

It happened that Don Ferardo had occasion to go to Venice about certain his own affairs, leaving his daughter the only steward of his household, who spared not to feast Philautus her friend, with all kinds of delights & delicates, reserving only her honesty as the chief stay of her honour. Her father being gone she sent for her friend to supper, who came not as he was accustomed solitarily alone, but accompanied with his friend Euphues. The gentlewoman whether it were for niceness or for niggardness of courtesy, gave him such a cold welcome that he repented that he was come.

Euphues though he knew himself worthy every way to have a good countenance, yet could he not perceive her willing anyway to lend him a friendly look. Yet lest he should seem to want gestures, or to be dashed out of conceit with her coy countenance, he addressed him to a gentlewoman called Livia, unto whom he uttered this speech. "Fair lady, if it be the guise of Italy to welcome strangers with strangeness, I must needs say the custom is strange and the country barbarous, if the manner of ladies to salute gentlemen with coyness, then I am enforced to think the women without courtesy to use such welcome, and the men past shame that will come. But hereafter I will either bring a stool on mine arm for an unbidden guest, or a visard on my face, for a shameless gossip." Livia replied.

"Sir, our country is civil, & our gentlewomen are courteous, but in Naples it is counted a jest, at every word to say, 'In faith you are welcome.'" As she was yet talking, supper was set on the board, then Philautus spake thus unto Lucilla. "Yet gentlewoman I was the bolder to bring my shadow with me," meaning Euphues, "knowing that he should be the better welcome for my sake"; unto whom the gentlewoman replied: "Sir as I never when I saw you thought that you came without your shadow, so now I cannot a little marvel to see you so overshot in bringing a new shadow with you." Euphues though he perceived her coy nip, seemed not to care for it, but taking her by the hand said.

"Fair lady seeing the shade doth often shield your beauty from the parching sun, I hope you will the better esteem of the shadow, and by so much the less it ought to be offensive, by how much the less it is able to offend you, and by so much the more you ought to like it, by how much the more you use to lie in it."

"Well gentlemen," answered Lucilla, "in arguing of the

shadow, we forgo the substance: pleaseth it you therefore to sit down to supper." And so they all sat down, but Euphues fed of one dish which ever stood before him, the beauty of Lucilla.

Here Euphues at the first sight was so kindled with desire, that almost he was like to burn to coals. Supper being ended, the order was in Naples that the gentlewomen would desire to hear some discourse, either concerning love or learning: And although Philautus was requested, yet he posted it over to Euphues, whom he knew most fit for that purpose: Euphues being thus tied to the stake by their importunate entreaty, began as followeth.

"He that worst may is alway enforced to hold the candle, the weakest must still to the wall, where none will, the devil himself must bear the cross: But were it not gentlewomen that your list[31] stands for law, I would borrow so much leave as to resign mine office to one of you, whose experience in love hath made you learned, and whose learning hath made you so lovely: for me to entreat of the one being a novice, or to discourse of the other being a truant, I may well make you weary but never the wiser, and give you occasion rather to laugh at my rashness, than to like my reasons. Yet I care the less to excuse my boldness to you, who were the cause of my blindness. And since I am at mine own choice either to talk of love or of learning, I had rather for this time be deemed an unthrift in rejecting profit, than a stoic in renouncing pleasure.

"It hath been a question often disputed, but never determined, whether the qualities of the mind, or the composition of the man, cause women most to like, or whether beauty or wit move men most to love. Certes by how much the more the mind is to be preferred before the body, by so much the more the graces of the one are to be preferred before the gifts of the other, which if it be so, that the contemplation of the inward quality ought to be respected more, than the view of the outward beauty, then doubtless women either do or should love those best whose virtue is best, not measuring the deformed man with the reformed mind. The foul toad hath a fair stone in his head, the fine gold is found in the filthy earth, the sweet kernel lieth in the hard shell. Virtue is harbored in the heart of him that most men esteem misshapen. Contrariwise if we respect more the outward shape, than the inward habit, good God into how many mischiefs do we fall? into what blindness are we led? Do we not commonly see that in painted pots is hidden the deadliest poison? that in the greenest grass is the greatest serpent? in the clearest water the ugliest toad? Doth not experience teach us that in the most curious sepulchre are enclosed rotten bones? That the cypress tree beareth a fair leaf but no fruit? That the estridge[32] carrieth fair feathers, but rank flesh? How frantic are those lovers which are carried away with the gay glistering of the fine face? the beauty whereof is parched with the summer's blaze, & chipped with the winter's blast, which is of so short continuance that it fadeth before one perceive it flourish, of so small profit that it poisoneth those that possess it, of so little value with the wise, that they account it a delicate bait with a deadly hook, a sweet panther with a devouring paunch, a sour poison in a silver pot. Here I could enter into discourse of such fine dames as being in love with their own looks, make such coarse account of their passionate lovers: for commonly if they be adorned with beauty, they be straight-laced, and made so high in the instep, that they disdain them most that most desire them. It is a world to see the doting of their lovers, and their dealing with them, the revealing of whose subtile trains would cause me to shed tears, & you gentlewomen to shut your modest ears. Pardon me gentlewomen if I unfold every wile, & show every wrinkle of women's disposition. Two things do they cause their servants to vow unto them, secrecy, & sovereignty, the one to conceal their enticing sleights, by the other to assure themselves of their only service. Again, but ho there, if I should have waded any further, & sounded the depth of their deceit, I should either have procured your displeasure, or incurred the suspicion of fraud, either armed you to practice the like subtlety, or accused myself of perjury. But I mean not to offend your chaste minds, with the rehearsal of their unchaste manners, whose ears I perceive to glow, and hearts to be grieved at that which I have already uttered, not that amongst you there be any such, but that in your sex there should be any such. Let not gentlewomen therefore make too much of their painted sheath, let them not be so curious in their own conceit, or so currish to their loyal lovers. When the black crow's-foot shall appear in their eye, or the black ox tread on their foot, when their beauty shall be like the blasted rose, their wealth wasted, their bodies worn, their faces wrinkled, their fingers crooked, who will like of them in their age, who loved none in their youth? If you will be cherished when you be old, be courteous while you be young, if you look for comfort in your hoary hairs, be not coy when you have your golden locks, if you would be embraced in the waning of your bravery, be not squeamish in the waxing of your beauty, if you desire to be kept like the roses when they have lost their colour, smell sweet as the rose doth in the bud, if you would be tasted for old wine, be in the mouth a pleasant grape, so shall you be cherished for your courtesy, comforted for your honesty, embraced for your amity, so shall you be preserved with the sweet rose, and drunk with the pleasant wine. Thus far I am bold gentlewomen, to counsel those that be coy that they weave not the web of their own woe, nor spin the thread of their own thraldom by their own overthwartness. And seeing we are even in the bowels of love, it shall not be amiss to examine whether man or woman be soonest allured, whether be most constant the male or the female. And in this point I mean not to be mine own carver, lest I should seem either to pick a thank with men, or a quarrel with women. If therefore it might stand with your pleasure (Mistress Lucilla) to give your censure I would take the contrary, for sure I am though your judgement be sound, yet affection will shadow it."

Lucilla seeing his pretence thought to take advantage of his large proffer, unto whom she said. "Gentleman in my opinion women are to be won with every wind, in whose sex there is neither force to withstand the assaults of love, neither constancy to remain faithful. And because your discourse hath hitherto bred delight, I am loth to hinder you in the sequel of your devices." Euphues perceiving himself to be taken napping, answered as followeth.

"Mistress Lucilla, if you speak as you think, these gentlewomen present have little cause to thank you, if you cause me to commend women, my tale will be accounted a mere trifle, & your words the plain truth: Yet knowing promise to be debt, I will pay it with performance. And I would the gentlemen here present were as ready to credit my proof, as the gentlewomen are willing to hear their own praises, or I as able to overcome, as Mistress Lucilla would be content to be overthrown. Howsoever the matter shall fall out, I am of the surer side, for if my reasons be weak, then is our sex strong, if forcible, then your judgment feeble, if I find truth on my side, I hope I shall for my wages win the good will of women, if I want proof, then gentlewomen of necessity you must yield to men. But to the matter.

"Touching the yielding to love, albeit their hearts seem tender, yet they harden them like the stone of Sicilia,[33] the which the more it is beaten, the harder it is: for being framed as it were of the perfection of men, they be free from all such cogitations as may any way provoke them to uncleanness, insomuch as they abhor the light love of youth which is grounded upon lust, & dissolved upon every light occasion. When they see the folly of men turn to fury, their delight to doting, their affection to frenzy, when they see them as it were pine in pleasure, and to wax pale through their own peevishness, their suits, their service, their letters, their labours, their loves, their lives, seem to them so odious, that they harden their hearts against such concupiscence, to the end they might convert them from rashness to reason, from such lewd disposition, to honest discretion: hereof it cometh that men accuse women of cruelty, because they themselves want civility, they account them full of wiles in not yielding to their wickedness, faithless for resisting their filthiness. But I had almost forgot myself, you shall pardon me Mistress Lucilla for this time, if thus abruptly, I finish my discourse: it is neither for want of good will, or lack of proof, but that I feel in myself such alteration, that I can scarcely utter one word. Ah Euphues, Euphues."

The gentlewomen were struck into such a quandary with this sudden change, that they all changed colour. But Euphues taking Philautus by the hand and giving the gentlewomen thanks for their patience and his repast, bade them all farewell, and went immediately to his chamber. But Lucilla who now began to fry in the flames of love, all the company being departed to their lodgings, entered into these terms and contrarieties.

"Ah wretched wench Lucilla how art thou perplexed? what a doubtful fight dost thou feel betwixt faith and fancy? hope & fear? conscience and concupiscence? O my Euphues, little dost thou know the sudden sorrow that I sustain for thy sweet sake. Whose wit hath betwitched me, whose rare qualities have deprived me of mine old quality, whose courteous behaviour without curiosity, whose comely feature without fault, whose filed speech without fraud, hath wrapped me in this misfortune. And canst thou Lucilla be so light of love in forsaking Philautus to fly to Euphues? canst thou prefer a stranger before thy countryman? a starter before thy companion? Why Euphues doth perhaps desire my love, but Philautus hath deserved it. Why Euphues' feature is worthy as good as I, But Philautus his faith is worthy a better. Aye but the latter love is most fervent. Aye but the first ought to be most faithful. Aye but Euphues hath greater perfection, Aye but Philautus hath deeper affection.

"Ah fond wench, dost thou think Euphues will deem thee constant to him, when thou hast been unconstant to his friend? Weenest thou that he will have no mistrust of thy faithfulness, when he hath had trial of thy fickleness? Will he have no doubt of thine honour, when thou thyself callest thine honesty in question? Yes, yes, Lucilla, well doth he know that the glass once crazed will with the least clap be cracked, that the cloth which staineth with milk, will soon lose his colour with vinegar, that the eagle's wing will waste the feather as well of the phoenix, as of the pheasant, that she that hath been faithless to one, will never be faithful to any. But can Euphues convince me of fleeting, seeing for his sake I break my fidelity? Can he condemn me of disloyalty, when he is the only cause of my disliking? May he justly condemn me of treachery, who hath this testimony as trial of my good will? Doth not he remember that the broken bone once set together, is stronger than ever it was? That the greatest blot is taken off with the pumice? That though the spider poison the fly, she cannot infect the bee? That although I have been light to Philautus, yet I may be lovely to Euphues? It is not my desire, but his deserts that moveth my mind to this choice, neither the want of the like good will in Philautus, but the lack of the like good qualities that removeth my fancy from the one to the other.

"For as the bee that gathereth honey out of the weed, when she espieth the fair flower flyeth to the sweetest: or as the kind spaniel though he hunt after birds, yet forsakes them to retrieve the partridge: or as we commonly feed on beef hungrily at the first, yet seeing the quail more dainty, change our diet: So I, although I loved Philautus for his good properties, yet seeing Euphues to excel him, I ought by nature to like him better: By so much the more therefore my change is to be excused, by how much the more my choice is excellent: and by so much the less I am to be condemned, by how much the more Euphues is to be commended. Is not the diamond of more value than the ruby, because he is of more virtue? Is not the emerald preferred before the sapphire for his wonderful property? Is not Euphues more praiseworthy than Philautus being more witty? But fie Lucilla, why dost thou flatter thyself in thine own folly? Canst thou feign Euphues thy friend, whom by thine own words thou hast made thy foe? Didest not thou accuse women of inconstancy? didest not thou account them easy to be won? didest not thou condemn them of weakness? what sounder argument can he have against thee, than thine own answer? what better proof, than thine own speech? what greater trial, than thine own talk? If thou hast belied women, he will judge thee unkind, if thou have revealed the truth, he must needs think thee unconstant, if he perceive thee to be won with a nut, he will imagine that thou wilt be lost with an apple: If he find thee wanton before thou be wooed, he will guess thou wilt be wavering when thou art wedded.

"But suppose that Euphues love thee, that Philautus leave thee, will thy father thinkest thou give thee liberty to live after thine own lust? Will he esteem him worthy to inherit his possessions, whom he accounteth unworthy to enjoy thy person? Is it like that he will match thee in marriage with a stranger, with a Grecian, with a mean man? Aye but what knoweth my father whether he be wealthy, whether his revenues be able to countervail my father's lands, whether his birth be noble, yea, or no? Can anyone make doubt of his gentle blood, that seeth his gentle conditions? Can his honour be called into question, whose honesty is so great? is he to be thought thriftless, who in all qualities of the mind is peerless? No, no, the tree is known by his fruit, the gold by his touch, the son by the sire. And as the soft wax receiveth whatsoever print be in the seal, and showeth no other impression, so the tender babe being sealed with his father's gifts representeth his image most lively. But were I once certain of Euphues' good will, I would not so superstitiously account of my father's ill will. Time hath weaned me from my mother's teat, and age rid me from my father's correction, when children are in their swathe clouts, then are they subject to the whip, and ought to be careful of the rigour of their parents. As for me seeing I am not fed with their pap, I am not to be led by their persuasions. Let my father use what speeches he list, I will follow mine own lust. Lust Lucilla, what sayst thou? No, no, mine own love I should have said, for I am as far from lust, as I am from reason, and as near to love as I am to folly. Then stick to thy determination, & shew thyself, what love can do, what love dares do, what love hath done. Albeit I can no way quench the coals of desire with forgetfulness, yet will I rake them up in the ashes of modesty, seeing I dare not discover my love for maidenly shamefacedness I will dissemble it till time I have opportunity. And I hope so to behave myself as Euphues shall think me his own, and Philautus persuade himself I am none but his. But I would to God Euphues would repair hither, that the sight of him might mitigate some part of my martyr-dom."

She having thus discoursed with herself her own miseries, cast herself on the bed: and there let her lie, and return we to Euphues, who was so caught in the gin of folly, that he neither could comfort himself nor durst ask counsel of his friend, suspecting that which indeed was true, that Phi-lautus was corrival with him and cock-mate[34] with Lucilla. Amidst therefore these his extremities between hope and fear, he uttered these or the like speeches.

"What is he Euphues that knowing thy wit, and seeing thy folly: but will rather punish thy lewdness, than pity thy heaviness? Was there ever any so fickle so soon to be allured? any ever so faithless to deceive his friend? ever any so foolish to bathe himself in his own misfortune? Too true it is that as the sea crab swimmeth always against the stream, so wit always striveth against wisdom: And as the bee is oftentimes hurt with her own honey, so is wit not seldom plagued with his own conceit.

"O ye gods have ye ordained for every malady a medicine, for every sore a salve, for every pain a plaster, leaving only love remediless? Did ye deem no man so mad to be entangled with desire, or thought ye them worthy to be tormented that were so misled? have ye dealt more favourable with brute beasts than with reasonable creatures.

"The filthy sow when she is sick, eateth the sea crab and is immediately recured: the tortoise having tasted the viper, sucketh *origanum* and is quickly revived: the bear ready to

pine, licketh up the ants and is recovered: the dog having surfeited, to procure his vomit eateth grass, and findeth remedy: the hart being pierced with the dart, runneth out of
hand to the herb *dictanum*, and is healed. And can men by
no herb, by no art, by no way procure a remedy for the
impatient disease of love? Ah well I perceive that love is not
unlike the fig tree, whose fruit is sweet, whose root is more
bitter than the claw of a bitter,[35] or like the apple in Persia,
whose blossom savoreth like honey, whose bud is more sour
than gall.

"But O impiety. O broad blasphemy against the heavens.
Wilt thou be so impudent Euphues, to accuse the gods of
iniquity? No fond fool, no. Neither is it forbidden us by the
gods to love, by whose divine providence we are permitted
to live, neither do we want remedies to recure our maladies,
but reason to use the means. But why go I about to hinder
the course of love, with the discourse of law? hast thou not
read Euphues, that he that loppeth the vine causeth it to
spread fairer? that he that stoppeth the stream forceth it to
swell higher? that he that casteth water on the fire in the
smith's forge, maketh it to flame fiercer? Even so he that
seeketh by counsel to moderate his overlashing affections,
increaseth his own misfortune. Ah my Lucilla, would thou
wert either less fair or I more fortunate, either I wiser or
thou milder, either would I were out of this mad mood,
either I would we were both of one mind. But how should
she be persuaded of my loyalty, that yet had never one simple
proof of my love? will she not rather imagine me to be entangled with her beauty, than with her virtue. That my fancy
being so lewdly changed at the first, will be as lightly changed
at the last, that there is nothing which is permanent that is violent? yes, yes, she must needs conjecture so, although it be
nothing so, for by how much the more my affection cometh
on the sudden, by so much the less will she think it certain.
The rattling thunderbolt hath but his clap, the lightning but his
flash, and as they both come in a moment, so do they both
end in a minute.

"Aye but Euphues, hath she not heard also that the dry touchwood is kindled with lime, that the greatest mushrompe[36] groweth in one night? that the fire quickly burneth the flax? that love easily entereth into the sharp wit without resistance, & is harboured there without repentance?

"If therefore the gods have endued her with as much bounty as beauty. If she have no less wit than she hath comeliness, certes she will neither conceive sinisterly of my sudden suit, neither be coy to receive me into her service, neither suspect me of lightness, in yielding so lightly, neither reject me disdainfully, for loving so hastily. Shall I not then hazard my life to obtain my love? and deceive Philautus to receive Lucilla? Yes Euphues, where love beareth sway, friendship can have no shew: As Philautus brought me for his shadow the last supper, so will I use him for my shadow till I have gained his saint. And canst thou wretch be false to him that is faithful to thee? Shall his courtesy be cause of thy cruelty? Wilt thou violate the league of faith, to inherit the land of folly? Shall affection be of more force than friendship, love than law, lust than loyalty? Knowest thou not that he that loseth his honesty hath nothing else to lose?

"Tush the case is light where reason taketh place, to love and to live well, is not granted to Jupiter. Who so is blinded with the caul [37] of beauty, discerneth no colour of honesty. Did not Gyges cut Candaules[38] a coat by his own measure? Did not Paris though he were a welcome guest to Menelaus serve his host a flippery prank? [39] If Philautus had loved Lucilla, he would never have suffered Euphues to have seen her. Is it not the prey that enticeth the thief to rifle? Is it not the pleasant bait, that causeth the fleetest fish to bite? Is it not a byword amongst us, that gold maketh an honest man an ill man? Did Philautus account Euphues too simple to decipher beauty, or superstitious not to desire it? Did he deem him a saint in rejecting fancy, or a sot in not discerning?

"Thought he him a stoic that he would not be moved, or a stock that he could not?

"Well, well, seeing the wound that bleedeth inward is

most dangerous, that the fire kept close burnest most furious, that the oven dammed up baketh soonest, that sores having no vent fester inwardly, it is high time to unfold my secret love, to my secret friend. Let Philautus behave himself never so craftily, he shall know that it must be a wily mouse that shall breed in the cat's ear, and because I resemble him in wit, I mean a little to dissemble with him in wiles. But O my Lucilla, if thy heart be made of that stone which may be mollified only with blood, would I had sipped of that river in Caria[40] which turneth those that drink of it to stones. If thine ears be anointed with the oil of Syria that bereaveth hearing, would mine eyes had been rubbed with the syrup of the cedar tree which taketh away sight.

"If Lucilla be so proud to disdain poor Euphues, would Euphues were so happy to deny Lucilla, or if Lucilla be so mortified to live without love, would Euphues were so fortunate to live in hate. Aye but my cold welcome foretelleth my cold suit, aye but her privy glances signify some good fortune. Fie fond fool Euphues, why goest thou about to allege those things to cut off thy hope which she perhaps would never have found, or to comfort myself with those reasons which she never meaneth to propose: Tush it were no love if it were certain, and a small conquest it is to overthrow those that never resisteth.

"In battles there ought to be a doubtful fight, and a desperate end, in pleading a difficult entrance, and a diffused determination, in love a life without hope, and a death without fear. Fire cometh out of the hardest flint with the steel. Oil out of the dryest jet by the fire, love out of the stoniest heart by faith, by trust, by time. Had Tarquinius used his love with colours of continuance, Lucretia[41] would either with some pity have answered his desire, or with some persuasion have stayed her death. It was the heat of his lust, that made her haste to end her life, wherefore love in neither respect is to be condemned, but he of rashness to attempt a lady furiously, and she of rigor to punish his folly in her own flesh, a fact (in mine opinion) more worthy the name of cruelty than chastity, and fitter for a monster in the deserts, than a matron of Rome. Penelope no less constant than she, yet more wise, would be weary to unweave that in the night, she spun in the day, if Ulysses had not come home the sooner.[42] There is no woman, Euphues, but she will yield in time, be not therefore dismayed either with high looks or forward words."

Euphues having thus talked with himself, Philautus entered the chamber, and finding him so worn and wasted with continual mourning, neither joying in his meat, nor rejoicing in his friend, with watery eyes uttered this speech.

"Friend and fellow, as I am not ignorant of thy present weakness, so I am not privy of the cause, and although I suspect many things, yet can I assure myself of no one thing. Therefore my good Euphues, for these doubts and dumps of mine, either remove the cause or reveal it. Thou hast hitherto found me a cheerful companion in thy mirth, and now shalt thou find me as careful with thee in thy moan. If altogether thou mayst not be cured, yet mayst thou be comforted. If there be any thing that either by my friends may be procured, or by my life attained, that may either heal thee in part, or help thee in all, I protest to thee by the name of a friend, that it shall rather be gotten with the loss of my body, than lost by getting a kingdom. Thou hast tried me, therefore trust me, thou hast trusted me in many things, therefore try me in this one thing. I never yet failed, and now I will not faint. Be bold to speak & flush not: thy sore is not so angry but I can salve it, the wound not so deep but I can search it, thy grief not so great but I can ease it. If it be ripe it shall be lanced, if it be broken it shall be tainted, be it never so desperate it shall be cured. Rise therefore Euphues, & take heart at grass,[43] younger thou shalt never be, pluck up thy stomach, if love itself have stung thee it shall not stifle thee. Though thou be enamoured of some lady thou shalt not be enchanted. They that begin to pine of a consumption, without delay preserve themselves with cullises,[44] he that feeleth his stomach inflamed with heat, cooleth it eftsoons with conserves: delays breed dangers, nothing so perilous as procrastination." Euphues hearing this comfort & friendly counsel, dissembled his sorrowing heart, with a smiling face, answering him forthwith as followeth.

"True it is Philautus that he which toucheth the nettle tenderly, is soonest stung, that the fly which playeth with the fire is singed in the flame, that he that dallieth with women is drawn to his woe. And as the adamant draweth the heavy iron, the harp the fleet dolphin, so beauty allureth the chaste mind to love, & the wisest wit to lust: The example whereof I would it were no less profitable than the experience to me is like to be perilous. The vine watered with wine is soon withered, the blossom in the fattest ground is quickly blasted, the goat the fatter she is the less fertile she is: yea, man the more witty he is the less happy he is. So it is Philautus (for why should I conceal it from thee, of whom I am to take counsel) that since my last & first being with thee at the house of Ferardo, I have felt such a furious battle in mine own body, as if it be not speedily repressed by policy, it will carry my mind (the grand captain in this fight) into endless captivity. Ah Livia, Livia, thy courtly grace without coyness, thy blazing beauty without blemish, thy courteous demeanor without curiosity, thy sweet speech savoured with wit, thy comely mirth tempered with modesty, thy chaste looks yet lovely, thy sharp taunts yet pleasant, have given me such a check, that sure I am at the next view of thy virtues, I shall take thee mate: And taking it not of a pawn, but of a prince, the loss is to be accounted the less. And though they be commonly in a great choler that receive the mate, yet would I willingly take every minute x. mates, to enjoy Livia for my loving mate. Doubtless if ever she herself have been scorched with the flames of desire, she will be ready to quench the coals with courtesy in another, if ever she have been attached of love, she will rescue him that is drenched in desire, if ever she have been taken with the fever of fancy, she will help his ague, who by a quotidian fit is converted into frenzy: Neither can there be under so delicate a hue lodged deceit, neither in so beautiful a mold a malicious mind. True it is that the disposition of the mind, followeth the composition of the body: how then can she be in mind any way imperfect, who in body is perfect every way? I know my success will be good, but I know not how to have access to my goddess, neither do I want courage to discover my love to my friend, but some colour to cloak my coming to the house of Ferardo, for if they be in Naples as jealous as they be in the other parts of Italy, then it behooveth me to walk circumspectly, & to forge some cause for mine often coming. If therefore Philautus, thou canst set but this feather to mine arrow, thou shalt see me shoot so near, that thou wilt account me for a cunning archer. And verily if I had not loved thee well, I would have swallowed mine own sorrow in silence, knowing that in love nothing is so dangerous, as to participate the .eans thereof to another, & that two may keep counsel if one be away. I am therefore enforced perforce to challenge that courtesy at thy hands, which erst thou didest promise with thy heart, the performance whereof shall bind me to Philautus, and prove thee faithful to Euphues. Now if thy cunning be answerable to thy good will, practise some pleasant conceit upon thy poor patient: one dram of Ovid's art, some of Tibullis' drugs, one of Propertius' pills,[45] which may cause me either to purge my new disease, or recover my hoped desire. But I fear me where so strange a sickness is to be recured of so unskillful a physician, that either thou wilt be too bold to practice, or my body too weak to purge. But seeing a desperate disease is to be committed to a desperate doctor, I will follow thy counsel and become thy cure, desiring thee to be as wise in ministering thy physic, as I have been willing to put my life into thy hands."

Philautus thinking all to be gold that glistered, and all to be gospel that Euphues uttered, answered his forged gloze with this friendly close.

"In that thou hast made me privy to thy purpose, I will not conceal my practise, in that thou cravest my aid, assure thyself I will be the finger next the thumb, insomuch as thou shalt never repent thee of the one or the other. For[46] persuade thyself that thou shalt find Philautus during life ready to comfort thee in thy misfortunes, and succour thee in thy necessity. Concerning Livia though she be fair, yet is she not so amiable as my Lucilla, whose servant I have been the term of three years, but lest comparison should seem odious, chiefly where both the parties be without comparison, I will omit that, and seeing that we had both rather be talking with them, than tattling of them, we will immediately go to them. And truly Euphues I am not a little glad, that I shall have thee, not only a comfort in my life, but also a companion in my love: As thou hast been wise in thy choice, so I hope thou shalt be fortunate in thy chance. Livia is a wench of more wit than beauty, Lucilla of more beauty than wit, both of more honesty than honour, and yet both of such honour, as in all Naples there is not one in birth, to be compared with any of them both. How much therefore have we to rejoice in our choice? Touching our access be thou secure, I will flap Ferardo in the mouth with some conceit, and fill his old head so full of new fables that thou shalt rather be earnestly entreated to repair to his house, than evil entreated to leave it. As old men are very suspicious to mistrust everything, so are they very credulous to believe anything, the blind man doth eat many a fly:" "Yea, but," said Euphues, "take heed my Philautus, that thou thyself swallow not a gudgeon," which word Philautus did not mark, until he had almost digested it. "But," said Philautus, "let us go devoutly to the shrine of our saints there to offer our devotion, for my books teach me, that such a wound must be healed where it was first hurt, and for this disease we will use a common remedy, but yet comfortable. The eye that blinded thee, shall make thee see, the scorpion that stung thee shall heal the, a sharp sore hath a short cure, let us go:" to the which Euphues consented willingly, smiling to himself to see how he had brought Philautus into a fool's paradise.

Here you may see gentlemen the falsehood in fellowship, the fraud in friendship, the painted sheath with the leaden dagger, the fair words that make fools fain, but I will not trouble you with superfluous addition unto whom I fear me I have been tedious, with the bare discourse of this rude history.

Philautus and Euphues repaired to the house of Ferardo, where they found Mistress Lucilla and Livia accompanied with other gentlewomen neither being idle, nor well employed, but playing at cards. But when Lucilla beheld Euphues she could scarcely contain herself from embracing him, had not womanly shamefacedness, and Philautus his presence, stayed her wisdom.

Euphues on the other side was fallen into such a trance, that he had not the power either to succour himself, or salute the gentlewomen. At the last Lucilla, began as one that best might be bold, on this manner.

"Gentlemen although your long absence gave me occasion to think that you disliked your late entertainment, yet your coming at the last hath cut off my former suspicion: And by so much the more you are welcome by how much the more you were wished for. But you gentleman," taking Euphues by the hand, "were the rather wished for, for that your discourse being left unperfect, caused us all to long (as women are wont for things that like them) to have an end thereof." Unto whom Philautus replied as followeth.

"Mistress Lucilla though your courtesy made us nothing to doubt of our welcome, yet modesty caused us to pinch courtesy who should first come: as for my friend I think he was never wished for here so earnestly of any as of himself, whether it might be to renew his talk or to recant his sayings, I cannot tell." Euphues taking the tale out of Philautus' mouth, answered: "Mistress Lucilla, to recant verities were heresy, and renew the praises of women flattery: the only cause I wished myself here, was to give thanks for so good entertainment the which I could no ways deserve, & to breed a greater acquaintance if it might be to make amends." Lucilla inflamed with his presence, said, "Nay Euphues you shall not escape so, for if my courtesy, as you say, were the cause of your coming, let it also be the occasion of the ending your former discourse, otherwise I shall think your proof naked, and you shall find my reward nothing." Euphues now as willing to obey as she to command, addressed himself to a farther conclusion, who seeing all the gentlewomen ready to give him the hearing, proceeded as followeth.

"I have not yet forgotten that my last talk with these gentlewomen, tended to their praises, and therefore the end must tie up the just proof, otherwise I should set down Venus' shadow without the lively substance.

"As there is no one thing which can be reckoned either concerning love or loyalty wherein women do not excel men, yet in fervency above all others, they so far exceed, that men are liker to marvel at them, than to imitate them, and readier to laugh at their virtues than emulate them. For as they be hard to be won without trial of great faith, so are they hard to be lost without great cause of fickleness. It is long before the cold water seethe, yet being once hot, it is long before it be cooled, it is long before salt come to his saltness, but being once seasoned, it never loseth his savour.

"I for mine own part am brought into a paradise by the only imagination of women's virtues, and were I persuaded that all the devils in hell were women, I would never live devoutly to inherit heaven, or that they were all saints in heaven, I would live more strictly for fear of hell. What could Adam have done in his paradise before his fall without a woman, or how would he have rise again after his fall without a woman? Artificers are wont in their last works to excel themselves, yea, God when he had made all things, at the last, made man as most perfect, thinking nothing could be framed more excellent, yet after him he created a woman, the express image of eternity, the lively picture of nature, the only steel glass[47] for man to behold his infirmities, by comparing them with women's perfections. Are they not more gentle, more witty, more beautiful than men? Are not men so bewitched with their qualities that they become mad for love, and women so wise that they detest lust.

"I am entered into so large a field, that I shall sooner want time than proof, and so cloy you with variety of praises that I fear me I am like to infect women with pride, which yet they have not, and men with spite which yet I would not. For as the horse if he knew his own strength were no ways to be bridled, or the unicorn his own virtue, were never to be caught, so women if they knew what excellency were in them, I fear me men should never win them to their wills, or wean them from their mind."

Lucilla began to smile, saying, "In faith Euphues, I would have you stay there, for as the sun when he is at the highest beginneth to go down, so when the praises of women are at the best, if you leave not, they will begin to fail," but Euphues (being rapt with the sight of his saint) answered, "No no Lucilla." But whilst he was yet speaking Ferardo entered, whom they all dutifully welcomed home, who rounding[48] Philautus in the ear, desired him to accompany him immediately without farther pausing, protesting it should be as well for his preferment as for his own profit. Philautus consenting, Ferardo said to his daughter.

"Lucilla the urgent affairs I have in hand, will scarce suffer me to tarry with you one hour, yet my return I hope will be so short, that my absence shall not breed thy sorrow: In the mean season I commit all things into thy custody wishing thee to use thy accustomable courtesy. And seeing I must take Philautus with me, I will be so bold to crave you gentleman (his friend) to supply his room desiring you to take this hasty warning for a hearty welcome and so to spend this time of mine absence in honest mirth. And thus I leave you."

Philautus knew well the cause of this sudden departure, which was to redeem certain lands that were mortgaged in his father's time to the use of Ferardo who on that condition had before time promised him his daughter in marriage. But return we to Euphues.

Euphues was surprised with such incredible joy at this strange event, that he had almost sounded,[49] for seeing his corrival to be departed, and Ferardo to give him so friendly entertainment, doubted not in time to get the good will of Lucilla: Whom finding in place convenient without company, with a bold courage and comely gesture, he began to assay her in this sort.

"Gentlewoman, my acquaintance being so little, I am afraid my credit will be less, for that they commonly are soonest believed, that are best beloved, and they liked best, whom we have known longest, nevertheless the noble mind suspecteth no guile without cause, neither condemneth any wight without proof, having therefore notice of your heroical heart, I am the better persuaded of my good hap. So it is Lucilla, that coming to Naples but to fetch fire, as the byword is, not to make my place of abode, I have found such flames that I can neither quench them with the water of free will, neither cool them with wisdom. For as the hop the pole being never so high groweth to the end, or as the dry beech kindled at the root, never leaveth until it come to the top, or as one drop of poison disperseth itself into every vein, so affection having caught hold of my heart, and the sparkles of love kindled my liver, will suddenly, though secretly flame up into my head, and spread itself into every sinew. It is your beauty (pardon my abrupt boldness) lady that hath taken every part of me prisoner, and brought me unto this deep distress, but seeing women when one praiseth them for their deserts, deem that he flattereth them to obtain his desire, I am here present to yield myself to such trial, as your courtesy in this behalf shall require: Yet will you commonly object this to such as serve you & starve to win your good will, that hot love is soon cold, that the bavin[50] though it burn bright, is but a blaze, that scalding water if it stand a while turneth almost to ice, that pepper though it be hot in the mouth is cold in the maw, that the faith of men though it try in their words, it freezeth in their works: Which things (Lucilla) albeit they be sufficient to reprove the lightness of someone, yet can they not convince every one of lewdness, neither ought the constancy of all, to be brought in question through the subtilty of a few. For although the worm entereth almost into every wood, yet he eateth not the cedar tree: Though the stone cylindrus at every thunder clap, roll from the hill, yet the pure sleek stone mounteth at the noise, though the rust fret the hardest steel, yet doth it not eat into the emerald, though polypus change his hue, yet the salamander keepeth his colour, though Proteus transform himself into every shape, yet Pygmalion retaineth his old form, though Aeneas were too fickle to Dido, yet Troilus was too faithful to Cressida,[51] though others seem counterfeit in their deeds, yet Lucilla persuade yourself that Euphues will be always current in his dealings. But as the true gold is tried by the touch, the pure flint by the stroke of the iron, so the loyal heart of the faithful lover, is known by the trial of his lady: of the which trial (Lucilla) if you shall account Euphues worthy, assure yourself, he will be as ready to offer himself a sacrifice for your sweet sake, as yourself shall be willing to employ him in your service. Neither doth he desire to be trusted anyway, until he shall be tried every way, neither doth he crave credit at the first, but a good countenance till time his desire shall be made manifest by his deserts. Thus not blinded by light affection, but dazzled with your rare perfection, and boldened by your exceeding courtesy, I have unfolded mine entire love, desiring you having so good leisure, to give so friendly an answer, as I may receive comfort, and you commendation."

Lucilla although she were contented to hear this desired discourse, yet did she seem to be somewhat displeased: And truly I know not whether it be peculiar to that sex to dissemble with those, whom they most desire, or whether by craft they have learned outwardly to loathe that, which inwardly they most love: yet wisely did she cast this in her head, that if she should yield at the first assault he would think her a light huswife,[52] if she should reject him scornfully a very haggard, minding therefore that he should neither take hold of her promise, neither unkindness of her preciseness, she fed him indifferently, with hope and despair, reason and affection, life and death. Yet in the end arguing wittily upon certain questions, they fell to such agreement as poor Philautus would not have agreed unto if he had been present, yet always keeping the body undefiled. And thus she replied.

"Gentleman as you may suspect me of idleness in giving ear to your talk, so may you convince me of lightness in answering such toys, certes as you have made mine ears glow at the rehearsal of your love, so have you galled my heart with the remembrance of your folly. Though you came to Naples as a stranger, yet were you welcome to my father's house as a friend. And can you then so much transgress the bounds of honour (I will not say of honesty) as to solicit a suit more sharp to me than death? I have hitherto God be thanked, lived without suspicion of lewdness, and shall I now incur the danger of sensual liberty? What hope can you have to obtain my love, seeing yet I could never afford you a good look? Do you therefore think me easily enticed to the bent of your bow, because I was easily entreated to listen to your late discourse? Or seeing me (as finely you gloze) to excel all other in beauty, did you deem that I would exceed all other in beastliness? But yet I am not angry Euphues but in an agony, for who is she that will fret or fume with one that loveth her, if this love to delude me be not dissembled. It is that which causeth me most to fear, not that my beauty is unknown to myself but that commonly we poor wenches are deluded through light belief, and ye men are naturally inclined craftily to lead your life. When the fox preacheth the geese perish. The crocodile shroudeth greatest treason under most pitiful tears:[53] in a kissing mouth there lieth a galling mind. You have made so large proffer of your service, and so fair promises of fidelity, that were I not over chary of mine honesty, you would inveigle me to shake hands with chastity. But certes I will either lead a virgin's life in earth (though I lead apes in hell)[54] or else follow thee rather than thy gifts: yet am I neither so precise to refuse thy proffer, neither so peevish to disdain thy good will: so excellent always are the gifts which are made acceptable by the virtue of the giver. I did at the first entrance discern thy love but yet dissemble it. Thy wanton glances, thy scalding sighs, thy loving signs, caused me to blush for shame, and to look wan for fear, lest they should be perceived of any. These subtile shifts, these painted practises (if I were to be won) would soon wean me from the teat of Vesta to the toys of Venus. Besides this thy comely grace, thy rare qualities, thy exquisite perfection, were able to move a mind half mortified to transgress the bonds of maidenly modesty. But God shield Lucilla, that thou shouldest be so careless of thine honour as to commit the state thereof to a stranger. Learn thou by me Euphues to despise things that be amiable, to forgo delightful practises, believe me it is piety to abstain from pleasure.

"Thou art not the first that hath solicited this suit, but the first that goeth about to seduce me, neither discernest thou more than other, but darest more than any, neither hast thou more art to discover thy meaning, but more heart to open thy mind. But thou preferrest me before thy lands, thy livings, thy life: thou offerest thyself a sacrifice for my security, thou profferest me the whole and only sovereignty of thy service: Truly I were very cruel and hardhearted if I should not love thee: hardhearted albeit I am not, but truly love thee I cannot, whom I doubt to be my lover.

"Moreover I have not been used to the court of Cupid, wherein there be more sleights than there be hares in Athon, than bees in Hybla,[55] than stars in heaven. Besides this, the common people here in Naples are not only both very suspicious of other men's matters and manners, but also very jealous over other men's children and maidens: either therefore dissemble thy fancy, or desist from thy folly.

"But why shouldest thou desist from the one, seeing thou canst cunningly dissemble the other. My father is now gone to Venice, and as I am uncertain of his return, so am I not privy to the cause of his travel: But yet is he so from hence that he seeth me in his absence. Knowest thou not Euphues that kings have long arms & rulers large reaches? neither let this comfort thee, that at his departure he deputed thee in Philautus' place. Although my face cause him to mistrust my loyalty, yet my faith enforceth him to give me this liberty, though he be suspicious of my fair hue, yet is he secure of my firm honesty. But alas Euphues, what truth can there be found in a traveler? what stay in a stranger? whose words & bodies both watch but for a wind, whose feet are ever fleeting, whose faith plighted on the shore, is turned to perjury when they hoist sail. Who more traitorous to Phyllis than Demophon? yet he a traveler. Who more perjured to Dido than Aeneas? and he a stranger: both these queens, both they caitiffs. Who more false to Ariadne than Theseus? yet he a sailor. Who more fickle to Medea than Jason? yet he a starter: both these daughters to great princes, both they unfaithful of promises.[56] Is it then likely that Euphues will be faithful to Lucilla being in Naples but a sojourner? I have not yet forgotten the invective (I can no otherwise term it) which thou madest against beauty, saying it was a deceitful bait with a deadly hook, & a sweet poison in a painted pot. Canst thou then be so unwise to swallow the bait which will breed thy bane? To swill the drink that will expire thy date? To desire the wight that will work thy death? But it may be that with the scorpion thou canst feed on the earth, or with the quail and roebuck, be fat with poison or with beauty live in all bravery. I fear me thou hast the stone continens[57] about thee, which is named of the contrary, that though thou pretend faith in thy words, thou devisest fraud in thy heart: that though thou seem to prefer love, thou art inflamed with lust. And what for that? Though thou have eaten the seeds of rocket, which breed incontinency, yet have I chewed the leaf cress which maintaineth modesty. Though thou bear in thy bosom the herb araxa most noisome to virginity, yet have I the stone that groweth in the Mount Tmolus, the upholder of chastity. You may gentleman account me for a cold prophet, thus hastily to divine of your disposition, pardon me Euphues if in love I cast beyond the moon, which bringeth us women to endless moan. Although I myself were never burnt, whereby I should dread the fire, yet the scorching of others in the flames of fancy, warneth me to beware:

Though I as yet never tried any faithless, whereby I should
be fearful, yet have I read of many that have been perjured,
which causeth me to be careful: though I am able to convince none by proof, yet am I enforced to suspect one upon
probabilities. Alas we silly souls which have neither wit to
decipher the wiles of men, nor wisdom to dissemble our affection, neither craft to train in young lovers, neither courage
to withstand their encounters, neither discretion to discern
their doubling, neither hard hearts to reject their complaints,
we I say are soon enticed, being by nature simple, and easily
entangled, being apt to receive the impression of love. But
alas it is both common and lamentable, to behold simplicity
entrapped by subtility, and those that have most might, to be
infected with most malice. The spider weaveth a fine web to
hang the fly, the wolf weareth a fair face to devour the lamb,
the merlin striketh at the partridge, the eagle often snappeth
at the fly, men are always laying baits for women, which are
the weaker vessels: but as yet I could never hear man by such
snares to entrap man: For true it is that men themselves have
by use observed, that it must be a hard winter, when one
wolf eateth another. I have read that the bull being tied to
the fig tree loseth his strength, that the whole herd of deer
stand at the gaze, if they smell a sweet apple, that the dolphin
by the sound of music is brought to the shore. And then no
marvel it is that if the fierce bull be tamed with the fig tree,
if that women being as weak as sheep, be overcome with a
fig, if the wild deer be caught with an apple, that the tame
damsel is won with a blossom, if the fleet dolphin be allured
with harmony, that women be entangled with the melody of
men's speech, fair promises and solemn protestations. But
folly it were for me to mark their mischiefs, sith I am neither
able, neither they willing to amend their manners, it becometh me rather to shew what our sex should do, than to
open what yours doth. And seeing I cannot by reason restrain
your importunate suit, I will by rigour done on myself, cause
you to refrain the means. I would to God Ferardo were in
this point like to Lysander,[58] which would not suffer his

daughters to wear gorgeous apparel, saying it would rather make them common than comely. I would it were in Naples a law, which was a custom in Egypt, that women should always go barefoot, to the intent they might keep themselves always at home, that they should be ever like to that snail, which hath ever his house on his head. I mean so to mortify myself that instead of silks I will wear sackcloth, for ouches and bracelets, leer and caddies,[59] for the lute use the distaff, for the pen, the needle, for lover's sonnets, David's psalms. But yet I am not so senseless altogether to reject your service: which if I were certainly assured to proceed of a simple mind, it should not receive so simple a reward. And what greater trial can I have of thy simplicity & truth, than thine own request which desireth a trial. Aye, but in the coldest flint there is hot fire, the bee that hath honey in her mouth, hath a sting in her tail, the tree that beareth the sweetest fruit, hath a sour sap, yea the words of men, though they seem smooth as oil, yet their hearts are as crooked as the stalk of ivy. I would not Euphues that thou shouldest condemn me of rigour, in that I seek to assuage thy folly by reason, but take this by the way that although as yet I am disposed to like of none, yet whensoever I shall love any I will not forget thee, in the mean season account me thy friend, for thy foe I will never be."

Euphues was brought into a great quandary and as it were a cold shivering, to hear this new kind of kindness, such sweet meat, such sour sauce, such fair words, such faint promises, such hot love, such cold desire, such certain hope, such sudden change, and stood like one that had looked on Medusa's head, and so had been turned into a stone.

Lucilla seeing him in this pitiful plight and fearing he would take stand if the lure were not cast out, took him by the hand and wringing him softly with a smiling countenance began thus to comfort him.

"Methinks Euphues changing so your colour upon the sudden, you will soon change your copy: is your mind on your meat? a penny for your thought."

"Mistress," quoth he, "if you would buy all my thoughts at that price, I should never be weary of thinking, but seeing it is too dear, read it, and take it for nothing."

"It seems to me," said she, "that you are in some brown study, what colours you might best wear for your lady."

"Indeed Lucilla you level shrewdly at my thought, by the aim of your own imagination, for you have given unto me a true love's knot wrought of changeable silk, and you deem me that I am devising how I might have my colours changeable also, that they might agree: But let this with such toys and devices pass, if it please you to command me any service, I am here ready to attend your leisure." "No service Euphues, but that you keep silence until I have uttered my mind: and secrecy when I have unfolded my meaning."

"If I should offend in the one I were too bold, if in the other too beastly."

"Well then Euphues," said she, "so it is that for the hope that I conceive of thy loyalty and the happy success that is like to ensue of this our love, I am content to yield thee the place in my heart which thou desirest and deservest above all other: which consent in me if it may anyways breed thy contentation, sure I am that it will every way work my comfort. But as either thou tenderest mine honour or thine own safety, use such secrecy in this matter that my father have no inkling hereof, before I have framed his mind fit for our purpose. And though women have small force to overcome men by reason, yet have they good fortune to undermine them by policy. The soft drops of rain pierce the hard marble, many strokes overthrow the tallest oak, a silly woman in time may make such a breach into a man's heart as her tears may enter without resistance, then doubt not but I will so undermine mine old father, as quickly I will enjoy my new friend. Tush Philautus was liked for fashion's sake, but never loved for fancy's sake, & this I vow by the faith of a virgin, and by the love I bear thee, (for greater bands to confirm my vow I have not) that my father shall sooner martyr me in the fire than marry me to Philautus. No no Euphues thou only hast won me by love, and shalt only wear me by law, I force not Philautus his fury, so I may have Euphues his friendship, neither will I prefer his possessions before thy person, neither esteem better of his lands than of thy love. Ferardo shall sooner disherit me of my patrimony, than dishonour me in breaking my promise. It is not his great manors, but thy good manners, that shall make my marriage. In token of which my sincere affection, I give thee my hand in pawn and my heart forever to be thy Lucilla."

Unto whom Euphues answered in this manner.

"If my tongue were able to utter the joys that my heart hath conceived, I fear me though I be well beloved, yet I should hardly be believed. Ah my Lucilla how much am I bound to thee, which preferrest mine unworthiness before thy father's wrath, my happiness before thine own misfortune, my love before thine own life? how might I excel thee in courtesy, whom no mortal creature can exceed in constancy? I find it now for a settled truth, which erst I accounted for a vain talk, that the purple dye will never stain, that the pure civet will never lose his savour, that the green laurel will never change his colour, that beauty can never be blotted with discourtesy: As touching secrecy in this behalf, assure thyself, that I will not so much as tell it to myself. Command Euphues to run, to ride, to undertake any exploit be it never so dangerous, to hazard himself in any enterprise, be it never so desperate:" As they were thus pleasantly conferring the one with the other, Livia (whom Euphues made his stale)[60] entered in to the parlor, unto whom Lucilla spake in these terms.

"Dost thou not laugh Livia to see my ghostly father keep me here so long at shrift?" "Truly," answered Livia, "methinks that you smile at some pleasant shift, either he is slow in enquiring of your faults, or you slack in answering of his questions," and thus being supper time they all sat down, Lucilla well pleased, no man better content than Euphues, who after his repast having no opportunity to confer with his lover, had small lust to continue with the gentlewomen any longer, seeing therefore he could frame no means to work his delight, he coined an excuse to hasten his departure, promising the next morning to trouble them again as a guest more bold than welcome, although indeed he thought himself to be the better welcome in saying that he would come.

But as Ferardo went in post, so he returned in haste, having concluded with Philautus, that the marriage should immediately be consummated which wrought such a content in Philautus that he was almost in an ecstasy through the extremity of his passions: such is the fulness and force of pleasure, that there is nothing so dangerous as the fruition, yet knowing that delays bring dangers, although he nothing doubted of Lucilla, whom he loved, yet feared he the fickleness of old men, which is always to be mistrusted. He urged therefore Ferardo to break with his daughter who being willing to have the match made, was content incontinently to procure the means: finding therefore his daughter at leisure, and having knowledge of her former love, spake to her as followeth.

"Dear daughter, as thou hast long time lived a maiden, so now thou must learn to be a mother, and as I have been careful to bring thee up a virgin, so am I now desirous to make thee a wife. Neither ought I in this matter to use any persuasions, for that maidens commonly nowadays are no sooner born, but they begin to bride it: neither to offer any great portions for that thou knowest thou shalt inherit all my possessions. Mine only care hath been hitherto to match thee with such an one, as should be of good wealth able to maintain thee, of great worship able to compare with thee in birth, of honest conditions to deserve thy love, and an Italian born to enjoy my lands. At the last I have found one answerable to my desire, a gentleman of great revenues, of a noble progeny, of honest behaviour, of comely personage, born and brought up in Naples, Philautus (thy friend as I guess) thy husband Lucilla, if thou like it, neither canst thou dislike him, who wanteth nothing that should cause thy liking, neither hath anything that should breed thy loathing. And surely I rejoice the more, that thou shalt be linked to him in marriage, whom thou hast loved as I hear being a maiden, neither can there any jars kindle between them, where the minds be so united, neither any jealousy arise, where love hath so long been settled. Therefore Lucilla to the end the desire of either of you may now be accomplished, to the delight of you both, I am here come to finish the contract by giving hands, which you have already begun between yourselves by joining of hearts, that as God doth witness the one in your consciences, so the world may testify the other by your conversations, and therefore Lucilla make such answer to my request, as may like me and satisfy thy friend."

Lucilla abashed with this sudden speech of her father, yet boldened by the love of her friend, with a comely bashfulness answered him in this manner.

"Reverend sir, the sweetness that I have found in the undefiled estate of virginity, causeth me to loathe the sour sauce which is mixed with matrimony, and the quiet life which I have tried being a maiden, maketh me to shun the cares that are always incident to a mother, neither am I so wedded to the world that I should be moved with great possessions, neither so bewitched with wantonness, that I should be enticed with any man's proportion, neither if I were so disposed would I be so proud to desire one of noble progeny, or so precise to choose one only in mine own country, for that commonly these things happen always to the contrary. Do we not see the noble to match with the base, the rich with the poor, the Italian oftentimes with the Portingale? [61] As love knoweth no laws, so it regardeth no conditions, as the lover maketh no pause where he liketh, so he maketh no conscience of these idle ceremonies. In that Philautus is the man that threateneth such kindness at my hands, and such courtesy at yours, that he should account me his wife before he woo me, certainly he is like for me to make his reckoning twice, because he reckoneth without his hostess. And in this Philautus would either shew himself of great wisdom to persuade, or me of great lightness to be allured: although the loadstone draw iron, yet it cannot move gold, though the jet gather up the light straw, yet can it not take up the pure steel. Although Philautus think himself of virtue sufficient to win his lover, yet shall he not obtain Lucilla. I cannot but smile to hear, that a marriage should be solemnized, where never was any mention of assuring, and that the wooing should be a day after the wedding. Certes if when I looked merrily on Philautus, he deemed it in the way of marriage, or if seeing me disposed to jest, he took me in good earnest, then sure he might gather some presumption of my love, but no promise: But methinks it is good reason, that I should be at mine own bridal, and not given in the church, before I know the bridegroom. Therefore dear father in mine opinion as there can be no bargain, where both be not agreed, neither any indentures sealed, where the one will not consent, so can there be no contract where both be not content, no bans asked lawfully where one of the parties forbiddeth them, no marriage made where no match was meant: But I will hereafter frame myself to be coy, seeing I am claimed for a wife because I have been courteous, and give myself to melancholy, seeing I am accounted won in that I have been merry: And if every gentleman be made of the metal that Philautus is, then I fear I shall be challenged of as many as I have used to company with, and be a common wife to all those that have commonly resorted hither.

"My duty therefore ever reserved, I here on my knees forswear Philautus for my husband, although I accept him for my friend, and seeing I shall hardly be induced ever to match with any, I beseech you, if by your fatherly love I shall be compelled, that I may match with such a one as both I may love, and you may like."

Ferardo being a grave and wise gentleman, although he were thoroughly angry, yet he dissembled his fury, to the end he might by craft discover her fancy, and whispering Philautus in the ear (who stood as though he had a flea in his ear) desired him to keep silence, until he had undermined her by subtilty, which Philautus having granted, Ferardo began to sift his daughter with this device.

"Lucilla thy colour sheweth thee to be in a great choler, and thy hot words bewray thy heavy wrath, but be patient, seeing all my talk was only to try thee, I am neither so unnatural to wrest thee against thine own will, neither so malicious to wed thee to any, against thine own liking: for well I know what jars, what jealousy, what strife, what storms ensue, where the match is made rather by the compulsion of the parents, than by consent of the parties, neither do I like thee the less, in that thou likest Philautus so little, neither can Philautus love thee the worse, in that thou lovest thyself so well, wishing rather to stand to thy chance, than to the choice of any other. But this grieveth me most, that thou art almost vowed to the vain order of the Vestal Virgins, despising, or at the least not desiring the sacred bands of Juno her bed.[62] If thy mother had been of that mind when she was a maiden, thou haddest not now been born to be of this mind to be a virgin: Weigh with thyself what slender profit they bring to the common wealth, what slight pleasure to themselves, what great grief to their parents which joy most in their offspring, and desire most to enjoy the noble and blessed name of a grandfather.

"Thou knowest that the tallest ash is cut down for fuel, because it beareth no good fruit, that the cow that gives no milk is brought to the slaughter, that the drone that gathereth no honey is contemned, that the woman that maketh herself barren by not marrying, is accounted among the Grecian ladies worse than a carrion, as Homer reporteth.[63] Therefore Lucilla if thou have any care to be a comfort to my hoary hairs, or a commodity to thy common weal, frame thyself to that honourable estate of matrimony, which was sanctified in paradise, allowed of the patriarchs, hallowed of the old prophets, and commended of all persons. If thou like any, be not ashamed to tell it me, which only am to exhort thee, yea, and as much as in me lieth to command thee, to love one: If he be base thy blood will make him noble, if beggarly thy goods shall make him wealthy, if a stranger thy freedom may enfranchise him: if he be young he is the more fitter to be thy fere, if he be old the liker to thine aged father. For I had rather thou shouldest lead a life to thine own liking in earth, than to thy great torments lead apes in hell. Be bold therefore to make me partner of thy desire, which will be partaker of thy disease,[64] yea, and a furtherer of thy delights, as far as either my friends, or my lands, or my life will stretch."

Lucilla perceiving the drift of the old fox her father, weighed with herself what was best to be done, at the last not weighing her father's ill will, but encouraged by love, shaped him an answer which pleased Ferardo but a little, and pinched Philautus on the parson's side[65] on this manner.

"Dear father Ferardo, although I see the bait you lay to catch me, yet I am content to swallow the hook, neither are you more desirous to take me napping, than I willing to confess my meaning. So it is that love hath as well inveigled me as others, which make it as strange as I. Neither do I love him so meanly that I should be ashamed of his name, neither is his personage so mean that I should love him shamefully: It is Euphues that lately arrived here at Naples, that hath battered the bulwark of my breast, and shall shortly enter as conqueror into my bosom: What his wealth is I neither know it nor weigh it, what his wit is all Naples doth know it, and wonder at it, neither have I been curious to enquire of his progenitors, for that I know so noble a mind could take no original but from a nobleman, for as no bird can look again[66] the sun, but those that be bred of the eagle, neither any hawk soar so high as the brood of the hobby, so no wight can have such excellent qualities except he descend of a noble race, neither be of so high capacity, unless he issue of a high progeny. And I hope Philautus will not be my foe, seeing I have chosen his dear friend, neither you father be displeased in that Philautus is displaced. You need not muse that I should so suddenly be entangled, love gives no reason of choice, neither will it suffer any repulse. Myrrha was enamoured of her natural father, Byblis of her brother, Phaedra of her son-in-law:[67] If nature can no way resist the fury of affection, how should it be stayed by wisdom?"

Ferardo interrupting her in the middle of her discourse, although he were moved with inward grudge, yet he wisely repressed his anger, knowing that sharp words would but sharpen her froward will, and thus answered her briefly.

"Lucilla, as I am not presently to grant my good will, so mean I not to reprehend thy choice, yet wisdom willeth me to pause, until I have called what may happen to my remembrance, and warneth thee to be circumspect, lest thy rash conceit bring a sharp repentance. As for you Philautus I would not have you despair seeing a woman doth oftentimes change her desire." Unto whom Philautus in few words made answer.

"Certainly Ferardo I take the less grief in that I see her so greedy after Euphues, and by so much the more I am content to leave my suit, by how much the more she seemeth to disdain my service, but as for hope because I would not by any means taste one dram thereof, I will abjure all places of her abode and loathe her company, whose countenance I have so much loved, as for Euphues," and there staying his speech, he flang[68] out of the doors and repairing to his lodging uttered these words.

"Ah most dissembling wretch Euphues, O counterfeit companion, couldest thou under the shew of a steadfast friend cloak the malice of a mortal foe? under the colour of simplicity shroud the image of deceit? Is thy Livia turned to my Lucilla, thy love to my lover, thy devotion to my saint? Is this the courtesy of Athens, the cavilling of scholars, the craft of Grecians? Couldest thou not remember Philautus that Greece is never without some wily Ulysses, never void of some Sinon,[69] never to seek of some deceitful shifter? Is it not commonly said of Grecians that craft cometh to them by kind, that they learn to deceive in their cradle? Why then did his pretended courtesy bewitch thee with such credulity? shall my good will be the cause of his ill will? because I was content to be his friend, thought he me meet to be made his fool? I see now that as the fish scolopidus[70] in the flood Araris at the waxing of the moon is as white as the driven snow, and at the waning as black as the burnt coal, so Euphues, which at the first increasing of our familiarity, was very zealous, is now at the last cast become most faithless. But why rather exclaim I not against Lucilla, whose wanton looks caused Euphues to violate his plighted faith? Ah wretched wench canst thou be so light of love, as to change with every wind? so unconstant as to prefer a new lover before thine old friend? Ah well I wot that a new broom sweepeth clean, and a new garment maketh thee leave off the old though it be fitter, and new wine causeth thee to forsake the old though it be better, much like to the men in the island Scyrum,[71] which pull up the old tree when they see the young begin to spring, and not unlike unto the widow of Lesbos, which changed all her old gold for new glass, have I served thee three years faithfully, and am I served so unkindly? shall the fruit of my desire be turned to disdain? But unless Euphues had inveigled thee thou hadst yet been constant, yea but if Euphues had not seen thee willing to be won, he would never have wooed thee, but had not Euphues enticed thee with fair words, thou wouldst never have loved him, but haddest thou not given him fair looks, he would never have liked thee: Aye, but Euphues gave the onset, aye, but Lucilla gave the occasion, aye, but Euphues first broke his mind, aye, but Lucilla first bewrayed her meaning. Tush why go I about to excuse any of them, seeing I have just cause to accuse them both? Neither ought I to dispute which of them hath proffered me the greatest villainy, sith that either of them hath committed perjury. Yet although they have found me dull in perceiving their falsehood, they shall not find me slack in revenging their folly. As for Lucilla seeing I mean altogether to forget her, I mean also to forgive her, lest in seeking means to be revenged, mine old desire be renewed." Philautus having thus discoursed with himself, began to write to Euphues as followeth.

"Although hitherto Euphues I have shrined thee in my heart for a trusty friend, I will shun thee hereafter as a trothless foe, and although I cannot see in thee less wit than I was wont, yet do I find less honesty, I perceive at the last (although being deceived it be too late) that musk although it be sweet in the smell, is sour in the smack, that the leaf of the cedar tree though it be fair to be seen, yet the syrup depriveth sight, that friendship though it be plighted by shaking the hand, yet it is shaken off by fraud of the heart. But thou hast not much to boast of, for as thou hast won a fickle lady, so hast thou lost a faithful friend. How canst thou be secure of her constancy when thou hast had such trial of her lightness?

"How canst thou assure thyself that she will be faithful to thee, which hath been faithless to me? Ah Euphues, let not my credulity be an occasion hereafter for thee to practise the like cruelty. Remember this that yet there hath never been any faithless to his friend, that hath not also been fruitless to his God. But I weigh this treachery the less, in that it cometh from a Grecian in whom is no troth. Though I be weak to wrestle for a revenge, yet God who permitteth no guile to be guiltless, will shortly requite this injury, though Philautus have no policy to undermine thee, yet thine own practices will be sufficient to overthrow thee.

"Couldest thou Euphues for the love of a fruitless pleasure, violate the league of faithful friendship? Diddest thou weigh more the enticing looks of a lewd wench, than the entire love of a loyal friend? If thou diddest determine with thyself at the first to be false, why didest thou swear to be true? If to be true, why art thou false? If thou wast minded both falsely and forgedly to deceive me, why diddest thou flatter and dissemble with me at the first? If to love me, why doest thou flinch at the last? If the sacred bands of amity did delight thee, why diddest thou break them? if dislike thee, why didest thou praise them? Dost thou not know that a perfect friend should be like the glazeworm,[72] which shineth most bright in the dark? or like the pure frankincense which smelleth most sweet when it is in the fire? or at the least not unlike to the damask rose which is sweeter in the still than on the stalk? But thou Euphues, dost rather resemble the swallow which in the summer creepeth under the eaves of every house, and in the winter leaveth nothing but dirt behind her, or the humblebee which having sucked honey out of the fair flower doth leave it & loathe it, or the spider which in the finest web doth hang the fairest fly. Doth thou think Euphues that thy craft in betraying me, shall any whit cool my courage in revenging thy villainy? or that a gentleman of Naples will put up such an injury at the hands of a scholar? And if I do, it is not for want of strength to maintain my just quarrel, but of will which thinketh scorn to get so vain a conquest. I know that Menelaus[73] for his ten years' war endured ten years' woe, that after all his strife he won but a strumpet, that for all his travels he reduced [74] (I cannot say reclaimed) but a straggler: which was as much in my judgement, as to strive for a broken glass which is good for nothing. I wish thee rather Menelaus' care, than myself his conquest, that thou being deluded by Lucilla mayst rather know what it is to be deceived, than I having conquered thee should prove what it were to bring back a dissembler. Seeing therefore there can no greater revenge light upon thee, than that as thou hast reaped where another hath sown, so another may thresh that which thou hast reaped: I will pray that thou mayst be measured unto with the like measure that thou hast meten[75] unto others: that as thou hast thought it no conscience to betray me, so others may deem it no dishonesty to deceive thee, that as Lucilla made it a light matter to forswear her old friend Philautus, so she may make it a mock to forsake her new fere Euphues. Which if it come to pass as it is like by my compass, then shalt thou see the troubles, & feel the torments which thou hast already thrown into the hearts and eyes of others. Thus hoping shortly to see thee as hopeless, as myself is hapless, I wish my wish were as effectually ended as it is heartily looked for. And so I leave thee.

> Thine once
> Philautus"

Philautus dispatching a messenger with this letter speedily to Euphues, went into the fields to walk there either to digest his choler or chew upon his melancholy. But Euphues having read the contents was well content, setting his talk at naught and answering his taunts in these gibing terms.

"I remember Philautus how valiantly Ajax[76] boasted in the feats of arms, yet Ulysses bare away the armour, and it may be that though thou crake[77] of thine own courage, thou mayst easily lose the conquest. Dost thou think Euphues such a dastard that he is not able to withstand thy courage, or such a dullard that he cannot descry thy craft. Alas good soul. It fareth with thee as with the hen, which when the puttock[78] hath caught her chicken beginneth to cackle: and thou having lost thy lover beginneth to prattle. Tush Philautus, I am in this point of Euripides his mind, who thinks it lawful for the desire of a kingdom to transgress the bounds of honesty, and for the love of a lady to violate and break the bands of amity.

"The friendship between man and man as it is common so is it of course, between man and woman, as it is seldom so is it sincere, the one proceedeth of the similitude of manners, the other of the sincerity of the heart: if thou haddest learned the first point of hawking thou wouldst have learned to have held fast, or the first note of descant thou wouldest have kept thy *sol. fa.* to thyself.

"But thou canst blame me no more of folly in leaving thee to love Lucilla, than thou mayst reprove him of foolishness that having a sparrow in his hand letteth her go to catch the pheasant, or him of unskillfulness that seeing the heron, leaveth to level his shot at the stock dove, or that woman of coyness, that having a dead rose in her bosom, throweth it away to gather the fresh violet. Love knoweth no laws: Did not Jupiter transform himself into the shape of Amphitrio to embrace Alcmaena? Into the form of a swan to enjoy Leda? Into a bull to beguile Io? Into a shower of gold to win Danaë? Did not Neptune change himself into a heifer, a ram, a flood, a dolphin, only for the love of those he lusted after? Did not Apollo convert himself into a shepherd, into a bird, into a lion, for the desire he had to heal his disease?[79]

If the gods thought no scorn to become beasts, to obtain their best beloved, shall Euphues be so nice in changing his copy to gain his lady? No, no: he that cannot dissemble in love, is not worthy to live. I am of this mind, that both might and malice, deceit and treachery, all perjury, any impiety may lawfully be committed in love, which is lawless. In that thou arguest Lucilla of lightness, thy will hangs in the light of thy wit: Dost thou not know that the weak stomach if it be cloyed with one diet doth soon surfeit? That the clown's garlic cannot eat the courtier's disease so well as the pure treacle? that far-fet[80] and dear-bought is good for ladies? That Euphues being a more dainty morsel than Philautus, ought better to be accepted? Tush Philautus set thy heart at rest, for thy hap willeth thee to give over all hope both of my friendship, and her love, as for revenge thou art not so able to lend a blow as I to ward it, neither more venturous to challenge the combat, than I valiant to answer the quarrel. As Lucilla was caught by fraud so shall she be kept by force, and as thou wast too simple to espy my craft, so I think thou wilt be too weak to withstand my courage, but if thy revenge stand only upon thy wish, thou shalt never live to see my woe, or to have thy will, and so farewell.

Euphues."

This letter being dispatched, Euphues sent it and Philautus read it, who disdaining those proud terms, disdained also to answer them, being ready to ride with Ferardo.

Euphues having for a space absented himself from the house of Ferardo, because he was at home, longed sore to see Lucilla which now opportunity offered unto him, Ferardo being gone again to Venice with Philautus, but in his absence one Curio a gentleman of Naples of little wealth and less wit haunted Lucilla her company, & so enchanted her, that Euphues was also cast off with Philautus which thing being unknown to Euphues, caused him the sooner to make his repair to the presence of his lady, whom he finding in her muses began pleasantly to salute in this manner.

"Mistress Lucilla, although my long absence might breed

your just anger, (for that lovers desire nothing so much as often meeting) yet I hope my presence will dissolve your choler (for that lovers are soon pleased when of their wishes they be fully possessed.) My absence is the rather to be excused in that your father hath been always at home, whose frowns seemed to threaten my ill fortune, and my presence at this present the better to be accepted in that I have made such speedy repair to your presence."

Unto whom Lucilla answered with this gleek.

"Truly Euphues you have missed the cushion, for I was neither angry with your long absence, neither am I well pleased at your presence, the one gave me rather a good hope hereafter never to see you, the other giveth me a greater occasion to abhor you."

Euphues being nipped on the head, with a pale countenance, as though his soul had forsaken his body replied as followeth.

"If this sudden change Lucilla, proceed of any desert of mine, I am here not only to answer the fact, but also to make amends for my fault: if of any new motion or mind to forsake your new friend, I am rather to lament your inconstancy than revenge it, but I hope that such hot love cannot be so soon cold, neither such sure faith, be rewarded with so sudden forgetfulness."

Lucilla not ashamed to confess her folly, answered him with this frump.

"Sir whether your deserts or my desire have wrought this change, it will boot you little to know, neither do I crave amends, neither fear revenge, as for fervent love, you know there is no fire so hot but it is quenched with water, neither affection so strong but is weakened with reason, let this suffice thee that thou know I care not for thee."

"Indeed," said Euphues, "to know the cause of your alteration would boot me little seeing the effect taketh such force. I have heard that women either love entirely or hate deadly, and seeing you have put me out of doubt of the one, I must needs persuade myself of the other. This change will cause

Philautus to laugh me to scorn, & double thy lightness in turning so often. Such was the hope that I conceived of thy constancy, that I spared not in all places to blaze thy loyalty, but now my rash conceit will prove me a liar, and thee a light huswife."

"Nay," said Lucilla, "now shalt thou not laugh Philautus to scorn, seeing you have both drunk of one cup, in misery Euphues it is a great comfort to have a companion. I doubt not, but that you will both conspire against me to work some mischief, although I nothing fear your malice: whosoever accounteth you a liar for praising me, may also deem you a lecher for being enamoured of me, and whosoever judgeth me light in forsaking of you, may think thee as lewd in loving of me, for thou that thoughtest it lawful to deceive thy friend, must take no scorn to be deceived of thy foe."

"Then I perceive Lucilla," said he, "that I was made thy stale, and Philautus thy laughingstock: whose friendship (I must confess indeed) I have refused to obtain thy favour: and sithens another hath won that we both have lost, I am content for my part, neither ought I to be grieved seeing thou art fickle."

"Certes Euphues," said Lucilla, "you spend your wind in waste for your welcome is but small, & your cheer is like to be less, fancy giveth no reason of his change neither will be controlled for any choice, this is therefore to warn you, that from henceforth you neither solicit this suit neither offer any way your service, I have chosen one (I must needs confess) neither to be compared to Philautus in wealth, nor to thee in wit, neither in birth to the worst of you both, I think God gave it me for a just plague, for renouncing Philautus, & choosing thee, and sithens I am an ensample to all women of lightness, I am like also to be a mirror to them all of unhappiness, which ill luck I must take by so much the more patiently, by how much the more I acknowledge myself to have deserved it worthily." "Well Lucilla," answered Euphues, "this case breedeth my sorrow the more, in that it is so sudden, and by so much the more I lament it, by how much the less I looked for it. In that my welcome is so cold and my cheer so simple, it nothing toucheth me, seeing your fury is so hot, and my misfortune so great, that I am neither willing to receive it, nor you to bestow it: if tract of time, or want of trial had caused this metamorphosis my grief had been more tolerable, and your fleeting more excusable, but coming in a moment undeserved, unlooked for, unthought of, it increaseth my sorrow and thy shame."

"Euphues," quoth she, "you make a long harvest for a little corn, and angle for the fish that is already caught. Curio, yea, Curio, is he that hath my love at his pleasure, and shall also have my life at his commandment, and although you deem him unworthy to enjoy that which erst you accounted no wight worthy to embrace, yet seeing I esteem him more worth than any, he is to be reputed as chief. The wolf chooseth him for her make,[81] that hath or doth endure most travail for her sake. Venus was content to take the blacksmith with his polt foot. Cornelia here in Naples disdained not to love a rude miller.[82] As for changing, did not Helen the pearl of Greece thy countrywoman first take Menelaus, then Theseus, and last of all Paris? [83] if brute beasts give us ensamples that those are most to be liked, of whom we are best beloved, or if the princess of beauty Venus, and her heirs Helen, and Cornelia, shew that our affection standeth on our free will: then am I rather to be excused than accused. Therefore good Euphues be as merry as you may be, for time may so turn that once again you may be."

"Nay Lucilla," said he, "my harvest shall cease, seeing others have reaped my corn, as for angling for the fish that is already caught, that were but mere folly. But in my mind if you be a fish you are either an eel which as soon as one hath hold of her tail, will slip out of his hand, or else a minnow which will be nibbling at every bait but never biting. But what fish so ever you be you have made both me and Philautus to swallow a gudgeon. If Curio be the person, I would neither wish thee a greater plague, nor him a deadlier poison. I for my part think him worthy of thee, and thou unworthy of him, for although he be in body deformed, in mind foolish, an innocent born, a beggar by misfortune, yet doth he deserve a better than thyself, whose corrupt manners have stained thy heavenly hue, whose light behaviour hath dimmed the lights of thy beauty, whose unconstant mind hath betrayed the innocency of so many a gentleman. And in that you bring in the example of a beast to confirm your folly, you show therein your beastly disposition, which is ready to follow such beastliness. But Venus played false: and what for that? seeing her lightness serveth for an example, I would wish thou mightest try her punishment for a reward, that being openly taken in an iron net[84] all the world might judge whether thou be fish or flesh, and certes in my mind no angle will hold thee, it must be a net. Cornelia loved a miller, and thou a miser, can her folly excuse thy fault? Helen of Greece my countrywoman born, but thine by profession, changed and rechanged at her pleasure I grant. Shall the lewdness of others animate thee in thy lightness? Why then dost thou not haunt the stews because Lais[85] frequented them? why doest thou not love a bull seeing Pasiphaë[86] loved one? why art thou not enamoured of thy father knowing that Myrrha was so incensed? these are set down that we viewing their incontinency, should fly the like impudency, not follow the like excess, neither can they excuse thee of any inconstancy. Merry I will be as I may, but if I may hereafter as thou meanest, I will not, and therefore farewell Lucilla, the most inconstant that ever was nursed in Naples, farewell Naples the most cursed town in all Italy, and women all farewell."

Euphues having thus given her his last farewell, yet being solitary began afresh to recount his sorrow on this manner.

"Ah Euphues into what a quandary art thou brought? in what sudden misfortune art thou wrapped? it is like to fare with thee as with the eagle, which dyeth neither for age, nor with sickness, but with famine, for although thy stomach hunger yet thy heart will not suffer thee to eat. And why shouldest thou torment thyself for one in whom is neither faith nor fervency? O the counterfeit love of women. Oh inconstant sex. I have lost Philautus, I have lost Lucilla, I have lost that which I shall hardly find again, a faithful friend. Ah foolish Euphues, why diddest thou leave Athens the nurse of wisdom, to inhabit Naples the nourisher of wantonness? Had it not been better for thee to have eaten salt with the philosophers in Greece, than sugar with the courtiers of Italy? But behold the course of youth which always inclineth to pleasure, I forsook mine old companions to search for new friends, I rejected the grave and fatherly counsel of Eubulus, to follow the brainsick humour of mine own will. I addicted myself wholly to the service of women to spend my life in the laps of ladies, my lands in maintenance of bravery, my wit in the vanities of idle sonnets. I had thought that women had been as we men, that is true, faithful, zealous, constant, but I perceive they be rather woe unto men, by their falsehood, jealousy, & inconstancy. I was half persuaded that they were made of the perfection of men, & would be comforters, but now I see they have tasted of the infection of the serpent, and will be corasives.[87] The physician sayeth it is dangerous to minister physic unto the patient that hath a cold stomach and a hot liver, lest in giving warmth to the one, he inflame the other, so verily it is hard to deal with a woman whose words seem fervent, whose heart is congealed into hard ice, lest trusting their outward talk, he be betrayed with their inward treachery. I will to Athens there to toss my books, no more in Naples to live with fair looks. I will so frame myself as all youth hereafter shall rather rejoice to see mine amendment than be animated to follow my former life. Philosophy, physic, divinity, shall be my study. O the hidden secrets of nature, the express image of moral virtues, the equal balance of justice, the medicines to heal all diseases, how they begin to delight me. The *Axiomaes* of Aristotle, the *Maxims* of Justinian, the *Aphorisms* of Galen,[88] have suddenly made such a breach into my mind that I seem only to desire them which did only erst detest them. If wit be employed in the honest study of learning what thing so precious as wit? if in the idle trade of love what thing more pestilent than wit? The proof of late hath been verified in me, whom nature hath endued with a little wit, which I have abused with an obstinate will, most true it is that the thing the better it is the greater is the abuse, and that there is nothing but through the malice of man may be abused.

"Doth not the fire (an element so necessary that without it man cannot live) as well burn the house as burn in the house if it be abused? Doth not treacle as well poison as help if it be taken out of time? Doth not wine if it be immoderately taken kill the stomach, inflame the liver, murther the drunken? Doth not physic destroy if it be not well tempered? Doth not law accuse if it be not rightly interpreted? Doth not divinity condemn if it be not faithfully construed? Is not poison taken out of the honeysuckle by the spider, venom out of the rose by the canker, dung out of the maple tree by the scorpion? Even so the greatest wickedness is drawn out of the greatest wit, if it be abused by will, or entangled with the world, or inveigled with women.

"But seeing I see mine own impiety, I will endeavour myself to amend all that is past, and to be a mirror of godliness hereafter. The rose though a little it be eaten with the canker yet being distilled yieldeth sweet water, the iron though fretted with the rust yet being burnt in the fire shineth brighter, and wit although it hath been eaten with the canker of his own conceit, and fretted with the rust of vain love, yet being purified in the still of wisdom, and tried in the fire of zeal, will shine bright and smell sweet in the nostrils of all young novices.

"As therefore I gave a farewell to Lucilla, a farewell to Naples, a farewell to women, so now do I give a farewell to the world, meaning rather to macerate myself with melancholy than pine in folly, rather choosing to die in my study amidst my books, than to court it in Italy, in the company of ladies."

Euphues having thus debated with himself, went to his bed,

there either with sleep to deceive his fancy, or with musing to renew his ill fortune, or recant his old follies.

But it happened immediately Ferardo to return home, who hearing this strange event was not a little amazed, and was now more ready to exhort Lucilla from the love of Curio, than before to the liking of Philautus. Therefore in all haste, with watery eyes, and a woeful heart, began on this manner to reason with his daughter.

"Lucilla (daughter I am ashamed to call thee, seeing thou hast neither care of thy father's tender affection, nor of thine own credit) what sprite hath enchanted thy spirit that every minute thou alterest thy mind? I had thought that my hoary hairs should have found comfort by thy golden locks, and my rotten age great ease by thy ripe years. But alas I see in thee neither wit to order thy doings neither will to frame thyself to discretion, neither the nature of a child, neither the nurture of a maiden, neither (I cannot without tears speak it) any regard of thine honour, neither any care of thine honesty.

"I am now enforced to remember thy mother's death, who I think was a prophetess in her life, for oftentimes she would say that thou haddest more beauty than was convenient for one that should be honest, and more cockering than was meet for one that should be a matron.

"Would I had never lived to be so old or thou to be so obstinate, either would I had died in my youth in the court, or thou in thy cradle, I would to God that either I had never been born, or thou never bred. Is this the comfort that the parent reapeth for all his care? Is obstinacy paid for obedience, stubbornness rendered for duty, malicious desperateness, for filial fear? I perceive now that the wise painter saw more than the foolish parent can, who painted love going downward, saying it might well descend, but ascend it could never. Danaus[89] whom they report to be the father of fifty children, had among them all but one that disobeyed him in a thing most dishonest, but I that am father to one more than I would be although one be all, have that one most disobedient to me in a request lawful and reasonable. If Danaus seeing but one of his daughters without awe became himself without mercy, what shall Ferardo do in this case who hath one and all most unnatural to him in a most just cause? Shall Curio enjoy the fruit of my travails, possess the benefit of my labours, inherit the patrimony of mine ancestors, who hath neither wisdom to increase them, nor wit to keep them? wilt thou Lucilla bestow thyself on such an one as hath neither comeliness in his body, nor knowledge in his mind, nor credit in his country. Oh I would thou haddest either been ever faithful to Philautus, or never faithless to Euphues, or would thou wouldest be more fickle to Curio. As thy beauty hath made thee the blaze of Italy, so will thy lightness make thee the byword of the world. O Lucilla, Lucilla, would thou wert less fair or more fortunate, either of less honour or greater honesty? either better minded, or soon buried. Shall thine old father live to see thee match with a young fool? shall my kind heart be rewarded with such unkind hate? Ah Lucilla thou knowest not the care of a father, nor the duty of a child, and as far art thou from piety, as I from cruelty.

"Nature will not permit me to disherit my daughter, and yet it will suffer thee to dishonour thy father. Affection causeth me to wish thy life, and shall it entice thee to procure my death? It is mine only comfort to see thee flourish in thy youth, and is it thine, to see me fade in mine age? to conclude, I desire to live to see thee prosper, & thou to see me perish. But why cast I the effect of this unnaturalness in thy teeth, seeing I myself was the cause? I made thee a wanton and thou hast made me a fool, I brought thee up like a cockney, and thou hast handled me like a cockscomb (I speak it to mine own shame) I made more of thee than became a father, & thou less of me than beseemed a child. And shall my loving care be cause of thy wicked cruelty? yea yea, I am not the first that hath been too careful, nor the last that shall be handled so unkindly, it is common to see fathers too fond, and children too froward. Well Lucilla the tears which thou seest trickle down my cheeks and the drops of blood (which thou canst not see) that fall from my heart, enforce me to make an end of my talk, and if thou have any duty of a child, or care of a friend, or courtesy of a stranger, or feeling of a Christian, or humanity of a reasonable creature, then release thy father of grief, and acquit thyself of ungratefulness, otherwise thou shalt but hasten my death, and increase thine own defame, which if thou do the gain is mine, and the loss thine, and both infinite."

Lucilla either so bewitched that she could not relent or so wicked that she would not yield to her father's request answered him on this manner.

"Dear father as you would have me to shew the duty of a child, so ought you to shew the care of a parent, and as the one standeth in obedience so the other is grounded upon reason. You would have me as I owe duty to you to leave Curio, and I desire you as you owe me any love, that you suffer me to enjoy him. If you accuse me of unnaturalness in that I yield not to your request, I am also to condemn you of unkindness, in that you grant not my petition. You object I know not what to Curio, but it is the eye of the master that fatteth the horse, and the love of the woman, that maketh the man. To give reason for fancy were to weigh the fire, and measure the wind. If therefore my delight be the cause of your death, I think my sorrow would be an occasion of your solace. And if you be angry because I am pleased, certes I deem you would be content if I were deceased: which if it be so that my pleasure breed your pain, and mine annoy your joy, I may well say that you are an unkind father, and I an unfortunate child. But good father either content yourself with my choice, or let me stand to the main chance, otherwise the grief will be mine, and the fault yours and both untolerable."

Ferardo seeing his daughter, to have neither regard of her own honour nor his request, conceived such an inward grief, that in short space he died, leaving Lucilla the only heir of his lands, and Curio to possess them: but what end came of her, seeing it is nothing incident to the history of

Euphues, it were superfluous to insert it, and so incredible that all women would rather wonder at it than believe it, which event being so strange, I had rather leave them in a muse what it should be, than in a maze in telling what it was.

Philautus having intelligence of Euphues his success, and the falsehood of Lucilla, although he began to rejoice at the misery of his fellow, yet seeing her fickleness, could not but lament her folly, and pity his friend's misfortune. Thinking that the lightness of Lucilla enticed Euphues to so great liking.

Euphues and Philautus having conference between themselves, casting discourtesy in the teeth each of the other, but chiefly noting disloyalty in the demeanor of Lucilla, after much talk renewed their old friendship both abandoning Lucilla as most abominable. Philautus was earnest to have Euphues tarry in Naples, and Euphues desirous to have Philautus to Athens, but the one was so addicted to the court, the other so wedded to the university, that each refused the offer of the other, yet this they agreed between themselves that though their bodies were by distance of place severed, yet the conjunction of their minds should neither be separated, by the length of time, nor alienated by change of soil. "I for my part," said Euphues, "to confirm this league give thee my hand and my heart," and so likewise did Philautus, and so shaking hands they bid each other farewell.

SIR PHILIP SIDNEY

THE ARCADIA

1590

Sir Philip Sidney (1554–1586)

Every schoolboy knows Sir Philip Sidney as the mortally wounded general who, offered a cup of water, gave it instead to a dying soldier, with the words, "Thy necessity is even greater than mine." The act was no mere histrionic gesture, but was typical of the most nearly perfect gentleman that Elizabethan England produced.

Sidney was born on the family estate of Penshurst on November 30, 1554. Although he was not of noble birth, few men have had more powerful connections. He was the godson of King Philip of Spain; the grandson of Northumberland, the most influential man in England; and the nephew and heir of Leicester, Queen Elizabeth's favorite. His mother, Mary Dudley, was a girlhood playmate and lifelong friend of Queen Elizabeth. His father, Sir Henry Sidney, grew up with Prince Edward, and when the latter died after a short reign as Edward VI, he died in Sir Henry's arms.

Educated at home for the first ten years of his life, Philip was then sent to the famous Free Grammar School at Shrewsbury. From 1567 to 1572 he was in residence at Oxford. He left without taking a degree and went abroad on the grand tour to complete his education. A few years later he made a second trip to Europe, this time as Elizabeth's emissary to Emperor Rudolph II of Germany. On his way back to England he met the great Protestant general, William of Orange. Orange, like many Protestant statesmen, looked to Sidney as the potential leader of the fight against Roman Catholic Spain. It was a role he yearned to play, for he saw more clearly than most Englishmen of his time that Spain stood in the way of England's greatness.

He received his first taste of fighting in Ireland, where his father was serving as Elizabeth's deputy governor. In 1578 he defended Sir Henry's Irish policies with A DISCOURSE ON IRISH AFFAIRS, and in the same year composed a masque, THE LADY OF MAY, for the Queen's entertainment. When Stephen Gosson published THE SCHOOL OF ABUSE (1579), a vehement attack on poets and playwrights, Sidney retaliated with A DEFENSE OF POESIE. This landmark of English literary criticism defended "poesie" as a noble calling and uttered a plea for a new, vigorous school of poetry, dedicated to the serious treatment of original subject matter in simple and modern language. While they did not exactly compose this school themselves, certain young poets like Sidney, Spenser, Dyer, and Greville were meeting together to discuss one another's work and were experimenting endlessly to regularize and standardize English verse. The bond between Sidney and Spenser was close: THE SHEPHEARDS CALENDAR was dedicated to Sidney, and THE FAERIE QUEENE might have been less complete than it is but for Sidney's encouragement. Sidney's own contribution to the new poetry was his impassioned sonnet sequence, ASTROPHEL AND STELLA, inspired by his unrequited love for Penelope Devereux Rich. It was the first of the great Elizabethan sonnet sequences.

In 1579 Sidney presented the Queen with a paper bluntly listing the reasons why she should not marry the Catholic Duke of Anjou. Tradition has it that his frankness cost him banishment from the court, but most scholars are agreed that his exile was self-imposed because of ill health and financial troubles. During this absence from court, he wrote THE ARCADIA and presented it to his sister, the Countess of Pembroke. Displeased with his first attempt, he wrote a second version, much more complex in plot, sounder in characterization, and loftier in tone. Perhaps he was never satisfied with the work, for he left a deathbed injunction that the manuscript be destroyed. Fortunately, this injunction was disregarded, and THE ARCADIA was published posthumously—

like all of Sidney's literary work—in 1590. It soon became the most popular book of the English Renaissance.

In 1581 Sidney served the first of his two terms in Parliament. A year later he was appointed to the Ordnance Office and for the next few years was busy preparing for the coming war with Spain. He was married on September 21, 1583, to Frances Walsingham, and in January of 1584 was knighted. One of the first Englishmen to recognize the importance of sea power, he sponsored Drake's plan to attack Spain through her colonies and was on the point of joining the expedition when he was ordered abroad as governor of the Dutch city of Flushing.

He arrived at Flushing on November 18, 1585. Almost immediately he gained the confidence of the Dutch, something no other English leader had been able to accomplish, and in July, 1586, won military fame by capturing the town of Axel without the loss of a single soldier. A few months later, during a skirmish near Zutphen he was struck by a bullet in the thigh. Typically, he had discarded the thigh-pieces that would have saved him, in deference to the Lord Marshal, Sir William Pelham, who was unable to wear his because of a leg wound. Lest his troops be dismayed at seeing him unhorsed, he insisted on remaining mounted, despite the agony of the long ride back to his headquarters. He was expected to recover and grew steadily better, but infection set in and caused his death on October 17, 1586. Four months later he was buried in Saint Paul's Cathedral. The funeral, attended by seven hundred mourners, was, in the words of one of Sidney's biographers, "memorable for its solemn splendour even in an age when every funeral was a pageant."

Despite his astuteness and foresight, his courage and martial skill, Sidney made no great mark in politics, statesmanship, or war: his spirit was too fine and fastidious for pre-eminence in these fields. Far more important were his contributions to literature. But it was as a personality that he left his deepest imprint on his age. His father said of him: "In troth I speak it without flattery of him, or of myself, he hath the most rare virtues that ever I found in any man." He was the Elizabethan embodiment of Chaucer's "verray, parfit gentil knyght," and when he died, the entire civilized world felt his loss.

The standard edition of Sidney is Albert Feuillerat's THE COMPLETE WORKS OF SIR PHILIP SIDNEY, 4 vols., Cambridge University Press, 1922–1926; this contains the original version as well as the final versions of THE ARCADIA. The best modern biographies are Mona Wilson's SIR PHILIP SIDNEY, Oxford University Press, 1932, and Alfred H. Bill's ASTROPHEL OR THE LIFE AND DEATH OF THE RENOWNED SIR PHILIP SIDNEY, Rinehart & Company, 1937. Special studies of interest are M. S. Golman's SIR PHILIP SIDNEY AND THE ARCADIA, Illinois Studies in Language and Literature, XVII, 1–2, 1934, and K. O. Myrick's SIR PHILIP SIDNEY AS A LITERARY CRAFTSMAN, Harvard University Press, 1935.

The text is taken from the reprint of the 1590 edition of THE ARCADIA in Feuillerat's COMPLETE WORKS.

THE COUNTESS OF PEMBROKE'S ARCADIA
WRITTEN BY SIR PHILIP SIDNEY

[*The main thread in the tangled skein of THE ARCA_
DIA revolves around the love of two Grecian princes,
Pyrocles of Macedon and Musidorus of Thessaly, for the
princesses Philoclea and Pamela, daughters of Basilius, King
of Arcadia. In response to a warning from the Oracle of
Delphos, Basilius has retired to a forest with his two daughters and his wife, Gynecia. As the selection below begins,
Pyrocles is telling Musidorus the results of his having disguised himself as a woman in order to be near Philoclea.*]

[From BOOK 1, CHAPTERS 14 AND 15]

Now THUS I had (as methought) well played my first
act, assuring myself, that under that disguisement, I
should find opportunity to reveal myself to the owner
of my heart. But who would think it possible (though I feel
it true) that in almost eight weeks' space, I have lived here
(having no more company but her parents, and I being familiar, as being a woman, and watchful, as being a lover) yet
could never find opportunity to have one minute's leisure of
privy conference: the cause whereof is, as strange, as the
effects are to me miserable. And (alas) this it is.

"At the first sight that Basilius had of me (I think Cupid
having headed his arrows with my misfortune) he was
stricken (taking me to be such as I profess) with great affection towards me, which since is grown to such a doting love,
that (till I was fain to get this place, sometimes to retire unto
freely) I was even choked with his tediousness. You never
saw fourscore years dance up and down more lively in a

young lover: now, as fine in his apparel, as if he would make me in love with a cloak; and verse for verse with the sharpest-witted lover in Arcadia. Do you not think that this is a sallet[1] of wormwood, while mine eyes feed upon the ambrosia of Philoclea's beauty.

"But this is not all; no this is not the worst; for he (good man) were easy enough to be dealt with: but (as I think) love and mischief having made a wager, which should have most power in me, have set Gynecia also on such a fire towards me, as will never (I fear) be quenched but with my destruction. For she (being a woman of excellent wit, and of strong-working thoughts) whether she suspected me by my over-vehement shows of affection to Philoclea (which love forced me unwisely to utter, while hope of my mask foolishly encouraged me) or that she hath taken some other mark of me, that I am not a woman: or what devil it is hath revealed it unto her, I know not; but so it is, that all her countenances, words and gestures, are miserable portraitures of a desperate affection. Whereby a man may learn, that these avoidings of company, do but make the passions more violent, when they meet with fit subjects. Truly it were a notable dumb shew of Cupid's kingdom, to see my eyes (languishing with over-vehement longing) direct themselves to Philoclea: & Basilius as busy about me as a bee, & indeed as cumbersome; making such suits to me, who neither could if I would; nor would if I could, help him: while the terrible wit of Gynecia, carried with the beere[2] of violent love, runs through us all. And so jealous is she of my love to her daughter, that I could never yet begin to open my mouth to the unevitable Philoclea but that her unwished presence gave my tale a conclusion, before it had a beginning.

"And surely if I be not deceived, I see such shews of liking, and (if I be acquainted with passions) of almost a passionate liking in the heavenly Philoclea, towards me, that I may hope her ears would not abhor my discourse. And for good Basilius, he thought it best to have lodged us together, but that the eternal hatefulness of my destiny, made Gynecia's jealousy stop that, and all other my blessings. Yet must I confess, that one way her love doth me pleasure: for since it was my foolish fortune, or unfortunate folly, to be known by her, that keeps her from bewraying me to Basilius. And thus (my Musidorus) you have my tragedy played unto you by myself, which I pray the gods may not in deed prove a tragedy . . .

". . . Now farewell dear cousin," said he, "from me, no more Pyrocles, nor Daiphantus[3] now, but Zelmane:[4] Zelmane is my name, Zelmane is my title, Zelmane is the only hope of my advancement." And with that word going out, and seeing that the coast was clear, Zelmane dismissed Musidorus, who departed as full of care to help his friend, as before he was to dissuade him.

Zelmane returned to the lodge, where (inflamed by Philoclea, watched by Gynecia, and tired by Basilius) she[5] was like a horse, desirous to run, and miserably spurred, but so short-reined, as he cannot stir forward: Zelmane sought occasion to speak with Philoclea; Basilius with Zelmane; and Gynecia hindered them all. If Philoclea happened to sigh (and sigh she did often) as if that sigh were to be waited on, Zelmane sighed also; whereto Basilius and Gynecia soon made up four parts of sorrow. Their affection increased their conversation; and their conversation increased their affection. The respect borne bred due ceremonies; but the affection shined so through them, that the ceremonies seemed not ceremonious. Zelmane's eyes were (like children afore sweetmeat) eager, but fearful of their ill-pleasing governors. Time in one instant, seeming both short, and long unto them: short, in the pleasingness of such presence: long, in the stay of their desires.

[From BOOK II, CHAPTER I]

In these pastoral pastimes a great number of days were sent to follow their flying predecessors, while the cup of poison (which was deeply tasted of this noble company) had left no sinew of theirs without mortally searching into it; yet never manifesting his venomous work, till once, that the night (parting away angrily, that she could distill no more sleep into the eyes of lovers) had no sooner given place to the breaking out of the morning light, and the sun bestowed his beams upon the tops of the mountains, but that the woeful Gynecia (to whom rest was no ease) had left her loathed lodging, and gotten herself into the solitary places those deserts were full of, going up and down with such unquiet motions, as a grieved & hopeless mind is wont to bring forth. There appeared unto the eyes of her judgement the evils she was like to run into, with ugly infamy waiting upon them: she felt the terrors of her own conscience: she was guilty of a long-exercised virtue, which made this vice the fuller of deformity. The uttermost of the good she could aspire unto, was a mortal wound to her vexed spirits: and lastly no small part of her evils was, that she was wise to see her evils. Insomuch, that having a great while thrown her countenance ghastly about her (as if she had called all the powers of the world to witness of her wretched estate) at length casting up her watery eyes to heaven, "O sun," said she, "whose unspotted light directs the steps of mortal mankind, art thou not ashamed to impart the clearness of thy presence to such a dust-creeping worm as I am? O you heavens (which continually keep the course allotted unto you) can none of your influences prevail so much upon the miserable Gynecia, as to make her preserve a course so long embraced by her? O deserts, deserts, how fit a guest am I for you, since my heart can people you with wild ravenous beasts, which in you are wanting? O virtue, where dost thou hide thyself? or what hideous thing is this which doth eclipse thee? or is it true that thou wert never but a vain name, and no essential thing, which hast thus left thy professed servant, when she had most need of thy lovely presence? O imperfect proportion of reason, which can too much foresee, & too little prevent? Alas, alas," said she, "if there were but one hope for all my pains, or but one excuse for all my faultiness. But wretch that I am, my torment is beyond all succour, & my evil deserving doth exceed my evil fortune. For nothing else did my husband take this strange resolution to live so solitarily: for nothing else have the winds delivered this strange guest to my country: for nothing else have the destinies reserved my life to this time, but that only I (most wretched I) should become a plague to myself, and a shame to womankind. Yet if my desire (how unjust soever it be) might take effect, though a thousand deaths followed it, and every death were followed with a thousand shames; yet should not my sepulcher receive me without some contentment. But alas, though sure I am, that Zelmane is such as can answer my love; yet as sure I am that, this disguising must needs come for some foretaken conceit. And then, wretched Gynecia, where canst thou find any small ground-plot for hope to dwell upon? No, no, it is Philoclea his heart is set upon: it is my daughter I have borne to supplant me. But if it be so, the life I have given thee (ungrateful Philoclea) I will sooner with these hands bereave thee of, than my birth shall glory, she hath bereaved me of my desires. In shame there is no comfort, but to be beyond all bounds of shame."

Having spoken thus, she began to make a piteous war with her fair hair, when she might hear (not far from her) an extremely doleful voice, but so suppressed with a kind of whispering note, that she could not conceive the words distinctly. But (as a lamentable tune is the sweetest music to a woeful mind) she drew thither near-away, in hope to find some companion of her misery. And as she passed on, she was stopped with a number of trees, so thickly placed together, that she was afraid she should (with rushing through) stop the speech of the lamentable party, which she was so desirous to understand. And therefore setting her down as softly as she could (for she was now in distance to hear) she might first perceive a lute excellently well played upon, and then the same doleful voice accompanying it with these verses.

> In vain, mine eyes, you labour to amend
>   With flowing tears your fault of hasty sight:
> Since to my heart her shape you so did send;
>   That her I see, though you did lose your light.
>
> In vain, my heart, now you with sight are burn'd,
>   With sighs you seek to cool your hot desire:

> Since sighs (into mine inward furnace turn'd)
> For bellows serve to kindle more the fire.
>
> Reason, in vain (now you have lost my heart)
> My head you seek, as to your strongest fort:
> Since there mine eyes have play'd so false a part,
> That to your strength your foes have sure resort.
> Then since in vain I find were all my strife,
> To this strange death I vainly yield my life.

The ending of the song served but for a beginning of new plaints, as if the mind (oppressed with too heavy a burthen of cares) was fain to discharge itself of all sides, & as it were, paint out the hideousness of the pain in all sorts of colours. For the woeful person (as if the lute had evil joined with the voice) threw it to the ground with such like words: "Alas, poor lute, how much art thou deceived to think, that in my miseries thou couldst ease my woes, as in my careless times thou was wont to please my fancies? The time is changed, my lute, the time is changed; and no more did my joyful mind then receive everything to a joyful consideration, than my careful mind now makes each thing taste like the bitter juice of care. The evil is inward, my lute, the evil is inward; which all thou doest doth serve but to make me think more freely of, and the more I think, the more cause I find of thinking, but less of hoping. And alas, what is then thy harmony, but the sweetmeats of sorrow? The discord of my thoughts, my lute, doth ill agree to the concord of thy strings; therefore be not ashamed to leave thy master, since he is not afraid to forsake himself."

And thus much spoken (instead of a conclusion) was closed up with so hearty a groaning, that Gynecia could not refrain to show herself, thinking such griefs could serve fitly for nothing, but her own fortune. But as she came into the little arbour of this sorrowful music, her eyes met with the eyes of Zelmane, which was the party that thus had indited herself of misery: so that either of them remained confused with a sudden astonishment. Zelmane fearing, lest she had heard some part of those complaints, which she had risen up that morning early of purpose, to breathe out in secret to herself. But Gynecia a great while stood still, with a kind of dull amazement, looking steadfastly upon her: at length returning to some use of herself, she began to ask Zelmane, what cause carried her so early abroad? But as if the opening of her mouth to Zelmane, had opened some great floodgate of sorrow (whereof her heart could not abide the violent issue) she sank to the ground, with her hands over her face, crying vehemently, "Zelmane help me, O Zelmane have pity on me." Zelmane ran to her, marvelling what sudden sickness had thus possessed her: and beginning to ask her the cause of her pain, and offering her service to be employed by her: Gynecia opening her eyes wildly upon her, pricked with the flames of love, and the torments of her own conscience: "O Zelmane, Zelmane," said she, "doest thou offer me physic, which art my only poison? Or wilt thou do me service, which hast already brought me into eternal slavery?" Zelmane then knowing well at what mark she shot, yet loth to enter into it; "Most excellent lady," said she, "you were best retire yourself into your lodging, that you the better may pass this sudden fit." "Retire myself?" said Gynecia. "If I had retired myself into myself, when thou to me (unfortunate guest) camest to draw me from myself; blessed had I been, and no need had I had of this counsel. But now alas, I am forced to fly to thee for succour, whom I accuse of all my hurt; and make thee judge of my cause, who art the only author of my mischief." Zelmane the more astonished, the more she understood her, "Madam," said she, "whereof do you accuse me, that I will not clear myself? Or wherein may I stead you, that you may not command me?" "Alas," answered Gynecia, "what shall I say more? Take pity of me, O Zelmane, but not as Zelmane, and disguise not with me in words, as I know thou doest in apparel."

Zelmane was much troubled with that word, finding herself brought to this strait. But as she was thinking what to answer her; they might see old Basilius pass hard by them, without ever seeing them: complaining likewise of love very freshly;

and ending his complaint with this song, love having renewed both his invention, and voice.

> Let not old age disgrace my high desire,
>   O heavenly soul, in human shape contain'd:
> Old wood inflam'd doth yield the bravest fire,
>   When younger doeth in smoke his virtue spend.
>
> Ne[5a] let white hairs, which on my face do grow,
>   Seem to your eyes of a disgraceful hue:
> Since whiteness doth present the sweetest show,
>   Which makes all eyes do honour unto you.
>
> Old age is wise and full of constant truth;
>   Old age well stay'd from ranging humor lives:
> Old age hath known whatever was in youth:
>   Old age o'ercome, the greater honour gives.
>   And to old age since you yourself aspire,
>   Let not old age disgrace my high desire.

Which being done, he looked very curiously upon himself, sometimes fetching a little skip, as if he had said, his strength had not yet forsaken him. But Zelmane having in this time gotten some leisure to think for an answer; looking upon Gynecia, as if she thought she did her some wrong: "Madam," said she, "I am not acquainted with those words of disguising, neither is it the profession of an Amazon, neither are you a party with whom it is to be used. If my service may please you, employ it, so long as you do me no wrong in misjudging of me." "Alas Zelmane," said Gynecia, "I perceive you know full little, how piercing the eyes are of a true lover. There is no one beam of those thoughts you have planted in me, but is able discern a greater cloud than you do go in. Seek not to conceal yourself further from me, nor force not the passion of love into violent extremities." Now was Zelmane brought to an exigent, when the king turning his eyes that way through the trees, perceived his wife and mistress together: so that framing the most lovely countenance he could, he came straightway towards them; and at the first word (thanking his wife for having entertained Zelmane,) desired her she would now return into the lodge, because he had certain matters of estate to impart to the Lady Zelmane. The queen (being nothing troubled with jealousy in that point) obeyed the king's commandment; full of raging agonies, and determinately bent, that as she would seek all loving means to win Zelmane, so she would stir up terrible tragedies, rather than fail of her intent. And so went she from them to the lodge-ward, with such a battle in her thoughts, and so deadly an overthrow given to her best resolutions, that even her body (where the field was fought) was oppressed withal: making a languishing sickness wait upon the triumph of passion; which the more it prevailed in her, the more it made her jealousy watchful, both over her daughter, and Zelmane; having ever one of them entrusted to her own eyes.

But as soon as Basilius was rid of his wife's presence, falling down on his knees, "O lady," said he, "which hast only had the power to stir up again those flames which had so long lain dead in me; see in me the power of your beauty; which can make old age come to ask counsel of youth; and a prince unconquered, to become a slave to a stranger. And when you see that power of yours, love that at least in me, since it is yours, although of me you see nothing to be loved." "Worthy prince," answered Zelmane, taking him up from his kneeling, "both your manner, and your speech are so strange unto me, as I know not how to answer it better than with silence." "If silence please you," said the king, "it shall never displease me, since my heart is wholly pledged to obey you: otherwise if you would vouchsafe mine ears such happiness, as to hear you, they shall convey your words to such a mind, which is with the humblest degree of reverence to receive them." "I disdain not to speak to you (mighty prince)," said Zelmane, "but I disdain to speak to any matter which may bring my honor into question." And therewith, with a brave counterfeited scorn she departed from the king; leaving him not so sorry for his short answer, as proud in himself that he had broken the matter. And thus did the king (feeding his mind with those thoughts) pass great time in writing verses, & making more of himself, than he was wont to do: that with a little help, he would have grown into a pretty kind of dotage.

But Zelmane being rid of this loving, but little-loved company, "Alas," said she, "poor Pyrocles, was there ever one, but I, that had received wrong, and could blame nobody? that having more than I desire, am still in want of that I would? Truly Love, I must needs say thus much on thy behalf; thou hast employed my love there, where all love is deserved; and for recompense hast sent me more love than ever I desired. But what wilt thou do Pyrocles? which way canst thou find to rid thee of thy intricate troubles? To her whom I would be known to, I live in darkness: and to her am revealed, from whom I would be most secret. What shift shall I find against the diligent love of Basilius? what shield against the violent passions of Gynecia? And if that be done, yet how am I the nearer to quench the fire that consumes me? Well, well, sweet Philoclea, my whole confidence must be builded in thy divine spirit, which cannot be ignorant of the cruel wound I have received by you."

[From BOOK II, CHAPTER 4]

The sweet-minded Philoclea was in their degree of well-doing, to whom the not knowing of evil serveth for a ground of virtue, and hold their inward powers in better form with an unspotted simplicity, than many, who rather cunningly seek to know what goodness is, than willingly take into themselves the following of it. But as that sweet & simple breath of heavenly goodness, is the easier to be altered, because it hath not passed through the worldly wickedness, nor feelingly found the evil, that evil carries with it; so now the Lady Philoclea (whose eyes and senses had received nothing, but according as the natural course of each thing required; which from the tender youth had obediently lived under her parents' behests, without framing out of her own will the fore-choosing of anything) when now she came to appoint[6] wherein her judgment was to be practised, in knowing faultiness by his first tokens, she was like a young fawn, who coming in

the wind of the hunters, doth not know whether it be a thing
or no to be eschewed; whereof at this time she began to get
a costly experience. For after that Zelmane had awhile lived
in the lodge with her, and that her only being a noble stranger
had bred a kind of heedful attention; her coming to that
lonely place (where she had nobody but her parents) a willingness of conversation; her wit & behaviour, a liking & silent
admiration; at length the excellency of her natural gifts,
joined with the extreme shews she made of most devout hon-
ouring Philoclea, (carrying thus in one person the only two
bands of good will, loveliness & lovingness) brought forth in
her heart a yielding to a most friendly affection; which when
it had gotten so full possession of the keys of her mind, that it
would receive no message from her senses, without that affection were the interpreter; then straight grew an exceeding delight still to be with her, with an unmeasurable liking of all
that Zelmane did: matters being so turned in her, that where
at first liking her manners did breed good will, now good will
became the chief cause of liking her manners: so that within
a while Zelmane was not prized for her demeanor, but the
demeanor was prized because it was Zelmane's. Then followed
that most natural effect of conforming one's self to that.
which she did like, and not only wishing to be herself such
another in all things, but to ground an imitation upon so
much an esteemed authority: so that the next degree was to
mark all Zelmane's doings, speeches, and fashions, and to take
them into herself, as a pattern of worthy proceeding. Which
when once it was enacted, not only by the commonalty of
passions, but agreed unto by her most noble thoughts, and
that by reason itself (not yet experienced in the issues of such
matters) had granted his royal assent; then friendship (a diligent officer) took care to see the statute thoroughly observed.
Then grew on that not only she did imitate the soberness of
her countenance, the gracefulness of her speech, but even
their particular gestures: so that as Zelmane did often eye her,
she would often eye Zelmane; & as Zelmane's eyes would
deliver a submissive, but vehement desire in their look, she,

though as yet she had not the desire in her, yet should her eyes answer in like piercing kindness of a look. Zelmane as much as Gynecia's jealousy would suffer, desired to be near Philoclea; Philoclea, as much as Gynecia's jealousy would suffer, desired to be near Zelmane. If Zelmane took her hand, and softly strained it, she also (thinking the knots of friendship ought to be mutual) would (with a sweet fastness) shew she was loth to part from it. And if Zelmane sighed, she should sigh also; when Zelmane was sad, she deemed it wisdom, and therefore she would be sad too. Zelmane's languishing countenance with crossed arms, and sometimes cast-up eyes, she thought to have an excellent grace: and therefore she also willingly put on the same countenance: till at the last (poor soul, ere she were aware) she accepted not only the band, but the service; not only the sign, but the passion signified. For whether it were, that her wit in continuance did find, that Zelmane's friendship was full of impatient desire, having more than ordinary limits, & therefore she was content to second Zelmane, though herself knew not the limits; or that in truth, true love (well considered) have an infective power. At last she fell in acquaintance with love's harbinger, wishing. First she would wish, that they two might live all their lives together, like two of Diana's nymphs. But that wish, she thought not sufficient, because she knew, there would be more nymphs besides them, who also would have their part in Zelmane. Then would she wish, that she were her sister, that such a natural band might make her more special to her. But against that, she considered, that though being her sister, if she happened to be married, she should be robbed of her. Then grown bolder, she would wish either herself, or Zelmane a man, that there might succeed a blessed marriage betwixt them. But when that wish had once displayed his ensign in her mind, then followed whole squadrons of longings, that so it might be, with a main battle of mislikings, and repinings against their creation, that so it was not. Then dreams by night began to bring more unto her, than she durst wish by day, whereout making[7] did make her know herself

the better by the image of those fancies. But as some diseases
when they are easy to be cured, they are hard to be known,
but when they grow easy to be known, they are almost impossible to be cured: so the sweet Philoclea, while she might
prevent it, she did not feel it, now she felt it, when it was
past preventing; like a river, no rampires[8] being built against
it, till already it have overflowed. For now indeed, Love
pulled off his mask, and shewed his face unto her, and told
her plainly, that she was his prisoner. Then needed she no
more paint her face with passions; for passions shone through
her face: Then her rosy colour was often increased with extraordinary blushing: and so another time, perfect whiteness
descended to a degree of paleness; now hot, then cold, desiring she knew not what, nor how, if she knew what. Then her
mind (though too late) by the smart was brought to think of
the disease, and her own proof taught her to know her
mother's mind; which (as no error gives so strong assault, as
that which comes armed in the authority of a parent, so)
greatly fortified her desires, to see, that her mother had the
like desires. And the more jealous her mother was, the more
she thought the jewel precious, which was with so many
looks guarded. But that prevailing so far, as to keep the two
lovers from private conference, then began she to feel the
sweetness of a lover's solitariness, when freely with words and
gestures, as if Zelmane were present, she might give passage
to her thoughts, and so as it were utter out some smoke of
those flames, wherewith else she was not only burned, but
smothered. As this night, that going from the one lodge to the
other by her mother's commandment, with doleful gestures
and uncertain paces, she did willingly accept the time's offer,
to be a while alone: so that going a little aside into the wood;
where many times before she had delighted to walk, her eyes
were saluted with a tuft of trees, so close set together, as with
the shade the moon gave through it, it might breed a fearful
kind of devotion to look upon it. But true thoughts of love
banish all vain fancy of superstition. Full well she did both
remember and like the place; for there had she often with

their shade beguiled Phœbus of looking upon her: There had she enjoyed herself often, while she was mistress of herself, and had no other thoughts, but such as might arise out of quiet senses. . . .

But . . . (laying all her fair length under one of the trees) for a while she did nothing but turn up and down, as if she had hoped to turn away the fancy that mastered her, and hid her face, as if she could have hidden herself from her own fancies. At length with a whispering note to herself; "O me unfortunate wretch," said she, "what poisonous heats be these, which thus torment me? How hath the sight of this strange guest invaded my soul? Alas, what entrance found this desire, or what strength had it thus to conquer me?" Then, a cloud passing between her sight and the moon, "O Diana," said she, "I would either the cloud that now hides the light of my virtue would as easily pass away, as you will quickly overcome this let; or else that you were forever thus darkened, to serve for an excuse of my outrageous folly." Then looking to the stars, which had perfectly as then beautified the clear sky: "My parents," said she, "have told me, that in these fair heavenly bodies, there are great hidden deities which have their working in the ebbing & flowing of our estates. If it be so, then (O you stars) judge rightly of me, & if I have with wicked intent made myself a prey to fancy, or if by any idle lusts I framed my heart fit for such an impression, then let this plague daily increase in me, till my name be made odious to womankind. But if extreme and unresistible violence have oppressed me, who will ever do any of you sacrifice (O you stars) if you do not succour me. No, no, you will not help me. No, no, you cannot help me: Sin must be the mother, and shame the daughter of my affection. And yet are these but childish objections (simple Philoclea) it is the impossibility that doeth torment me: for, unlawful desires are punished after the effect of enjoying; but unpossible desires are punished in the desire itself. O then, O ten times unhappy that I am, since wherein all other hope kindleth love; in me despair should be the bellows of my affection: and of all despairs the most miserable, which is drawn from impossibility. The most covetous man longs not to get riches out of a ground which never can bear anything; Why? because it is impossible. The most ambitious wight vexeth not his wits to climb into heaven; Why? because it is impossible. Alas then, O Love, why doest thou in thy beautiful sampler set such a work for my desire to take out, which is as much impossible? And yet alas, why do I thus condemn my fortune, before I hear what she can say for herself? What do I, silly wench, know what Love hath prepared for me? Do I not see my mother, as well, at least as furiously as myself, love Zelmane? And should I be wiser than my mother? Either she sees a possibility in that which I think impossible, or else impossible loves need not misbecome me. And do I not see Zelmane (who doth not think a thought which is not first weighed by wisdom and virtue) doth not she vouchsafe to love me with like ardour? I see it, her eyes depose it to be true; what then? and if she can love poor me, shall I think scorn to love such a woman as Zelmane? Away then all vain examinations of why and how. Thou lovest me, excellent Zelmane, and I love thee:" and with that, embracing the very ground whereon she lay, she said to herself (for even to herself she was ashamed to speak it out in words) "O my Zelmane, govern and direct me: for I am wholly given over unto thee."

[From BOOK II, CHAPTER 11]

But as he (who found no so good sacrifice, as obedience) was returning to the story of himself,[9] Philoclea came in, & by and by after her, Miso;[10] so as for that time they were fain to let Dorus[11] depart. But Pamela (delighted even to preserve in her memory, the words of so well a beloved speaker) repeated the whole substance to her sister, till their sober dinner being come and gone, to recreate themselves something, (even tired with the noisomeness of Miso's conversation) they determined to go (while the heat of the day lasted) to bathe themselves (such being the manner of the Arcadian nymphs often to do) in the river of Ladon, and take with

them a lute, meaning to delight them under some shadow. But
they could not stir, but that Miso with her daughter Mopsa
was after them: and as it lay in their way to pass by the other
lodge, Zelmane out of her window espied them, and so stole
down after them: which she might the better do because that
Gynecia was sick, and Basilius (that day being his birthday)
according to his manner, was busy about his devotions; and
therefore she went after, hoping to find some time to speak
with Philoclea: but not a word could she begin, but that Miso
would be one of the audience; so that she was driven to rec-
ommend thinking, speaking, and all, to her eyes, who diligently performed her trust, till they came to the river's side;
which of all the rivers of Greece had the prize for excellent
pureness and sweetness, insomuch as the very bathing in it,
was accounted exceeding healthful. It ran upon so fine and
delicate a ground, as one could not easily judge, whether the
river did more wash the gravel, or the gravel did purify the
river; the river not running forthright, but almost continually
winding, as if the lower streams would return to their spring,
or that the river had a delight to play with itself. The banks
of either side seeming arms of the loving earth, that fain
would embrace it; and the river a wanton nymph which still
would stir from it: either side of the bank being fringed with
most beautiful trees, which resisted the sun's darts from
overmuch piercing the natural coldness of the river. There
was . . .[12] among the rest a goodly cypress, who bowing her
fair head over the water, it seemed she looked into it, and
dressed her green locks, by that running river. There the
princesses determining to bathe themselves, though it was so
privileged a place, upon pain of death, as nobody durst presume to come thither, yet for the more surety, they looked
round about, and could see nothing but a water spaniel, who
came down the river, shewing that he hunted for a duck, &
with a snuffling grace, disdaining that his smelling force could
not as well prevail through the water, as through the air; &
therefore waiting with his eye, to see whether he could espy
the ducks getting up again: but then a little below them fail-

ing of his purpose, he got out of the river, & shaking off the
water (as great men do their friends, now he had no further
cause to use it) inweeded himself so, as the ladies lost the
further marking his sportfulness: and inviting Zelmane also to
wash herself with them, and she excusing herself with having
taken a late cold, they began by piecemeal to take away the
eclipsing of their apparel.

Zelmane would have put to her helping hand, but she was
taken with such a quivering, that she thought it more wisdom
to lean herself to a tree and look on, while Miso and Mopsa
(like a couple of forswat[13] melters) were getting the pure
silver of their bodies out of the ure[14] of their garments. But
as the raiments went off to receive kisses of the ground, Zelmane envied the happiness of all, but of the smock was even
jealous, and when that was taken away too, and that Philoclea
remained (for her Zelmane only marked) like a diamond
taken from out the rock, or rather like the sun getting from
under a cloud, and shewing his naked beams to the full view,
then was the beauty too much for a patient sight, the delight
too strong for a staid conceit: so that Zelmane could not
choose but run, to touch, embrace, and kiss her; But conscience made her come to herself, & leave Philoclea, who
blushing, and withal smiling, making shamefacedness pleasant,
and pleasure shamefaced, tenderly moved her feet, unwonted
to feel the naked ground, till the touch of the cold water
made a pretty kind of shrugging come over her body, like the
twinkling of the fairest among the fixed stars. But the river
itself gave way unto her, so that she was straight breast high;
which was the deepest that thereabout she could be: and
when cold Ladon had once fully embraced them, himself was
no more so cold to those ladies, but as if his cold complexion
had been heated with love, so seemed he to play about every
part he could touch.

"Ah sweet, now sweetest Ladon," said Zelmane, "why dost
thou not stay thy course to have more full taste of thy happiness? But the reason is manifest, the upper streams make such
haste to have their part of embracing, that the nether (though

lothly) must needs give place unto them. O happy Ladon,
within whom she is, upon whom her beauty falls, through
whom her eye pierceth. O happy Ladon, which art now an
unperfect mirror of all perfection, canst thou ever forget the
blessedness of this impression? if thou do, then let thy bed be
turned from fine gravel, to weeds & mud; if thou do, let some
unjust niggards make weirs to spoil thy beauty; if thou do,
let some greater river fall into thee, to take away the name
of Ladon. Oh Ladon, happy Ladon, rather slide than run by
her, lest thou shouldest make her legs slip from her; and then,
O happy Ladon, who would then call thee, but the most
cursed Ladon?" But as the ladies played them in the water,
sometimes striking it with their hands, the water (making
lines in his face) seemed to smile at such beating, and with
twenty bubbles, not to be content to have the picture of their
face in large upon him, but he would in each of those bubbles
set forth the miniature of them.

But Zelmane, whose sight was gainsaid by nothing but the
transparent veil of Ladon, (like a chamber where a great fire
is kept, though the fire be at one stay, yet with the continuance continually hath his heat increased) had the coals of her
affection so kindled with wonder, and blown with delight,
that now all her parts grudged, that her eyes should do more
homage, than they, to the princess of them. Insomuch that
taking up the lute, her wit began to be with a divine fury
inspired; her voice would in so beloved an occasion second
her wit; her hands accorded the lute's music to the voice; her
panting heart danced to the music; while I think her feet did
beat the time; while her body was the room where it should
be celebrated; her soul the queen which should be delighted.
And so together went the utterance and the invention, that
one might judge, it was Philoclea's beauty which did speedily
write it in her eyes; or the sense thereof, which did word by
word indite it in her mind, whereto she (but as an organ) did
only lend utterance. The song was to this purpose.

What tongue can her perfections tell
In whose each part all pens may dwell?

Her hair fine threads of finest gold
In curled knots man's thought to hold:
But that her forehead says in me
A whiter beauty you may see.
Whiter indeed; more white than snow,
Which on cold winter's face doth grow.
That doth present those even brows,
Whose equal line their angles bows,
Like to the moon when after change
Her horned head abroad doth range:
And arches be two heavenly lids,
Whose wink each bold attempt forbids.
For the black stars those spheres contain,
The matchless pair, even praise doth stain.
No lamp, whose light by art is got,
No sun, which shines, and seeth not,
Can liken them without all peer,
Save one as much as other clear:
Which only thus unhappy be,
Because themselves they cannot see.
    Her cheeks with kindly claret spread.
Aurora-like new out of bed,
Or like the fresh queen-apple's side,
Blushing at sight of Phoebus' pride.
    Her nose, her chin pure ivory wears:
No purer than the pretty ears.
So that therein appears some blood,
Like wine and milk that mingled stood
In whose incirclets if ye gaze,
Your eyes may tread a lover's maze.
But with such turns the voice to stray,
No talk untaught can find the way.
The tip no jewel needs to wear:
The tip is jewel of the ear.
    But who those ruddy lips can miss?
Which blessed still themselves do kiss.
Rubies, cherries, and roses new,
In worth, in taste, in perfect hue:
Which never part but that they show
Of precious pearl the double row,
The second sweetly fenced ward,

Her heav'nly-dewed tongue to guard.
Whence never word in vain did flow.
   Fair under these doth stately grow,
The handle of this precious work,
The neck, in which strange graces lurk.
Such be I think the sumptuous towers
Which skill doeth make in princes' bowers.
So good a say invites the eye,
A little downward to espy,
The lively clusters of her breasts,
Of Venus' babe the wanton nests:
Like pommels round of marble clear:
Where azur'd veins well mix'd appear.
With dearest tops of porphyry.
   Betwixt these two a way doth lie,
A way more worthy beauty's fame,
Than that which bears the milky name.
This leads into the joyous field,
Which only still doth lilies yield:
But lilies such whose native smell
The Indian odours doth excel.
Waist it is call'd, for it doth waste
Men's lives, until it be embrac'd.
   There may one see, and yet not see
Her ribs in white all armed be.
More white than Neptune's foamy face,
When struggling rocks he would embrace.
   In those delights the wand'ring thought
Might of each side astray be brought,
But that her navel doth unite,
In curious circle, busy sight:
A dainty seal of virgin wax,
Where nothing but impression lacks.
   Her belly then glad sight doth fill,
Justly entitled Cupid's hill.
A hill most fit for such a master,
A spotless mine of alabaster.
Like alabaster fair and sleek,
But soft and supple satin-like.
In that sweet seat the Boy doth sport:
Loath, I must leave his chief resort.

For such a use the world hath gotten,
The best things still must be forgotten.
   Yet never shall my song omit
Thighs, for Ovid's song more fit;
Which flanked with two sug'red flanks,
Lift up their stately swelling banks;
That Albion's cliffs in whiteness pass:
With haunches smooth as looking glass.
   But bow all knees, now of her knees
My tongue doth tell what fancy sees.
The knots of joy, the gems of love,
Whose motion makes all graces move.
Whose bought incav'd [15] doth yield such sight,
Like cunning painter shadowing white.
The gart'ring place with childlike sign,
Shews easy print in metal fine.
But then again the flesh doth rise
In her brave calves, like crystal skies.
Whose Atlas is a smallest small [16]
More white than whitest bone of all.
   Thereout steals out that round clean foot
This noble cedar's precious root:
In shew and scent pale violets,
Whose step on earth all beauty sets.
   But back unto her back, my Muse,
Where Leda's swan[17] his feathers mews,
Along whose ridge such bones are met,
Like comfits round in marchpane set.
   Her shoulders be like two white doves,
Perching within square royal rooves,[18]
Which leaded are with silver skin,
Passing the hate-sport ermelin.[19]
And thence those arms derived are;
The Phoenix' wings are not so rare
For faultless length, and stainless hue.
   Ah woe is me, my woes renew;
Now course doth lead me to her hand,
Of my first love the fatal band.
Where whiteness doeth forever sit:
Nature herself enamel'd it.
For therewith strange compact doeth lie

Warm snow, moist pearl, soft ivory.
There fall those sapphire-coloured brooks,
Which conduit-like with curious crooks,
Sweet islands make in that sweet land.
As for the fingers of the hand,
The bloody shafts of Cupid's war,
With amethysts they headed are.
  Thus hath each part his beauty's part,
But how the Graces do impart
To all her limbs a special grace,
Becoming every time and place.
Which doth even beauty beautify,
And most bewitched the wretched eye.
How all this is but a fair inn
Of fairer guests, which dwell within.
Of whose high praise, and praiseful bliss,
Goodness the pen, Heaven paper is.
The ink immortal fame doeth lend:
As I began, so must I end.
No tongue can her perfections tell,
In whose each part all tongues may dwell.

But as Zelmane was coming to the latter end of her song, she might see the same water spaniel which before had hunted, come and fetch away one of Philoclea's gloves; whose fine proportion, shewed well what a dainty guest was wont there to be lodged. It was a delight to Zelmane, to see that the dog was therewith delighted, and so let him go a little way withal, who quickly carried it out of sight among certain trees and bushes, which were very close together. But by & by he came again, & amongst the raiments. (Miso and Mopsa being preparing sheets against their coming out) the dog lighted upon a little book of four or five leaves of paper, & was bearing that away too. But then Zelmane (not knowing what importance it might be of) ran after the dog, who going straight to those bushes, she might see the dog deliver it to a gentleman who secretly lay there. But she hastily coming in, the gentleman rose up, & with a courteous (though sad) countenance presented himself unto her. Zelmane's eyes straight

willed her mind to mark him: for she thought, in her life she
had never seen a man of a more goodly presence, in whom
strong making took not away delicacy, nor beauty fierceness:
being indeed such a right manlike man, as nature often erring,
yet shews she would fain make. But when she had awhile (not
without admiration) viewed him, she desired him to deliver
back the glove & paper, because they were the Lady Philoclea's; telling him withal, that she would not willingly let
them know of his close lying in that prohibited place, while
they were bathing themselves; because she knew they would
be mortally offended withal. "Fair lady," answered he, "the
worst of the complaint is already passed, since I feel of my
fault in myself the punishment. But for these things I assure
you, it was my dog's wanton boldness, not my presumption."
With that he gave her back the paper: "But for the glove,"
said he, "since it is my Lady Philoclea's, give me leave to keep
it, since my heart cannot persuade itself to part from it. And
I pray you tell the lady (lady indeed of all my desires) that
owes[20] it, that I will direct my life to honour this glove with
serving her." "O villain," cried out Zelmane, madded with
finding an unlooked-for rival, and that he would make her a
messenger, "dispatch," said she, "and deliver it, or by the life
of her that owes it, I will make thy soul (though too base a
price) pay for it." And with that drew out her sword, which
(Amazon-like) she ever wore about her. The gentleman retired himself into an open place from among the bushes; &
then drawing out his too, he offered to deliver it unto her,
saying withal, "God forbid I should use my sword against
you, since (if I be not deceived) you are the same famous
Amazon, that both defended my lady's just title of beauty
against the valiant Phalantus, & saved her life in killing the
lion:[21] therefore I am rather to kiss your hands, with ac-
knowledging myself bound to obey you." But this courtesy
was worse than a bastinado to Zelmane: so that again with
rageful eyes she bade him defend himself, for no less than
his life should answer it. "A hard case," said he, "to teach
my sword that lesson, which hath ever used to turn itself

to a shield in a lady's presence." But Zelmane hearkening to no more words, began with such witty fury to pursue him with blows & thrusts, that nature & virtue commanded the gentleman to look to his safety. Yet still courtesy, that seemed incorporate in his heart, would not be persuaded by danger to offer any offence, but only to stand upon the best defensive guard he could; sometimes going back, being content in that respect to take on the figure of cowardice; sometime with strong and well-met wards; sometime cunning avoidings of his body; and sometimes feigning some blows, which himself pulled back before they needed to be withstood. And so with play did he a good while fight against the fight of Zelmane, who (more spited with that courtesy) that one that did nothing should be able to resist her) burned away with choler any motions, which might grow out of her own sweet disposition, determining to kill him if he fought no better; & so redoubling her blows, drove the stranger to no other shift, than to ward, and go back; at that time seeming the image of innocency against violence. But at length he found, that both in public and private respects, who stands only upon defence, stands upon no defence: For Zelmane seeming to strike at his head, and he going to ward it, withal stepped back as he was accustomed, she stopt her blow in the air, and suddenly turning the point, ran full at his breast; so as he was driven with the pommel of his sword (having no other weapon of defence) to beat it down: but the thrust was so strong, that he could not so wholly beat it away, but that it met with his thigh through which it ran. But Zelmane retiring her sword, and seeing his blood, victorious anger was conquered by the before-conquered pity; and heartily sorry, and even ashamed with herself she was, considering how little he had done, who well she found could have done more. Insomuch that she said, "Truly I am sorry for your hurt, but yourself gave the cause, both in refusing to deliver the glove, and yet not fighting as I know you could have done. But," said she, "because I perceive you disdain to fight with a woman, it may be before a year come about, you shall meet with a near kinsman of mine, Pyrocles Prince of Macedon, and I give you my word, he for me shall maintain this quarrel against you." "I would" answered Amphialus, "I had many more such hurts to meet and know that worthy prince, whose virtue I love & admire, though my good destiny hath not been to see his person."

But as they were so speaking, the young ladies came, to whom Mopsa (curious in anything, but her own good behaviour) having followed & seen Zelmane fighting, had cried, what she had seen, while they were drying themselves, & the water (with some drops) seemed to weep, that it should part from such bodies. But they careful of Zelmane (assuring themselves that any Arcadian would bear reverence to them) Pamela with a noble mind, and Philoclea with a loving (hastily hiding the beauties, whereof nature was proud, and they ashamed) they made quick work to come to save Zelmane. But already they found them in talk, & Zelmane careful of his wound. But when they saw him they knew it was their cousin-german, the famous Amphialus; whom yet with a sweet-graced bitterness they blamed for breaking their father's commandment, especially while themselves were in such sort retired. But he craved pardon, protesting unto them that he had only been to seek solitary places, by an extreme melancholy that had a good while possessed him, and guided to that place by his spaniel, where while the dog hunted in the river, he had withdrawn himself to pacify with sleep his overwatched eyes: till a dream waked him, and made him see that whereof he had dreamed, & withal not obscurely signified that he felt the smart of his own doings. But Philoclea (that was even jealous of herself for Zelmane) would needs have her glove, and not without so mighty a lour as that face could yield. As for Zelmane when she knew, it was Amphialus, "Lord Amphialus," said she, "I have long desired to know you, heretofore I must confess with more good will, but still with honoring your virtue, though I love not your person: & at this time I pray you let us take care of your wound, upon condition you shall hereafter promise, that a more knightly

combat shall be performed between us." Amphialus answered
in honorable sort, but with such excusing himself, that more
and more accused his love to Philoclea, & provoked more hate
in Zelmane. But Mopsa had already called certain shepherds
not far off (who knew & well observed their limits) to come
and help to carry away Amphialus, whose wound suffered
him not without danger to strain it: and so he leaving himself
with them, departed from them, faster bleeding in his heart,
than at his wound: which bound up by the sheets, wherewith
Philoclea had been wrapped, made him thank the wound, and
bless the sword for that favour.

[From BOOK II, CHAPTERS 16 and 17]

The chief recreation she [Zelmane] could find in her anguish, was sometime to visit that place, where first she was so
happy as to see the cause of her unhap. There would she kiss
the ground, and thank the trees, bliss[22] the air, & do dutiful
reverence to everything that she thought did accompany her at
their first meeting: then return again to her inward thoughts;
sometimes despair darkening all her imaginations, sometimes
the active passion of love cheering and clearing her invention,
how to unbar that cumbersome hindrance of her two ill-
matched lovers. But this morning Basilius himself gave her
good occasion to go beyond them. For having combed and
tricked himself more curiously, than any time forty winters
before, coming where Zelmane was, he found her given over
to her musical muses, to the great pleasure of the good old
Basilius, who retired himself behind a tree, while she with a
most sweet voice did utter those passionate verses.

> Lov'd I am, and yet complain of love:
> As loving not, accus'd in love I die.
> When pity most I crave, I cruel prove:
> Still seeking love, love found as much I fly.
>   Burnt in myself, I muse at others' fire:
> What I call wrong, I do the same, and more:
> Barr'd of my will, I have beyond desire:
> . I wail for want, and yet am chok'd with store.

This is thy work, thou god forever blind:
Though thousands old, a boy entitled still.
Thus children do the silly birds they find,
With stroking hurt, and too much cramming kill.
    Yet thus much love, O Love, I crave of thee:
    Let me be lov'd, or else not loved be.

Basilius made no great haste from behind the tree, till he perceived she had fully ended her music. But then loth to lose the precious fruit of time, he presented himself unto her, falling down upon both his knees, and holding up his hands, as the old governess of Danaë is painted, when she suddenly saw the golden shower, "O heavenly woman, or earthly goddess," said he, "let not my presence be odious unto you, nor my humble suit seem of small weight in your ears. Vouchsafe your eyes to descend upon this miserable old man, whose life hath hitherto been maintained but to serve as an increase of your beautiful triumphs. You only have overthrown me, & in my bondage consists my glory. Suffer not your own work to be despised of you: but look upon him with pity, whose life serves for your praise." Zelmane (keeping a countenance askances[23] she understood him not) told him, It became her evil to suffer such excessive reverence of him, but that it worse became her to correct him, to whom she owed duty: that the opinion she had of his wisdom was such, as made her esteem greatly of his words; but that the words themselves sounded so, as she could not imagine what they might intend. "Intend?" said Basilius, proud that that was brought in question, "what may they intend, but a refreshing of my soul, and a suaging[24] of my heat, and enjoying those your excellencies, wherein my life is upheld, and my death threatened?" Zelmane lifting up her face as if she had received a mortal injury of him, "And is this the devotion your ceremonies have been bent unto?" said she: "Is it the disdain of my estate, or the opinion of my lightness, that have emboldened such base fancies towards me? enjoying quoth you? now little joy come to them that yield to such enjoying." Poor Basilius was so appalled, that his legs bowed under him; his eyes looked as though he would gladly hide himself; and his old blood going to his heart, a general shaking all over his body possessed him. At length with a wan mouth; he was about to give a stammering answer, when it came into Zelmane's head by this device to make her profit of his folly; and therefore with a relented countenance, thus said unto him. "Your words (mighty prince) were unfit either for me to hear, or you to speak: but yet the large testimony I see of your affection makes me willing to suppress a great number of errors. Only thus much I think good to say, that the same words in my Lady Philoclea's mouth, as from one woman to another (so as there were no other body by) might have had a better grace; and perchance have found a gentler receipt."

Basilius (whose senses by desire were held open, and conceit was by love quickened) heard scarcely half her answer out, but that (as if speedy flight might save his life) he turned away, and ran with all the speed his body would suffer him, towards his daughter Philoclea: whom he found at that time dutifully watching by her mother, and Miso curiously watching her; having left Mopsa to do the like service to Pamela. Basilius forthwith calling Philoclea aside, (with all the conjuring words which desire could indite, and authority utter) besought her she would preserve his life, in whom her life was begun; she would save his grey hairs from rebuke, and his aged mind from despair; that if she were not cloyed with his company, and that she thought not the earth overburdened with him, she would cool his fiery grief, which was to be done but by her breath. That in fine, whatsoever he was, he was nothing but what it pleased Zelmane; all the powers of his spirit depending of her: that if she continued cruel, he could no more sustain his life, than the earth remain fruitful in the sun's continual absence. He concluded, she should in one payment requite all his deserts: and that she needed not disdain any service (though never so mean) which was warranted by the sacred name of a father. Philoclea more glad than ever she had known herself, that she might by this occasion, enjoy the private conference of Zelmane, yet had so sweet a feeling of virtue in her mind, that she would not suffer a vile colour to be cast over her fair thoughts; but with humble grace answered her father: That there needed neither promise nor persuasion to her, to make her do her uttermost for her father's service. That for Zelmane's favour, she would in all virtuous sort seek it towards him: and that as she would not pierce further into his meaning, than himself should declare, so would she interpret all his doings to be accomplished in goodness: and therefore desired, (if otherwise it were) that he would not impart it to her, who then should be forced to begin (by true obedience) a shew of disobedience: rather performing his general commandment, which had ever been, to embrace virtue, than any new particular, sprung out of passion, and contrary to the former. Basilius content to take that, since he could have no more (thinking it a great point, if by her means, he could get but a more free access unto Zelmane) allowed her reasons, & took her proffer thankfully, desiring only a speedy return of comfort. Philoclea was parting, and Miso straight behind her, like Alecto[25] following Prosperpina. But Basilius forced her to stay, though with much ado, she being sharp-set upon the fulfilling of a shrewd office, in overlooking Philoclea: and so said to Basilius, that she did as she was commanded, and could not answer it to Gynecia, if she were any whit from Philoclea: telling him true, that he did evil to take her charge from her. But Basilius, (swearing he would put out her eyes, if she stirred a foot to trouble his daughter) gave her a stop for that while.

So away departed Philoclea, with a new field of fancies for her travailing mind. For well she saw, her father was grown her adverse party, and yet her fortune such, as she must favour her rival; and the fortune of that fortune such, as neither that did hurt her, nor any contrary mean help her.

But she walked but a little on, before she saw Zelmane lying upon a bank, with her face so bent over Ladon, that (her tears falling into the water) one might have thought, that she began meltingly to be metamorphosed to the under-running river. But by and by, with speech she made known, as well that she lived, as that she sorrowed. "Fair streams," said she, "that do vouchsafe in your clearness to represent unto me my blubbered face, let the tribute-offer of my tears unto you, procure your stay awhile with me, that I may begin yet at last, to find some thing that pities me: and that all things of comfort and pleasure do not fly away from me. But if the violence of your spring command you to haste away, to pay your duties to your great prince, the sea, yet carry with you these few words, and let the uttermost ends of the world know them. A love more clear than yourselves, dedicated to a love (I fear) more cold than yourselves, with the clearness lays a night of sorrow upon me; and with the coldness inflames a world of fire within me." With that she took a willow stick, and wrote in a sandy bank these few verses.

> Over these brooks trusting to ease mine eyes,
> (Mine eyes even great in labour with their tears)
> I laid my face; my face wherein there lies
> Clusters of clouds, which no sun ever clears.
>   In wat'ry glass my wat'ry eyes I see:
>   Sorrows ill eas'd, where sorrows painted be.
>
> My thoughts imprison'd in my secret woes,
> With flamy breaths do issue oft in sound:
> The sound to this strange air no sooner goes,
> But that it doeth with Echo's force rebound.
>   And make me hear the plaints I would refrain:
>   Thus outward helps my inward griefs maintain.
>
> Now in this sand I would discharge my mind,
> And cast from me part of my burd'nous cares:
> But in the sand my tales foretold I find,
> And see therein how well the writer fares.
>   Since stream, air, sand, mine eyes and ears conspire:
>   What hope to quench, where each thing blows the fire?

And as soon as she had written them (a new swarm of thoughts stinging her mind) she was ready with her foot to give the newborn letters both death and burial. But Philoclea (to whom delight of hearing and seeing was before a stay from interrupting her) gave herself to be seen unto her, with such a lightning of beauty upon Zelmane, that neither she could look on, nor would look off. At last Philoclea (having a little mused how to cut the thread even, between her own hopeless affection, and her father's unbridled hope) with eyes, cheeks, and lips, (whereof each sang their part, to make up the harmony of bashfulness) began to say, "My father to whom I owe myself, & therefore . . ." [26] when Zelmane (making a womanish habit to be the armour of her boldness, giving up her life to the lips of Philoclea, and taking it again by the sweetness of those kisses) humbly besought her to keep her speech for a while within the paradise of her mind. For well she knew her father's errand, who should soon receive a sufficient answer. But now she demanded leave not to lose this long-sought-for commodity of time, to ease her heart thus far, that if in her agonies her destiny was to be condemned by Philoclea's mouth, at least Philoclea might know, whom she had condemned. Philoclea easily yielded to grant her own desire: and so making the green bank the situation, and the river the prospect of the most beautiful buildings of nature, Zelmane doubting how to begin, though her thoughts already had run to the end, with a mind fearing the unworthiness of every word that should be presented to her ears, at length brought it forth in this manner.

"Most beloved lady, the incomparable excellencies of yourself, (waited on by the greatness of your estate) and the importance of the thing (whereon my life consisteth), doth require both many ceremonies before the beginning, and many circumstances in the uttering my speech, both bold, and fearful. But the small opportunity of envious occasion (by the malicious eye hateful love doth cast upon me) and the extreme bent of my affection (which will either break out in words, or break my heart) compel me, not only to embrace the smallest time, but to pass by respects due unto you, in respect of your poor caitiff's life, who is now, or never to be preserved. I do therefore vow unto you, hereafter nevermore to omit all dutiful form: do you only now vouchsafe to hear the matter of a mind most perplexed. If ever the sound of love have come to your ears, or if ever you have understood, what force it hath had to conquer the strongest hearts, and change the most settled estates: receive here an example of those strange tragedies; one, that in himself containeth the particularities of all those misfortunes: and from henceforth believe that such a thing may be, since you shall see it is. You shall see (I say) a living image, and a present story of what love can do, when he is bent to ruin.

"But alas, whither goest thou my tongue? or how doth my heart consent to adventure the revealing his nearest-touching secret? But peace Fear, thou comest too late, when already the harm is taken. Therefore I say again, O only princess, attend here a miserable miracle of affection. Behold here before your eyes Pyrocles, Prince of Macedon, whom you only have brought to this game of fortune, and unused metamorphosis: whom you only have made neglect his country, forget his father, and lastly, forsake to be Pyrocles: the same Pyrocles, who (you heard) was betrayed by being put in a ship, which being burned, Pyrocles was drowned.[27] O most true presage: for these traitors, my eyes, putting me in a ship of desire, which daily burneth, those eyes (I say) which betrayed me, will never leave till they have drowned me. But be not, be not (most excellent lady) you that nature hath made to be the loadstar of comfort, be not the rock of shipwreck: you whom virtue hath made the princess of felicity, be not the minister of ruin: you, whom my choice hath made the goddess of my safety, O let not, let not, from you be poured upon me destruction. Your fair face hath many tokens in it of amazement at my words: think then what his amazement is, from whence they come: since no words can carry with them the life of the inward feeling. I desire, that my desire may be weighed in the balances of honour, and let virtue hold them. For if the highest love in no base person may aspire to grace, then may I hope your beauty will not be without pity. If otherwise you be (alas but let it never be so) resolved, yet shall not my death be comfortless, receiving it by your sentence."

The joy which wrought into Pygmalion's mind, while he found his beloved image was softer, & warmer in his folded arms, till at length it accomplished his gladness with a perfect woman's shape (still beautified with the former perfections) was even such, as by each degree of Zelmane's words creepingly entered into Philoclea: till her pleasure was fully made up with the manifesting of his being: which was such as in hope did overcome Hope. Yet Doubt would fain have played his part in her mind, and called in question, how she should be assured that Zelmane was Pyrocles. But Love straight stood up & deposed, that a lie could not come from the mouth of Zelmane. Besides, a certain spark of honour, which rose in her well-disposed mind, made her fear to be alone with him, with whom alone she desired to be (with all the other contradictions growing in those minds, which neither absolutely climb the rock of virtue, nor freely sink into the sea of vanity) but that spark soon gave place, or at least gave no more light in her mind, than a candle doth in the sun's presence. But even sick with a surfeit of joy, and fearful of she knew not what (as he that newly finds huge treasures, doubts whether he sleep or no; or like a fearful deer, which then looks most about, when he comes to the best feed) with a shrugging kind of tremor through all her principal parts, she gave these affectionate words for answer.

"Alas, how painful a thing it is to a divided mind to make a well-joined answer? how hard it is to bring inward shame to outward confession? and what handsomeness trow you can be observed in that speech, which is made one knows not to whom? Shall I say O Zelmane? Alas your words be against it. Shall I say Prince Pyrocles? wretch that I am, your shew is manifest against it. But this, this I may well say; If I had continued as I ought, Philoclea, you had either never been, or ever been Zelmane: you had either never attempted this change, set on with hope, or never discovered it, stopt with despair. But I fear me, my behaviour ill governed, gave you the first comfort: I fear me, my affection ill hid, hath given you this last assurance: I fear indeed, the weakness of my government before, made you think such a mask would be grateful unto me: & my weaker government since, makes you pull off the visor. What shall I do then? shall I seek farfetched inventions? shall I labour to lay marble colours over my ruinous thoughts? or rather, though the pureness of my virgin mind be stained, let me keep the true simplicity of my word. True it is, alas, too true it is, O Zelmane (for so I love to call thee, since in that name my love first began, and in the shade of that name my love shall best lie hidden,) that even while so thou wert, (what eye betwitched me I know not) my passions were fitter to desire, than to be desired. Shall I say then, I am sorry, or that my love must be turned to hate, since thou art turned to Pyrocles? how may that well be, since when thou wert Zelmane, the despair thou mightest not be thus, did most torment me. Thou hast then the victory: use it with virtue. Thy virtue won me; with virtue preserve me. Doest thou love me? keep me then still worthy to be beloved."

Then held she her tongue, and cast down a self-accusing look, finding, that in herself she had (as it were) shot out of the bow of her affection, a more quick opening of her mind, than she minded to have done. But Pyrocles so carried up with joy, that he did not envy the gods' felicity, presented her with some jewels of right princely value, as some little tokens of his love, & quality: and withal shewed her letters from his father King Euarchus, unto him, which even in the sea had amongst his jewels been preserved. But little needed those proofs to one, who would have fallen out with herself, rather than make any contrary conjectures to Zelmane's speeches; so that with such embracements, as it seemed their souls desired to meet, and their hearts to kiss, as their mouths did: which fain Pyrocles would have sealed with the chief arms of his desire, but Philoclea commanded the contrary: and yet they passed the promise of marriage.

THOMAS NASHE

THE UNFORTUNATE TRAVELLER

1594

Thomas Nashe (1567–1601)

Before Thomas Nashe died at the early age of thirty-four, his contemporaries had paid him the highest praise. Nashe's friend Robert Greene had called him "a young Juvenal," placing him with the great Latin satirists, and Thomas Lodge had described him as a "true English Aretine," equating him with Aretino, the biting poet and critic of the Italian Renaissance. Middleton regretted that Nashe died before his remarkable talents were fully expressed, and Dekker in true elegiac fashion blamed "dry-fisted patrons" for Nashe's "untimely death." But Nashe was also the object of attacks as unrestrained as the praise from his admirers, and not always without cause. He devoted his entire life to literary controversy, taking a strong stand on every issue with which he was confronted; consequently he was liked or disliked with vehemence.

Nashe's father was a minister reputedly of Puritan sympathies. Nashe, on the other hand, was scurrilous in his ridicule of the Puritans, just as if he had a background of strong discipline to rebel against and had to work hard to keep the rebellion going.

Nashe was a sizar at Cambridge as early as 1582 and received his B.A. there in 1585–1586. Altogether he was at the university for almost seven years, but if his later enemy, Gabriel Harvey, can be believed, he was known more as an "untoward fellow" than as a student. In any case, Nashe seems to have left the university under a cloud, without receiving his M.A. degree. One conjecture is that he then went on a not-so-grand tour of France and Italy and ob-

tained in the process some background material for his novel
THE UNFORTUNATE TRAVELLER.

Nashe appeared in London in 1588, a year or so after he
left Cambridge, and soon became known as part of a circle
of defiant young writers, including Greene, Lodge, Daniel,
and Marlowe. From this time on Nashe made his living,
such as it was, by his pen. He needed patronage and courted
the attention of Sir George Carey and the Earl of Southampton with little success. At times his financial straits reduced him to writing, as he admits, "amorous Villanellos
and Quipassas" for "new-fangled Galiardoes and senior
Fantasticos." But he lamented this necessity as "unedifying"
and worked untiringly to express in writing his sincere con-
victions. He stated his literary position by attacking un-
original translators, unnatural writers of heroic drama, and
unimaginative Puritans, and by praising the literary giant
Spenser and his own immediate society of professional writers,
especially Marlowe, Peele, and Greene. He soon established
his reputation as a young man to listen to, for he was at least
never dull.

Later Nashe was to wish for some peace from his enthu-
siasms, for almost from his arrival in London until his death
he was engaged in one long battle. In 1589, at the urging of
his friends, among them the publisher John Danter, Nashe
entered full sail into the Martin Marprelate controversy.
The Puritans were defying the crown's, and the Anglican
Church's, right of literary censorship, and Elizabeth's bishops
were defending their prerogative to register and examine
every work intended for publication. Nashe, who had long
been an uncritical anti-Puritan, entered the fray on the side
of the bishops and against Martin, the anonymous Puritan
champion. He wrote a series of pamphlets under the name
of Pasquil and was acknowledged as the outstanding anti-
Martinist writer. But then the controversy took a regrettable
turn. In 1590 Richard Harvey attacked Nashe, Greene, and
Lyly for extending the Martin Marprelate battle longer than
was necessary, and Nashe replied with a personal attack not

only on Richard but also on his brothers John and, especially, Gabriel. The fight became a picayune dispute between Nashe and Gabriel Harvey and exhausted the literary efforts of each for almost a decade. Finally, in 1599, the licensers of the press demanded that the two men cease their public bickering, and the Archbishop of Canterbury ordered the withdrawal of their pamphlets from sale, ironically by exercising the very power of censorship that Nashe had been defending.

Nashe's long fight with the Harveys was punctuated by a versatile list of writings much more important than the pamphlets on which he spent most of his time. PIERCE PENNILESS HIS SUPPLICATION TO THE DEVIL (1592) was an effective satire on contemporary society. CHRIST'S TEARS OVER JERUSALEM (1593) was a declaration of repentance for his sins, including his animosity to Harvey. SUMMERS' LAST WILL AND TESTAMENT, acted at Sir George Carey's home in 1593, was an initial attempt at comedy, written around the antics of Henry VIII's jester, Will Summers. His ambitious picaresque novel, THE UNFORTUNATE TRAVELLER, appeared in 1594, with a dedication to the Earl of Southampton. In the same year Nashe completed Marlowe's unfinished TRAGEDY OF DIDO, the former's single attempt at serious drama.

However, the work of greatest immediate consequence for Nashe was a play, THE ISLE OF DOGS, for which he contracted with the manager-producer Henslowe in 1597. The play is lost, but according to records it so excited the privy council by its criticism of current corruption that Henslowe's license was temporarily withdrawn. Nashe was sent to Fleet Prison and, upon release, banished for a while from London. He was, so he wrote to Sir Robert Cotten, "without a penny in his purse," but he was hardly subdued. The fight with Harvey continued for two more years, his LENTEN STUFF (1599) was as defiant as his early works, and the printed version of SUMMERS' LAST WILL (1600) contained a disdainful reference to the fuss about THE ISLE OF DOGS.

By 1601 Nashe was dead, but zealous and acknowledged

imitation of him continued for another half century, chiefly among the satirists of the Puritan sects. Nashe, so rebellious against authority, had pathetically spent his energy in defense of licensing and passed on a technique to the conservative opponents of the new individualism. The seventeenth century, centered around religious and political struggle, kept Nashe an anti-Martinist; the eighteenth century, straining to define universals, recognized Nashe as a powerful satirist of the foibles of Everyman.

The definitive edition of Nashe is R. B. McKerrow's THE WORKS OF THOMAS NASHE, 5 vols., Bullen, 1904–1910; these volumes contain invaluable notes to which the editors of this anthology are frequently indebted. Biographical studies of Nashe include McKerrow's careful essay and Donald J. McGinn's "Nashe's Share in the Marprelate Controversy," PMLA, LIX, 952–984. Special studies of interest are F. T. Bowers' "Thomas Nashe and the Picaresque Novel," STUDIES IN HONOR OF JOHN CALVIN METCALF, The University of Virginia Press, 1941, and Agnes M. C. Latham's "Satire on Literary Themes and Modes in Nashe's 'Unfortunate Traveller,' " ENGLISH STUDIES 1948, New Series, I, 85–100.

The text is taken from a collation of two 1594 editions of THE UNFORTUNATE TRAVELLER in McKerrow's collection.

THE UNFORTUNATE TRAVELLER

ABOUT THAT TIME[1] that the terror of the world and fever
quartan of the French, Henry the Eight (the only true
subject of chronicles), advanced his standard against
the two hundred and fifty towers of Turney and Turwin,
and had the Emperor and all the nobility of Flanders, Holland, & Brabant as mercenary attendants on his full-sailed
fortune, I, Jack Wilton, (a gentleman at least,) was a certain
kind of an appendix or page, belonging or appertaining in or
unto the confines of the English court; where what my credit
was, a number of my creditors that I cozened can testify:
Coelum petimus stultitia,[2] which of us all is not a sinner? Be
it known to as many as will pay money enough to peruse
my story, that I followed the court or the camp, or the
camp and the court, when Turwin lost her maidenhead,
and opened her gates to more than Jane Trosse did. There
did I (soft, let me drink before I go any further) reign sole
king of the cans and black jacks, prince of the pigmies, county
palatine of clean straw and provant,[3] and, to conclude, lord
high regent of rashers of the coals and red herring cobs.[4]
Paulo maiora canamus.[5] Well, to the purpose. What strate-
gemical acts and monuments do you think an ingenious infant of my years might enact? You will say, it were sufficient
if he slur a die,[6] pawn his master to the utmost penny, and
minister the oath of the pantofle artificially. These are signs
of good education, I must confess, and arguments of "in grace
and virtue" [7] to proceed. Oh, but *Aliquid latet quod non patet,*[8]
there's a further path I must trace: examples confirm; list,
lordings, to my proceedings. Whosoever is acquainted with
the state of a camp understands that in it be many quarters,
and yet not so many as on London Bridge. In those quarters

are many companies: Much company, much knavery, as true as that old adage, Much courtesy, much subtilty. Those companies, like a great deal of corn, do yield some chaff; the corn are cormorants, the chaff are good fellows, which are quickly blown to nothing with bearing a light heart in a light purse. Amongst this chaff was I winnowing my wits to live merrily, and by my troth so I did: the prince could but command men spend their blood in his service, I could make them spend all the money they had for my pleasure. But poverty in the end parts friends; though I was prince of their purses, & exacted of my unthrift subjects as much liquid allegiance as any kaiser in the world could do, yet where it is not to be had the king must lose his right: want cannot be withstood, men can do no more than they can do: what remained then, but the fox's case must help, when the lion's skin is out at the elbows?

There was a lord in the camp, let him be a lord of misrule if you will, for he kept a plain alehouse without welt or guard of any ivybush[9] and sold cider and cheese by pint and by pound to all that came, (at the very name of cider I can but sigh, there is so much of it in Rhenish wine nowadays.) Well, *Tendit ad sidera virtus*,[10] there's great virtue belongs (I can tell you) to a cup of cider, and very good men have sold it, and at sea it is *Aqua coelestis*;[11] but that's neither here nor there, if it had no other patron but this pair of quart pots to authorize it, it were sufficient. This great lord, this worthy lord, this noble lord, thought no scorn (Lord, have mercy upon us) to have his great velvet breeches larded with the droppings of this dainty liquor, & yet he was an old servitor, a cavalier of an ancient house, as might appear by the arms of his ancestors, drawn very amiably in chalk on the inside of his tent door.

He and no other was the man I chose out to damn with a lewd moneyless device; for coming to him on a day, as he was counting his barrels and setting the price in chalk on the head of them, I did my duty very devoutly, and told his aley honor I had matters of some secrecy to impart unto him, if it pleased him to grant me private audience. "With me, young Wilton," quoth he, "marry, and shalt: bring us a pint of cider of a fresh tap into the three cups here, wash the pot:" so into a back room he led me, where after he had spit on his finger, and picked off two or three motes of his old moth-eaten velvet cap, and sponged and wrung all the rheumatic drivel from his ill-favored goat's beard, he bade me declare my mind, and thereupon he drank to me on the same. I up with a long circumstance, alias, a cunning shift of the seventeens,[12] and discoursed unto him what entire affection I had borne him time out of mind, partly for the high descent and lineage from whence he sprung, and partly for the tender care and provident respect he had of poor soldiers, that, whereas the vastity of that place (which afforded them no indifferent supply of drink or of victuals) might humble them to some extremity, and so weaken their hands, he vouchsafed in his own person to be a victualler to the camp (a rare example of magnificence and honorable courtesy), and diligently provided that without far travel every man might for his money have cider and cheese his belly full; nor did he sell his cheese by the way[13] only, or his cider by the great, but abased himself with his own hands to take a shoemaker's knife (a homely instrument for such a high personage to touch) and cut it out equally, like a true justiciary, in little pennyworths that it would do a man good for to look upon. So likewise of his cider, the poor man might have his moderate draught of it (as there is a moderation in all things) as well for his doit or his dandiprat as the rich man for his half-souse or his denier.[14] "Not so much," quoth I, "but this tapster's linen apron which you wear to protect your apparel from the imperfections of the spigot, most amply bewrays your lowly mind. I speak it with tears, too few such noble men have we, that will draw drink in linen aprons. Why, you are every child's fellow; any man that comes under the name of a soldier and a good fellow, you will sit and bear company to the last pot, yea, and you take in as good part the homely phrase of mine host, here's to you, as if one saluted you by all the titles of your barony. These considerations, I say, which the world suffers to slip by in the channel of forgetfulness, have moved me, in ardent zeal of your welfare, to forewarn you of some dangers that have beset you and your barrels." At the name of dangers he start up, and bounced with his fist on the board so hard that his tapster overhearing him, cried, "Anon, anon, sir," by and by, and came and made a low leg and asked him what he lacked. He was ready to have stricken his tapster for interrupting him in attention of this his so much desired relation, but for fear of displeasing me he moderated his fury, & only sending for the other fresh pint, willed him look to the bar, & come when he is called with a devil's name. Well, at his earnest importunity, after I had moistened my lips to make my lie run glib to his journey's end, forward I went as followeth. "It chanced me the other night, amongst other pages, to attend where the King, with his lords and many chief leaders, sat in counsel: there, amongst sundry serious matters that were debated, and intelligences from the enemy given up, it was privily informed (no villains to these privy informers) that you, even you that I now speak to, had—(O would I had no tongue to tell the rest; by this drink it grieves me so I am not able to repeat it.)" Now was my drunken lord ready to hang himself for the end of the full point, and over my neck he throws himself very lubberly, and intreated me, as I was a proper young gentleman and ever looked for pleasure at his hands, soon to rid him out of this hell of suspense, and resolve him of the rest: then fell he on his knees, wrung his hands, and I think on my conscience, wept out all the cider that he had drunk in a week before: to move me to have pity on him, he rose & put his rusty ring on my finger, gave me his greasy purse with that single money[15] that was in it, promised to make me his heir, and a thousand more favours, if I would expire the misery of his unspeakable tormenting uncertainty. I, being by nature inclined to mercy (for indeed I knew two or three good wenches of that name), bade him harden his ears, and not make his eyes abortive before their time, and he should have the inside of my breast turned outward, hear such a tale as would tempt the utmost strength of life to attend it and not die in the midst of it. "Why," quoth I, "myself that am but a poor childish well-willer of yours, with the very thought that a man of your desert and state by a number of peasants and varlets should be so injuriously abused in huggermugger, have wept all my urine upward. The wheel under our city bridge carries not so much water over the city, as my brain hath welled forth gushing streams of sorrow: I have wept so immoderately and lavishly that I thought verily my palate had been turned to pissing conduit in London. My eyes have been drunk, outrageously drunk, with giving but ordinary intercourse through their sea-circled islands to my distilling dreariment. What shall I say? that which malice hath said is the mere overthrow and murther of your days. Change not your colour, none can slander a clear conscience to itself; receive all your fraught of misfortune in at once.

"It is buzzed in the King's head that you are a secret friend to the enemy, and under pretence of getting a license to furnish the camp with cider and such like provant, you have furnished the enemy, & in empty barrels sent letters of discovery and corn innumerable."

I might well have left here, for by this time his white liver had mixed itself with the white of his eye, and both were turned upwards, as if they had offered themselves a fair white for death to shoot at. The troth was, I was very loath mine host and I should part with dry lips: wherefore the best means that I could imagine to wake him out of his trance, was to cry loud in his ear, "Ho, host, what's to pay? will no man look to the reckoning here?" And in plain verity it took expected effect, for with the noise he started and bustled, like a man that had been scared with fire out of his sleep, and ran hastily to his tapster, and all to belaboured him about the ears, for letting gentlemen call so long and not look in to them. Presently he remembered himself, and had like to fall into his memento again, but that I met him halfways and asked his lordship what he meant to slip his neck out of the collar so suddenly, and, being revived, strike his tapster so hastily.

"Oh," quoth he, "I am bought and sold for doing my country such good service as I have done. They are afraid of me, because my good deeds have brought me into such estimation with the commonalty. I see, I see, it is not for the lamb to live with the wolf."

The world is well amended (thought I) with your cider-ships; such another forty years' nap together as Epeminedes[16] had, would make you a perfect wise man. "Answer me," quoth he, "my wise young Wilton, is it true that I am thus underhand dead and buried by these bad tongues?"

"Nay," quoth I, "you shall pardon me, for I have spoken too much already; no definitive sentence of death shall march out of my well-meaning lips; they have but lately sucked milk, and shall they so suddenly change their food and seek after blood?"

"Oh, but," quoth he, "a man's friend is his friend; fill the other pint, tapster: what said the King? did he believe it when he heard it? I pray thee say; I swear by my nobility, none in the world shall ever be made privy that I received any light of this matter by thee."

"That firm affiance," quoth I, "had I in you before, or else I would never have gone so far over the shoes, to pluck you out of the mire. Not to make many words, (since you will needs know,) the King says flatly, you are a miser and a snudge,[17] and he never hoped better of you." "Nay, then," quoth he, "questionless some planet that loves not cider hath conspired against me." "Moreover, which is worse, the King hath vowed to give Turwin one hot breakfast only with the bungs that he will pluck out of your barrels. I cannot stay at this time to report each circumstance that passed, but the only counsel that my long cherished kind inclination can possibly contrive, is now in your old days to be liberal: such victuals or provision as you have, presently distribute it frankly amongst poor soldiers; I would let them burst their bellies with cider and bathe in it, before I would run into my prince's ill opinion for a whole sea of it. The hunter pursuing the beaver for his stones, he bites them off, and leaves them behind for him to gather up, whereby he lives quiet. If greedy hunters and hungry tale-tellers pursue you, it is for a little pelf that you have; cast it behind you, neglect it, let them have it, lest it breed a farther inconvenience. Credit my advice, you shall find it prophetical: and thus have I discharged the part of a poor friend." With some few like phrases of ceremony, "Your honor's poor suppliant," and so forth, and "Farewell, my good youth, I thank thee and will remember thee," we parted.

But the next day I think we had a dole of cider, cider in bowls, in scuppets,[18] in helmets; and to conclude, if a man would have filled his boots full, there he might have had it: provant thrust itself into poor soldiers' pockets whether they would or no. We made five peals of shot into the town together of nothing but spigots and faucets of discarded empty barrels: every underfoot soldier had a distenanted tun, as Diogenes had his tub to sleep in. I myself got as many confiscated tapsters' aprons as made me a tent as big as any ordinary commander's in the field. But in conclusion, my well-beloved baron of double beer got him humbly on his marrowbones to the King, and complained he was old and stricken in years, and had never an heir to cast at a dog, wherefore if it might please His Majesty to take his lands into his hands, and allow him some reasonable pension to live, he should be marvelously well pleased: as for wars, he was weary of them; yet as long as His Highness ventured his own person, he would not flinch a foot, but make his withered body a buckler to bear off any blow advanced against him.

The King, marveling at this alteration of his cider-merchant (for so he often pleasantly termed him), with a little farther talk bolted out the whole complotment. Then was I pitifully whipt for my holiday lie, though they made themselves merry with it many a winter's evening after.

For all this, his good ass-headed honor, mine host, persevered in his former request to the King to accept his lands, & allow him a beadsmanry or out-brothership of brachet: which through his vehement instancy took effect, and the King jestingly said, since he would needs have it so, he would distrain on part of his land for impost of cider, which he was behind with.

This was one of my famous achievements, insomuch as I never light upon the like famous fool: but I have done a thousand better jests, if they had been booked in order as they were begotten. It is pity posterity should be deprived of such precious records; & yet there is no remedy: and yet there is too, for when all fails, well fare a good memory. Gentle readers (look you be gentle now since I have called you so), as freely as my knavery was mine own, it shall be yours to use in the way of honesty.

Even in this expedition of Turwin (for the King stood not long a thrumming of buttons there) it happened me fall in (I would it had fallen out otherwise for his sake) with an ugly mechanical captain. You must think in an army, where truncheons are in their state-house, it is a flat stab once to name a captain without cap in hand. Well, suppose he was a captain, and had never a good cap of his own, but I was fain to lend him one of my lord's cast velvet caps, and a weather-beaten feather, wherewith he threatened his soldiers afar off, as Jupiter is said with the shaking of his hair to make heaven & earth to quake. Suppose out of the parings of a pair of false dice I apparelled both him and myself many a time and oft: and surely, not to slander the devil, if any man ever deserved the golden dice the King of the Parthians sent to Demetrius,[19] it was I: I had the right vain of sucking up a die twixt the dints of my fingers; not a crevice in my hand but could swallow a quarter trey[20] for a need; in the line of life many a dead lift did there lurk, but it was nothing towards the maintenance of a family. This Monsieur Capitano eat up the cream of my earnings, and *Crede mihi, res est ingeniosa dare,*[21] any man is a fine fellow as long as he hath any money in his purse. That money is like the marigold, which opens and shuts with the sun: if fortune smileth or one be in favor, it floweth; if the evening of age comes on, or he falls into disgrace, it fadeth and is not to be found. I was my craft's master though I was but young, and could as soon decline *Nominativo hic asinus*[22] as a greater clerk; wherefore I thought it not convenient my soldado should have my purse any longer for his drum to play upon, but I would give him Jack Drum's entertainment[23] and send him packing.

This was my plot: I knew a piece of service of intelligence which was presently to be done, that required a man with all his five senses to effect it, and would overthrow any fool that should undertake it: to this service did I animate and egg my foresaid costs and charges, alias, Senor Velvet-cap, whose head was not encumbered with too much forecast; and coming to him in his cabin about dinner time, where I found him very devoutly paring of his nails for want of other repast, I entertained him with this solemn oration.

"Captain, you perceive how near both of us are driven, the dice of late are grown as melancholy as a dog, high men and low men both prosper alike, langrets, fullams,[24] and all the whole fellowship of them will not afford a man his dinner; some other means must be invented to prevent imminent extremity. My state, you are not ignorant, depends on trencher service; your advancement must be derived from the valour of your arm. In the delays of siege, desert hardly gets a day of hearing; 'tis gowns must direct and guns enact all the wars that is to be made against walls. Resteth no way for you to climb suddenly, but by doing some rare stratagem, the like not before heard of: and fitly at this time occasion is offered.

"There is a feat the King is desirous to have wrought on some great man of the enemy's side: marry, it requireth not so much resolution as discretion to bring it to pass; and yet resolution enough should be shown in it too, being so full of hazardous jeopardy as it is: hark in your ear, thus it is: without more drumbling[25] or pausing, if you will undertake it, and work it through stitch[26] (as you may, ere the King hath determined which way to go about it), I warrant you are made while you live, you need not care which way your staff falls; if it prove not so, then cut off my head."

Oh my auditors, had you seen him how he stretched out his limbs, scratched his scabbed elbows at this speech; how he set his cap over his eyebrows like a politician, and then folded his arms one in another, and nodded with the head, as who would say, let the French beware for they shall find me a devil: if (I say) you had seen but half the actions that he used, of shrugging up his shoulders, smiling scornfully, playing with his fingers on his buttons, and biting the lip, you would have laughed your face and your knees together. The iron being hot, I thought to lay on load, for in any case I would not have his humor cool. As before I laid open unto him the brief sum of the service, so now I began to urge the honorableness of it, and what a rare thing it was to be a right politician, how much esteemed of kings & princes, and how divers of mean parentage have come to be monarchs by it. Then I discoursed of the qualities and properties of him in every respect, how, like the wolf, he must draw the breath from a man long before he be seen, how, like a hare, he must sleep with his eyes open, how, as the eagle in his flying casts dust in the eyes of crows and other fowls, for to blind them, so he must cast dust in the eyes of his enemies, delude their sight by one means or other, that they dive not into his subtleties: how he must be familiar with all and trust none, drink, carouse, and lecher with him out of whom he hopes to wring any matter, swear and forswear, rather than be suspected, and, in a word, have the art of dissembling at his fingers' ends as perfect as any courtier.

"Perhaps," quoth I, "you may have some few greasy cavaliers that will seek to dissuade you from it, and they will not stick to stand on their three halfpenny honour, swearing and staring that a man were better be a hangman than an intelligencer, and call him a sneaking eavesdropper, a scraping hedgecreeper, and a piperly pickthank; but you must not be discouraged by their talk, for the most part of these beggarly contemners of wit are huge burlybond butchers like Ajax,[27] good for nothing but to strike right down blows on a wedge with a cleaving beetle, or stand hammering all day upon bars of iron. The whelps of a bear never grow but sleeping, and these bear-wards having big limbs shall be preferred though they do nothing. You have read stories, (I'll be sworn he never looked in book in his life,) how many of the Roman worthies were there that have gone as 'spials into their enemy's camp? Ulysses, Nestor, Diomed [28] went as spies together in the night into the tents of Rhesus, and intercepted Dolon, the spy of the Trojans: never any discredited the trade of intelligencers but Judas, and he hanged himself. Danger will put wit into any man. Architas made a wooden dove to fly;[29] by which proportion I see no reason that the veriest block in the world should despair of anything. Though nature be contrary inclined, it may be altered; yet usually those whom she denies her ordinary gifts in one thing, she doubles them in another. That which the ass wants in wit, he hath in honesty; who ever saw him kick or winch, or use any jade's tricks? though he live an hundred years you shall never hear that he breaks pasture. Amongst men, he that hath not a good wit, lightly hath a good iron memory, and he that hath neither of both, hath some bones to carry burthens. Blind men have better noses than other men: the bull's horns serve him as well as hands to fight withal: the lion's paws are as good to him as a poleaxe, to knock down any that resist him: the bore's tushes serve him in better stead than a sword and buckler: what need the snail care for eyes, when he feels the way with his two horns, as well as if he were as quick-sighted as a decipherer? There is a fish that having no wings supports herself in the air with her fins. Admit that you had neither wit nor capacity, as sure, in my judgement, there is none equal unto you in idiotism, yet if you have simplicity and secrecy, serpents themselves will think you a serpent; for what serpent is there but hides his sting? and yet, whatsoever be wanting, a good plausible tongue in such a man of employment can hardly be spared which, as the forenamed serpent with his winding tail fetcheth in those that come near him, so with a ravishing tale it gathers all men's hearts unto him: which if he have not, let him never look to engender by the mouth, as ravens and doves do, that is, mount or be great by undermining. Sir, I am ascertained that all these imperfections I speak of in you have their natural resiance.[30] I see in your face, that you were born, with the swallow, to feed flying, to get much treasure and honor by travel. None so fit as you for so important an enterprise: our vulgar politicians are but flies swimming on the stream of subtilty superficially in comparison of your singularity, their blind narrow eyes cannot pierce into the profundity of hypocrisy; you alone, with Palamed,[31] can pry into Ulysses' mad counterfeiting, you can discern Achilles from a chambermaid, though he be decked with his spindle and distaff: as Jove dining with Lycaon[32] could not be beguiled with human flesh drest like meat, so no human brain may go beyond you, none beguile you; you gull all, all fear you, love you, stoop to you. Therefore, good sir, be ruled by me, stoop your fortune so low as to bequeath yourself wholly to this business."

This silver-sounding tale made such sugared harmony in his ears, that with the sweet meditation, what a more than miraculous politician he should be, and what kingly promotion should come tumbling on him thereby, he could have found in his heart to have packed up his pipes and to have gone to heaven without a bait: yea, he was more inflamed and ravished with it than a young man called Taurimontanus[33] was with the Phrygian melody, who was so incensed and fired therewith, that he would needs run presently upon it, and set a courtezan's house on fire that had angered him.

No remedy there was but I must help to furnish him with money: I did so, as who will not make his enemy a bridge of gold to fly by? Very earnestly he conjured me to make no man living privy to his departure, in regard of his place and charge, and on his honor assured me his return should be very short and successful. Aye, aye, shorter by the neck (thought I); in the meantime let this be thy posy, I live in hope to 'scape the rope.

Gone he is; God send him good shipping to Wapping,[34] and by this time, if you will, let him be a pitiful poor fellow and undone forever: for mine own part, if he had been mine own brother, I could have done no more for him than I did, for straight after his back was turned, I went in all love and kindness to the marshal general of the field, & certified him that such a man was lately fled to the enemy, & got his place begged for another immediately. What became of him after you shall hear. To the enemy he went and offered his service, railing egregiously against the King of England; he swore, as he was a gentleman and a soldier, he would be revenged on him; and let but the King of France follow his counsel, he would drive him from Turwin walls yet ere three days to an end. All these were good humors, but the tragedy followeth. The French king hearing of such a prating fellow that was come, desired to see him, but yet he feared treason, willing one of his minions to take upon him his person, & he would stand by as a private person while he was examined. Why should I use any idle delays? In was Captain Gog's Wounds brought, after he was thoroughly searched; not a louse in his doublet was let pass, but was asked *Quevela*,[35] and charged to stand in the King's name; the molds of his buttons they turned out, to see if they were not bullets covered over with thread; the codpiece in his devil's breeches[36] (for they were then in fashion) they said plainly was a case for a pistol; if he had had ever a hobnail in his shoes it had hanged him, and he should never have known who had harmed him; but, as luck was, he had no mite of any metal about him, he took part with none of the four ages, neither the golden age, the silver age, the brazen, nor the iron age; only his purse was aged in emptiness, and I think verily a Puritan, for it kept itself from any pollution of crosses.[37] Standing before the supposed king, he was asked what he was, and wherefore he came. To which in a glorious bragging humor he answered, that he was a gentleman, a captain commander, a chief leader, that came from the King of England upon discontentment. Questioned of the particular cause, he had not a word to bless himself with, yet fain he would have patched out a polt-foot tale, but (God knows) it had not one true leg to stand on.

Then began he to smell on the villain so rammishly that none there but was ready to rent him in pieces, yet the minion king kept in his choler, and propounded unto him further, what of the King of England's secrets (so advantageable) he was privy to, as might remove him from the siege of Turwin in three days. He said diverse, diverse matters which asked longer conference, but in good honesty they were lies which he had not yet stamped. Hereat the true king stept forth, and commanded to lay hands on the losel, and that he should be tortured to confess the truth, for he was a spy and nothing else.

He no sooner saw the wheel and the torments set before him, but he cried out like a rascal, and said he was a poor captain in the English camp, suborned by one Jack Wilton (a nobleman's page), and no other, to come and kill the French king in a bravery and return, and that he had no other intention in the world.

This confession could not choose but move them all to laughter, in that he made it as light a matter to kill their king and come back, as to go to Islington[38] and eat a mess of cream and come home again, nay, and besides he protested that he had no other intention, as if that were not enough to hang him.

Adam never fell till God made fools; all this could not keep his joints from ransacking on the wheel, for they vowed either to make him a confessor or a martyr with a trice: when still he sung all one song, they told the King he was a fool, and that some shrewd head had knavishly wrought on him; wherefore it should stand with His Honour to whip him out of the camp and send him home. That persuasion took place, and soundly was he lashed out of their liberties, and sent home by a herald with this message, that so the King his master hoped to whip home all the English fools very shortly: answer was returned, that that shortly was a long-lie, and they were shrewd fools that should drive the Frenchman out of his kingdom, and make him glad, with Corinthian Dionysius[39] to play the schoolmaster.

The Herald being dismissed, our afflicted intelligencer was called *coram nobis*:[40] how he sped, judge you, but something he was adjudged too. The sparrow for his lechery liveth but a year, he for his treachery was turned on the toe,[41] *Plura dolor prohibet.*[42]

Here let me triumph a while, and ruminate a line or two on the excellence of my wit: but I will not breathe neither till I have disfraughted all my knavery.

Another Switzer captain that was far gone for want of the wench, I led astray most notoriously, for he being a monstrous unthrift of battle-axes (as one that cared not in his anger to bid fly out scuttles[43] to five score of them) and a notable emboweler of quart pots, I came disguised unto him in the form of a half crown wench, my gown and attire according to the custom then in request. Iwis I had my curtsies in cue,[44] or in quart pot rather, for they dived into the very entrails of the dust, and I simpered with my countenance like a porridge pot on the fire when it first begins to seethe. The sobriety of the circumstance is, that after he had courted me and all, and given me the earnest-penny of impiety, some six crowns at the least for an antepast to iniquity, I feigned an impregnable excuse to be gone, and never came at him after.

Yet left I not here, but committed a little more scutchery. A company of coistrel clerks (who were in band with Satan, and not of any soldier's collar nor hatband) pinched a number of good minds to Godward of their provant.[45] They would not let a dram of dead-pay overslip them; they would not lend a groat of the week to come, to him that had spent his money before this week was done. They outfaced the greatest and most magnanimous servitors in their sincere and finigraphical [46] clean shirts and cuffs. A louse (that was any gentleman's companion) they thought scorn of; their near-bitten beards must in a devil's name be dewed every day with rosewater; hogs could have ne'er a hair on their backs, for making them rubbing-brushes to rouse their crab-lice. They would in no wise permit that the motes in the sunbeams should be full-mouthed beholders of their clean phinifide apparel; their shoes shined as bright as slick-stone;[47] their hands troubled and foiled more water with washing, than the camel doth, that never drinks till the whole stream be troubled. Summarily, never any were so fantastical the one half as they.

My masters, you may conceive of me what you list, but I think confidently I was ordained God's scourge from above for their dainty finicality. The hour of their punishment could no longer be prorogued, but vengeance must have at them at all a ventures.[48] So it was, that the most of these above-named goose-quill braggadocios were mere cowards and cravens, and durst not so much as throw a pen-full of ink into the enemy's face, if proof were made: wherefore on the experience of their pusillanimity I thought to raise the foundation of my roguery.

What did I now but one day made a false alarum in the quarter where they lay, to try how they would stand to their tackling, and with a pitiful outcry warned them to fly, for there was treason afoot, they were environed and beset. Upon the first watch word of treason that was given, I think they betook them to their heels very stoutly, left their pen and inkhorns and paper behind them for spoil, resigned their desks, with the money that was in them, to the mercy of the van-quisher, and in fine, left me and my fellows (their fool-catchers) lords of the field: How we dealt with them, their disburdened desks can best tell, but this I am assured, we fared the better for it a fortnight of fasting days after.

I must not place a volume in the precincts of a pamphlet: sleep an hour or two, and dream that Turney and Turwin is won, that the King is shipped again into England, and that

I am close at hard-meat[49] at Windsor or at Hampton Court. What, will you in your indifferent opinions allow me for my travel no more seigniory over the pages than I had before? yes, whether you will part with so much probable friendly suppose or no, I'll have it in spite of your hearts. For your instruction and godly consolation, be informed, that at that time I was no common squire, no undertrodden torchbearer; I had my feather in my cap as big as a flag in the foretop; my French doublet gelt[50] in the belly as though (like a pig ready to be spitted) all my guts had been plucked out; a pair of side-paned hose[51] that hung down like two scales filled with Holland cheeses; my long stock that sat close to my dock,[52] and smothered not a scab or a lecherous hairy sinew on the calf of the leg; my rapier pendant like a round stick fastened in the tacklings for skippers the better to climb by; my cape cloak of black cloth, overspreading my back like a thorn-back, or an elephant's ear, that hangs on his shoulders like a country housewife's banskin,[53] which she thirls her spindle on, & in consummation of my curiosity, my hands without gloves, all a more French, and a black budge edging of a beard on the upper lip, & the like sable aglet of excrements in the rising of the ankle[54] of my chin. I was the first that brought in the order of passing into the court which I derived from the common word *qui passa* and the herald's phrase of *arms passant*, thinking in sincerity, he was not a gentleman, nor his arms current, who was not first past by the pages. If any prentice or other came into the court that was not a gentleman, I thought it was an indignity to the pre-eminence of the court to include such a one, and could not be saluted except we gave him arms passant, to make him a gentleman.

Besides, in Spain, none pass any far way but he must be examined what he is, and give three pence for his pass.

In which regard it was considered of by the common table of the cupbearers, what a perilsome thing it was to let any stranger or out-dweller approach so near the precincts of the Prince as the great chamber, without examining what he was, and giving him his pass: whereupon we established the like order, but took no money of them as they did; only for a sign that he had not past our hands unexamined, we set a red mark on their ears, and so let them walk as authentical.

I must not discover what ungodly dealing we had with the black jacks, or how oft I was crowned king of the drunkards with a court cup; let me quietly descend to the waning of my youthful days, and tell a little of the sweating sickness,[55] that made me in a cold sweat take my heels and run out of England.

This sweating sickness was a disease that a man then might catch and never go to a hothouse. Many masters desire to have such servants as would work till they sweat again, but in those days he that sweat never wrought again. That Scripture then was not thought so necessary which says, Earn thy living with the sweat of thy brows, for then they earned their dying with the sweat of their brows. It was enough if a fat man did but truss his points,[56] to turn him over the perch:[57] Mother Cornelius' tub,[58] why it was like hell, he that came into it never came out of it.

Cooks that stand continually basting their faces before the fire, were now all cashiered with this sweat into kitchen stuff: their hall [59] fell into the King's hands for want of one of the trade to uphold it.

Felt-makers and furriers, what the one with the hot steam of their wool new taken out of the pan, and the other with the contagious heat of their slaughter budge[60] and conyskins, died more thick than of the pestilence: I have seen an old woman at that season, having three chins, wipe them all away one after another, as they melted to water, and left herself nothing of a mouth but an upper chap. Look how in May or the heat of summer we lay butter in water for fear it should melt away, so then were men fain to wet their clothes in water as dyers do, and hide themselves in wells from the heat of the sun.

Then happy was he that was an ass, for nothing will kill an

ass but cold, and none died but with extreme heat. The fishes called sea-stars, that burn one another by excessive heat, were not so contagious as one man that had the sweat was to another. Masons paid nothing for hair to mix their lime, nor glovers to stuff their balls with, for then they had it for nothing; it dropped off men's heads and beards faster than any barber could shave it. O, if hair breeches had then been in fashion, what a fine world had it been for tailors; and so it was a fine world for tailors nevertheless, for he that could make a garment slightest and thinnest carried it away. Cutters, I can tell you, then stood upon it to have their trade one of the twelve companies, for who was it then that would not have his doublet cut to the skin, and his shirt cut into it too, to make it more cold. It was as much as a man's life was worth, once to name a frieze jerkin; it was high treason for a fat gross man to come within five miles of the court. I heard where they died up all in one family, and not a mother's child escaped, insomuch as they had but an Irish rug locked up in a press, and not laid upon any bed neither. If those that were sick of this malady slept of it, they never waked more. Physicians with their simples in this case waxed simple fellows, and knew not which way to bestir them.

Galen might go shoe the gander for any good he could do; his secretaries had so long called him divine, that now he had lost all his virtue upon earth. Hippocrates might well help almanac-makers, but here he had not a word to say; a man might sooner catch the sweat with plodding over him to no end, than cure the sweat with any of his impotent principles. Paracelsus, with his spirit of the buttery[61] and his spirits of minerals, could not so much as say, "God amend him," to the matter. *Plus erat in artifice quam arte*,[62] there was more infection in the physician himself than his art could cure. This mortality first began amongst old men, for they, taking a pride to have their breasts loose basted with tedious beards, kept their houses so hot with their hairy excrements, that not so much but their very walls sweat out saltpeter with the smothering perplexity: nay, a number of them had marvelous hot breaths, which sticking in the briars of their bushy beards, could not choose but (as close air long imprisoned) engender corruption.

Wiser was our brother Banks[63] of these latter days, who made his juggling horse a cut, for fear if at any time he should foist the stink sticking in his thick bushy tail might be noisome to his auditors. Should I tell you how many pursuants with red noses, and sergeants with precious[64] faces, shrunk away in this sweat, you would not believe me. Even as the salamander with his very sight blasteth apples on the trees, so a pursuant or a sergeant at this present, with the very reflex of his *fierie facies*,[65] was able to spoil a man afar off. In some places of the world there is no shadow of the sun; *diebus illis*[66] if it had been so in England, the generation of Brut[67] had died all and some. To knit up this description in a pursenet, so fervent & scorching was the burning air which inclosed them, that the most blessed man then alive would have thought that God had done fairly by him if he had turned him to a goat, for goats take breath, not at the mouth or nose only, but at the ears also.

Take breath how they would, I vowed to tarry no longer among them. As at Turwin I was a demi-soldier in jest, so now I became a martialist in earnest. Over sea with my implements I got me, where hearing the King of France and the Switzers[68] were together by the ears, I made towards them as fast as I could, thinking to thrust myself into that faction that was strongest. It was my good luck or my ill (I know not which) to come just to the fighting of the battle; where I saw a wonderful spectacle of bloodshed on both sides: here unwieldy Switzers wallowing in their gore, like an ox in his dung, there the sprightly French sprawling and turning on the stained grass, like a roach new taken out of the stream: all the ground was strewed as thick with battleaxes as the carpenter's yard with chips; the plain appeared like a quagmire, overspread as it was with trampled dead bodies. In one place might you behold a heap of dead murthered men overwhelmed with a falling steed instead of a tombstone, in another place a bundle of bodies fettered together in their own bowels; and as the tyrant Roman emperors[69] used to tie condemned living captives face to face to dead corses, so were the half living here mixed with squeezed carcasses long putrefied. Any man might give arms that was an actor in that battle, for there were more arms and legs scattered in the field that day than will be gathered up till doomsday: the French king himself in this conflict was much distressed, the brains of his own men sprinkled in his face, thrice was his courser slain under him, and thrice was he struck on the breast with a spear: but in the end, by the help of the Venetians, the Helvetians or Switzers were subdued, and he crowned a victor, a peace concluded, and the city of Milan surrendered unto him as a pledge of reconciliation.

That war thus blown over, and the several bands dissolved, like a crow that still follows aloof where there is carrion, I flew me over to Münster in Germany, which an Anabaptistical brother, named John Leyden,[70] kept at that instant against the Emperor and the Duke of Saxony. Here I was in good hope to set up my staff for some reasonable time, deeming that no city would drive it to a siege, except they were able to hold out: and prettily well had these Münsterians held out, for they kept the Emperor and the Duke of Saxony play for the space of a year; and longer would have done, but that Dame Famine came amongst them; whereupon they were forced by messengers to agree upon a day of fight, when according to their Anabaptistical error they might all be new christened in their own blood.

That day come, flourishing entered John Leyden the botcher into the field, with a scarf made of lists[71] like a bowcase, a cross on his breast like a thread bottom,[72] a round twilted [73] tailor's cushion buckled like a tankard-bearer's device to his shoulders for a target, the pike whereof was a packneedle,[74] a tough prentice's club for his spear, a great brewer's cow[75] on his back for a corselet, and on his head for a helmet a huge high shoe with the bottom turned upwards, embossed as full of hobnails as ever it might stick: his men were all base handicrafts, as cobblers and curriers and tinkers, whereof some had bars of iron, some hatchets, some cool-staves,[76] some dung-forks, some spades, some mattocks, some wood-knives, some addises[77] for their weapons: he that was best provided had but a piece of a rusty brown bill bravely fringed with cobwebs to fight for him. Perchance here and there you might see a fellow that had a canker-eaten skull [78] on his head, which served him and his ancestors for a chamber pot two hundred years, and another that had bent a couple of iron dripping pans armor-wise, to fence his back and his belly; another that had thrust a pair of dry old boots as a breastplate before his belly of his doublet, because he would not be dangerously hurt; another that had twilted all his truss full of counters, thinking, if the enemy should take him, he would mistake them for gold, and so save his life for his money. Very devout asses they were, for all they were so dunstically set forth, and such as thought they knew as much of God's mind as richer men: why, inspiration was their ordinary familiar, and buzzed in their ears like a bee in a box every hour what news from heaven, hell, and the land of Whipperginnie:[79] displease them who durst, he should have his mittimus to damnation *ex tempore;* they would vaunt there was not a pea's difference betwixt them and the Apostles; they were as poor as they, or as base trades as they, and no more inspired than they, and with God there is no respect of persons; only herein may seem some little diversity to lurk, that Peter wore a sword, and they count it flat hell-fire for any man to wear a dagger; nay, so grounded and graveled were they in this opinion, that now when they should come to battle, there's never a one of them would bring a blade (no, not an onion blade) about him, to die for it. It was not lawful, said they, for any man to draw the sword but the magistrate; and in fidelity, (which I had well-nigh forgot,) Jack Leyden, their magistrate, had the image or likeness of a piece of a rusty sword, like a lusty lad, by his side: now I remember me, it was but a foil neither, and he wore it to shew that he should have the foil of his enemies, which might have been an oracle for his two-hand interpretation. *Quid plura?* [80] His battle is pitched: by pitched, I do not mean set in order, for that was far from their order, only as sailors do pitch their apparel to make it storm-proof, so had most of them pitched their patched clothes to make them impierceable: a nearer way than to be at the charges of armour by half. And in another sort he might be said to have pitched the field, for he had pitched or rather set up his rest whether to fly if they were discomfited.

Peace, peace there in the belfry, service begins: upon their knees before they join falls John Leyden and his fraternity very devoutly, they pray, they howl, they expostulate with God to grant them victory, and use such unspeakable vehemence a man would think them the only well-bent men under heaven. Wherein let me dilate a little more gravely than the nature of this history requires, or will be expected of so young a practitioner in divinity: that not those that intermissively cry, "Lord, open unto us, Lord, open unto us," enter first into the kingdom; that not the greatest professors have the greatest portion in grace; that all is not gold that glisters. When Christ said, "The kingdom of heaven must suffer violence," he meant not the violence of long babbling prayers, nor the violence of tedious invective sermons without wit, but the violence of faith, the violence of good works, the violence of patient suffering. The ignorant snatch the kingdom of heaven to themselves with greediness, when we with all our learning sink into hell.

Where did Peter and John, in the third of the *Acts*, find the lame cripple but in the gate of the temple called beautiful? in the beautifullest gates of our temple, in the forefront of professors, are many lame cripples, lame in life, lame in good works, lame in everything; yet will they always sit at the gates of the temple; none be more forward than they to enter into matters of reformation, yet none more behindhand to enter into the true temple of the Lord by the gates of good life.

You may object that those which I speak against are more diligent in reading the Scriptures, more careful to resort unto sermons, more sober in their looks, more modest in their attire than any else. But I pray you let me answer you, Doth not Christ say that before the latter day the sun shall be turned into darkness, and the moon into blood? whereof what may the meaning be, but that the glorious sun of the Gospel shall be eclipsed with the dim cloud of dissimulation; that that which is the brightest planet of salvation shall be a means of error and darkness: and the moon shall be turned into blood, those that shine fairest, make the simplest shew, seem most to favour religion, shall rend out the bowels of the church, be turned into blood, and all this shall come to pass before the notable day of the Lord, whereof this age is the eve?

Let me use a more familiar example, since the heat of a great number outraged so excessively. Did not the devil lead Christ to the pinnacle or highest place of the temple to tempt him? If he led Christ, he will lead a whole army of hypocrites to the top or highest part of the temple, the highest step of religion and holiness, to seduce them and subvert them. I say unto you that which this our tempted Saviour with many other words besought his disciples, "Save yourselves from this forward generation. Verily, verily, the servant is not greater than his master:" Verily, verily, sinful men are not holier than holy Jesus, their maker. That holy Jesus again repeats this holy sentence, "Remember the words I said unto you, the servant is not holier nor greater than his master"; as if he should say, Remember then, imprint in your memory, your pride and singularity will make you forget them, the effects of them many years hence will come to pass. "Whosoever will seek to save his soul shall lose it:" whosoever seeks by headlong means to enter into heaven and disannul God's ordinance, shall, with the giants that thought to scale heaven in contempt of Jupiter, be overwhelmed with Mount Ossa and Pelion,[81] and dwell with the devil in eternal desolation.

Though the high priest's office was expired when Paul said unto one of them, "God rebuke thee, thou painted sepulcher," yet when a stander-by reproved him, saying, "Revilest thou the high priest?" he repented and asked forgiveness.

That which I suppose I do not grant: the lawfulness of

the authority they oppose themselves against is sufficiently proved: far be it my under-age arguments should intrude themselves as a green weak prop to support so high a building: let it suffice, if you know Christ, you know his Father also; if you know Christianity, you know the fathers of the church also. But a great number of you, with Philip,[82] have been long with Christ, and have not known him; have long professed yourselves Christians, and have not known his true ministers: you follow the French and Scottish fashion and faction, and in all points are like the Switzers, *Qui quaerunt cum qua gente cadunt*, that seek with what nation they may first miscarry.

In the days of Nero there was an odd fellow that had found out an exquisite way to make glass as hammer-proof as gold:[83] shall I say that the like experiment he made upon glass, we have practised on the Gospel? Aye, confidently will I: We have found out a sleight to hammer it to any heresy whatsoever. But those furnaces of falsehood and hammer-heads of heresy must be dissolved and broken as his was, or else I fear me the false glittering glass of innovation will be better esteemed of, than the ancient gold of the Gospel.

The fault of faults is this, that your dead-born faith is begotten by too-too infant fathers. Cato,[84] one of the wisest men in Roman histories canonized, was not born till his father was fourscore years old: none can be a perfect father of faith and beget men aright unto God, but those that are aged in experience, have many years imprinted in their mild conversation, and have, with Zaccheus,[85] sold all their possessions of vanities to enjoy the sweet fellowship, not of the human, but spiritual Messiahs.

Ministers and pastors, sell away your sects and schisms to the decrepit churches in contention beyond sea; they have been so long inured to war, both about matters of religion and regiment, that now they have no peace of mind but in troubling all other men's peace. Because the poverty of their provinces will allow them no proportionable maintenance for higher callings of ecclesiastical magistrates, they would reduce us to the president of their rebellious persecuted beggary: much like the sect of philosophers called Cynics, who when they saw they were born to no lands or possessions, nor had any possible means to support their estates, but they must live despised and in misery, do what they could, they plotted and consulted with themselves how to make their poverty better esteemed of than rich dominion and sovereignty. The upshot of their plotting and consultation was this, that they would live to themselves, scorning the very breath or company of all men; they professed (according to the rate of their lands) voluntary poverty, thin fare & lying hard, contemning and inveighing against all those as brute beasts whatsoever whom the world had given any reputation for riches or prosperity. Diogenes was one of the first and foremost of the ringleaders of this rusty morosity, and he for all his nice dogged disposition and blunt deriding of worldly dross and the gross felicity of fools, was taken notwithstanding a little after very fairly a coining money in his cell: so fares it up and down with our cynical reformed foreign churches; they will digest no grapes of great bishoprics forsooth, because they cannot tell how to come by them; they must shape their coats, good men, according to their cloth, and do as they may, not as they would, yet they must give us leave here in England that are their honest neighbors, if we have more cloth than they, to make our garment somewhat larger.

What was the foundation or groundwork of this dismal declining of Münster, but the banishing of their bishop, their confiscating and casting lots for church-livings, as the soldiers cast lots for Christ's garments, and, in short terms, their making the house of God a den of thieves? The house of God a number of hungry church robbers in these days have made a den of thieves. Thieves spend loosely what they have gotten lightly; sacrilege is no sure inheritance; Dionysius[86] was ne'er the richer for robbing of Jupiter of his golden coat, he was driven in the end to play the schoolmaster at Corinth. The name of religion, be it good or bad that is ruinated, God never suffers unrevenged: I'll say of it as Ovid said of eunuchs:

Qui primus pueris genitalia membra recidit,
Vulnera quae fecit debuit ipse pati.

Who first deprived young boys of their best part,
With selfsame wounds he gave he ought to smart.[87]

So would he that first gelt religion or church-livings had been first gelt himself or never lived; Cardinal Wolsey is the man I aim at, *Qui in suas poenas ingeniosus erat*, first gave others a light to his own overthrow. How it prospered with him and his instruments that after wrought for themselves, chronicles largely report, though not apply, and some parcel of their punishment yet unpaid I do not doubt but will be required of their posterity.

To go forward with my story of the overthrow of that usurper, John Leyden: he and all his army, as I said before, falling prostrate on their faces and fervently given over to prayer, determined never to cease, or leave soliciting of God, till he had shewed them from heaven some manifest miracle of success.

Note that it was a general received tradition both with John Leyden and all the crew of Cnipperdolings and Müncers,[88] if God at any time at their vehement outcries and clamors did not condescend to their requests, to rail on him and curse him to his face, to dispute with him and argue him of injustice for not being so good as his word with them, and to urge his many promises in the Scripture against him: so that they did not serve God simply, but that he should serve their turns; and after that tenure are many content to serve as bondmen to save the danger of hanging: but he that serves God aright, whose upright conscience hath for his mot, *Amor est mihi causa sequendi*, I serve because I love, he says, *Ego te potius, Domine, quam tua dona sequar*, I'll rather follow thee, O Lord, for thine own sake, than for any covetous respect of that thou canst do for me.

Christ would have no followers but such as forsook all and follow him, such as forsake all their own desires, such as abandon all expectations of reward in this world, such as neglected and contemned their lives, their wives and children, in comparison of him, and were content to take up their cross and follow him.

These Anabaptists had not yet forsook all and followed Christ, they had not forsook their own desires of revenge and innovation, they had not abandoned their expectation of the spoil of their enemies, they regarded their lives, they looked after their wives and children, they took not up their crosses of humility and followed him, but would cross him, upbraid him, and set him at nought, if he assured not by some sign their prayers and supplications. *Deteriora sequuntur*, they followed God as daring him. God heard their prayers, *Quod petitur poena est*, It was their speedy punishment that they prayed for. Lo, according to the sum of their impudent supplications, a sign in the heavens appeared, the glorious sign of the rainbow, which agreed just with the sign of their ensign that was a rainbow likewise.

Whereupon, assuring themselves of victory, (*Miseri quod volunt, facile credunt;* that which wretches would have they easily believe,) with shouts and clamors they presently ran headlong on their well-deserved confusion.

Pitiful and lamentable was their unpitied and well-performed slaughter. To see even a bear (which is the most cruellest of all beasts) too-too bloodily overmatched, and deformedly rent in pieces by an unconscionable number of curs, it would move compassion against kind, and make those that (beholding him at the stake yet uncoped with) wished him a suitable death to his ugly shape, now to recall their hardhearted wishes, and moan him suffering as a mild beast, in comparison of the foulmouthed mastiffs, his butchers: even such compassion did those overmatched ungracious Münsterians obtain of many indifferent eyes, who now thought them (suffering) to be sheep brought innocent to the shambles, when as before they deemed them as a number of wolves up in arms against the shepherds.

The Imperials themselves that were their executioners (like a father that weeps when he beats his child, yet still weeps and still beats) not without much ruth and sorrow prosecuted that lamentable massacre; yet drums and trumpets sounding nothing but stern revenge in their ears, made them so eager that their hands had no leisure to ask counsel of their effeminate eyes; their swords, their pikes, their bills, their bows, their calivers[89] slew, empierced, knocked down, shot through, and overthrew as many men every minute of the battle as there falls ears of corn before the scythe at one blow: yet all their weapons so slaying, empiercing, knocking down, shooting through, overthrowing, dissoul-joined[90] not half so many as the hailing thunder of the great ordinance: so ordinary at every foot-step was the imbruement of iron in blood, that one could hardly discern heads from bullets, or clotted hair from mangled flesh hung with gore.

This tale must at one time or other give up the ghost, and as good now as stay longer; I would gladly rid my hands of it cleanly, if I could tell how, for what with talking of cobblers, tinkers, rope-makers, botchers, and dirt-daubers, the mark is clean out of my muse's mouth, & I am as it were, more than duncified twixt divinity and poetry. What is there more as touching this tragedy that you would be resolved of? say quickly, for now is my pen on foot again. How John Leyden died, is that it? He died like a dog, he was hanged[91] & the halter paid for. For his companions, do they trouble you? I can tell you they troubled some men before, for they were all killed, & none escaped, no, not so much as one to tell the tale of the rainbow. Hear what it is to be Anabaptists, to be Puritans, to be villains; you may be counted illuminate botchers for a while, but your end will be, Good people, pray for us.

With the tragical catastrophe of this Münsterian conflict did I cashier the new vocation of my cavaliership. There was no more honorable wars in Christendom then towards; wherefore, after I had learned to be half an hour in bidding a man *bon jour* in German sunonimas,[92] I traveled along the country towards England as fast as I could.

What with wagons and bare tentoes[93] having attained to Middleborough, (good Lord, see the changing chances of us knights arrant[94] infants) I met with the right honorable Lord Henry Howard, Earl of Surrey,[95] my late master. Jesu, I was persuaded I should not be more glad to see heaven than I was to see him. O, it was a right noble lord, liberality itself (if in this iron age there were any such creature as liberality left on the earth), a prince in content because a poet without peer.

Destiny never defames herself but when she lets an excellent poet die: if there be any spark of Adam's paradised perfection yet embered up in the breasts of mortal men, certainly God hath bestowed that his perfectest image on poets. None come so near to God in wit, none more contemn the world, *Vatis avarus non temere est animus*, saieth Horace, *versus amat, hoc studet unum;* Seldom have you seen any poet possessed with avarice, only verses he loves, nothing else he delights in: and as they contemn the world, so contrarily of the mechanical world are none more contemned. Despised they are of the world, because they are not of the world: their thoughts are exalted above the world of ignorance and all earthly conceits.

As sweet angelical queristers[96] they are continually conversant in the heaven of arts: heaven itself is but the highest height of knowledge; he that knows himself & all things else, knows the means to be happy: happy, thrice happy, are they whom God hath doubled his spirit upon, and given a double soul unto to be poets.

My heroical master exceeded in this supernatural kind of wit; he entertained no gross earthly spirit of avarice, nor weak womanly spirit of pusillanimity and fear that are fained to be of the water, but admirable, airy, and fiery spirits, full of freedom, magnanimity, and bountihood. Let me not speak any more of his accomplishments, for fear I spend all my spirits in praising him, and leave myself no vigor of wit or effects of a soul to go forward with my history.

Having thus met him I so much adored, no interpleading was there of opposite occasions, but back I must return and bear half stakes with him in the lottery of travel. I was not altogether unwilling to walk along with such a good purse-bearer, yet musing what changeable humor had so suddenly seduced him from his native soil to seek out needless perils in those parts beyond sea, one night very boldly I demanded of him the reason that moved him thereto.

"Ah," quoth he, "my little page, full little canst thou perceive how far metamorphosed I am from myself, since I last saw thee. There is a little god called Love, that will not be worshiped of any leaden brains; one that proclaims himself sole king and emperor of piercing eyes, and chief sovereign of soft hearts; he it is that, exercising his empire in my eyes, hath exorcised and clean conjured me from my content.

"Thou know'st stately Geraldine,[97] too stately I fear for me to do homage to her statue or shrine; she it is that is come out of Italy to bewitch all the wise men of England; upon Queen Catherine Dowager[98] she waits, that hath a dowry of beauty sufficient to make her wooed of the greatest kings in Christendom. Her high exalted sunbeams have set the phoenix' nest of my breast on fire, and I myself have brought Arabian spiceries of sweet passions and praises to furnish out the funeral flame of my folly. Those who were condemned to be smothered to death by sinking down into the soft bottom of an high-built bed of roses, never died so sweet a death as I should die, if her rose-coloured disdain were my deaths-man.[99]

"Oh thrice imperial Hampton Court, Cupid's enchanted castle, the place where I first saw the perfect omnipotence of the Almighty expressed in mortality, 'tis thou alone that, tithing all other men solace in thy pleasant situation, affordest me nothing but an excellent begotten sorrow out of the chief treasury of all thy recreations.

"Dear Wilton, understand that there it was where I first set eye on my more than celestial Geraldine. Seeing her, I admired her; all the whole receptacle of my sight was unhabited with her rare worth.[100] Long suit and uncessant protestations got me the grace to be entertained. Did never unloving servant so prentice-like obey his never pleased mistress as I did her. My life, my wealth, my friends had all their destiny depending on her command.

"Upon a time I was determined to travel; the fame of Italy,

and an especial affection I had unto poetry, my second mistress, for which Italy was so famous, had wholly ravished me unto it. There was no dehortment[101] from it, but needs thither I would: wherefore, coming to my mistress as she was then walking with other ladies of estate in Paradise[102] at Hampton Court, I most humbly besought her of favour, that she would give me so much gracious leave to absent myself from her service, as to travel a year or two into Italy. She very discreetly answered me that if my love were so hot as I had often avouched, I did very well to apply the plaster of absence unto it, for absence, as they say, causeth forgetfulness: 'Yet nevertheless since it is Italy, my native country, you are so desirous to see, I am the more willing to make my will yours. Aye, *pete Italiam*, go and seek Italy, with Aeneas; but be more true than Aeneas;[103] I hope that kind wit-cherishing climate will work no change in so witty a breast. No country of mine shall it be more, if it conspire with thee in any new love against me. One charge I will give thee, and let it be rather a request than a charge: When thou comest to Florence (the fair city from whence I fetched the pride of my birth), by an open challenge defend my beauty against all comers.

" 'Thou hast that honourable carriage in arms that it shall be no discredit for me to bequeath all the glory of my beauty to thy well-governed arm. Fain would I be known where I was born, fain would I have thee known where fame sits in her chiefest theater. Farewell, forget me not; continued deserts will eternize me unto thee, thy wishes shall be expired when thy travel shall be once ended.'

"Here did tears step out before words, and intercepted the course of my kind-conceived speech, even as wind is allayed with rain: with heart-scalding sighs I confirmed her parting request, and vowed myself hers while living heat allowed me to be mine own; *Hinc illae lachrimae*,[104] here hence proceedeth the whole cause of my peregrination."

Not a little was I delighted with this unexpected love story, especially from a mouth out of which was nought wont to march but stern precepts of gravity & modesty. I swear unto you I thought his company the better by a thousand crowns, because he had discarded those nice terms of chastity and continency. Now I beseech God love me so well as I love a plain-dealing man; earth is earth, flesh is flesh, earth will to earth, and flesh unto flesh; frail earth, frail flesh, who can keep you from the work of your creation?

Dismissing this fruitless annotation *pro et contra;* towards Venice we progressed, and took Rotterdam in our way, that was clean out of our way: there we met with aged learning's chief ornament, that abundant and superingenious clerk, Erasmus, as also with merry Sir Thomas More,[105] our countryman, who was come purposely over a little before us, to visit the said grave father Erasmus: what talk, what conference we had then, it were here superfluous to rehearse, but this I can assure you, Erasmus in all his speeches seemed so much to mislike the indiscretion of princes in preferring of parasites and fools, that he decreed with himself to swim with the stream, and write a book forthwith in commendation of folly.[106] Quick-witted Sir Thomas More traveled in a clean contrary province, for he seeing most commonwealths corrupted by ill custom, & that principalities were nothing but great piracies, which, gotten by violence and murther, were maintained by private undermining and bloodshed, that in the chiefest flourishing kingdoms there was no equal or well-divided weal one with another, but a manifest conspiracy of rich men against poor men, procuring their own unlawful commodities under the name and interest of the commonwealth: he concluded with himself to lay down a perfect plot of a commonwealth or government, which he would entitle his *Utopia*.

So left we them to prosecute their discontented studies, and made our next journey to Wittenberg.[107]

At the very point of our entrance into Wittenberg, we were spectators of a very solemn scholastical entertainment of the Duke of Saxony thither. Whom, because he was the chief patron of their university, and had took Luther's part in banishing the Mass and all like papal jurisdiction out of their town, they crouched unto extremely. The chief ceremonies of their entertainment were these: first, the heads of their university (they were great heads of certainty) met him in their hooded hypocrisy and doctorly accoutrements, *secundum formam statuti;* [108] where by the orator of the university, whose pickerdeuant[109] was very plentifully besprinkled with rose water, a very learned or rather ruthful oration was delivered (for it rained all the while) signifying thus much, that it was all by patch & by piecemeal stolen out of Tully,[110] and he must pardon them, though in emptying their phrase-books, the world emptied his entrails, for they did it not in any ostentation of wit (which God knows they had not) but to shew the extraordinary good will they bore the Duke (to have him stand in the rain till he was through wet): a thousand *quemadmodums* and *quapropters*[111] he came over him with; every sentence he concluded with *Esse posse videatur:* [112] through all the nine worthies he ran with praising and comparing him; Nestor's[113] years he assured him of under the broad seal of their supplications, and with that crow-trodden verse in Virgil, *Dum iuga montis aper,*[114] he packed up his pipes and cried *Dixi.*[115]

That pageant overpast, there rushed upon him a miserable rabblement of junior graduates, that all cried upon him mightily in their gibberish, like a company of beggars, "God save Your Grace, God save Your Grace, Jesus preserve Your Highness, though it be but for an hour."

Some three halfpenny-worth of Latin here also had he thrown at his face, but it was choice stuff, I can tell you, as there is a choice even amongst rags gathered up from the dunghill. At the town's end met him the burghers and dunstical incorporationers of Wittenberg in their distinguished liveries, their distinguished livery faces, I mean, for they were most of them hot-livered drunkards, and had all the coat colours of sanguine, purple, crimson, copper, carnation, that were to be had, in their countenances. Filthy knaves, no cost had they bestowed on the town for his welcome, saving new painted their houghs[116] and bousing houses, which commonly are fairer than their churches, and over their gates set the town arms carousing a whole health to the Duke's arms, which sounded gulping after this sort, *Vanhotten, slotten, irk bloshen glotten gelderslike:* whatever the words were, the sense was this, Good drink is a medicine for all diseases.

A bursten-belly inkhorn orator called Vanderhulke,[117] they picked out to present him with an oration, one that had a sulphurous big swollen large face, like a Saracen, eyes like two Kentish oysters, a mouth that opened as wide every time he spake, as one of those old knit trap doors, a beard as though it had been made of a bird's nest plucked in pieces, which consisteth of straw, hair, and dirt mixed together. He was apparelled in black leather new liquored, & a short gown without any gathering in the back, faced before and behind with a boisterous bearskin, and a red nightcap on his head. To this purport and effect was this broccing double beer[118] oration.

"Right noble Duke (*ideo nobilis quasi no bilis,* for you have no bile or choler in you), know that our present incorporation of Wittenberg, by me the tongue-man of their thankfulness, a townsman by birth, a free German by nature, an orator by art, and a scrivener by education, in all obedience & chastity, most bountifully bid you welcome to Wittenberg: welcome, said I? O orificial [119] rhetoric, wipe thy everlasting mouth, and afford me a more Indian metaphor than that, for the brave princely blood of a Saxon. Oratory, uncask the barred hutch of thy compliments, and with the triumphantest troop in thy treasury do truage[120] unto him. What impotent speech with his eight parts may not specify, this unestimable gift, holding his peace, shall as it were (with tears I speak it) do whereby as it may seem or appear to manifest or declare, and yet it is, and yet it is not, and yet it may be a diminutive oblation meritorious to your high pusillanimity and indignity. Why should I go gadding and fisgigging after firkin flantado amfibologies? [121] wit is wit, and good will is good will. With all the wit I have, I here, according to the premises, offer up unto you the city's general good will, which is a gilded can, in manner and form following, for you and the heirs of your body lawfully begotten to drink healths in. The scholastical squitter-books[122] clout you up canopies and foot-cloths of verses. We that are good fellows, and live as merry as cup and can, will not verse[123] upon you as they do, but must do as we can, and entertain you if it be but a plain empty can. He hath learning enough that hath learned to drink to his first man.

"Gentle Duke, without paradox be it spoken, thy horses at our own proper costs and charges shall knead up to the knees all the while thou art here in spruce beer and Lübeck liquor. Not a dog thou bringest with thee but shall be banqueted with Rhenish wine and sturgeon. On our shoulders we wear no lambskin or miniver[124] like these academics, yet we can drink to the confusion of thy enemies. Good lamb's wool have we for their lambskins, and for their miniver, large minerals in our coffers. Mechanical men they call us, and not amiss, for most of us being Maechi,[125] that is, cuckolds and whore-masters, fetch our antiquity from the temple of Mecca, where Mahomet was hung up. Three parts of the world, America, Africa, and Asia, are of this our mechanic religion. Nero, when he cried, *O quantus artifex pereo*,[126] professed himself of our freedom, insomuch as *Artifex* is a citizen or craftsman, as well as *Carnifex* a scholar or hangman. Pass on by leave into the precincts of our abomination. Bonnie Duke, frolic in our bower, and persuade thyself that even as garlic hath three properties, to make a man wink, drink, and stink, so we will wink on thy imperfections, drink to thy favorites, and all thy foes shall stink before us. So be it. Farewell."

The Duke laughed not a little at this ridiculous oration, but that very night as great an ironical occasion was ministered, for he was bidden to one of the chief schools to a comedy handled by scholars. *Acolastus, the Prodigal Child*, [127] was the name of it, which was so filthily acted, so leathernly set forth, as would have moved laughter in Heraclitus.[128] One, as if he had been planing a clay floor, stampingly trod the stage so hard with his feet that I thought verily he had resolved to do the carpenter that set it up some utter shame. Another flung his arms like cudgels at a pear tree, insomuch as it was mightily dreaded that he would strike the candles that hung above their heads out of their sockets, and leave them all dark. Another did nothing but wink and make faces. There was a parasite, and he with clapping his hands and thripping[129] his fingers seemed to dance an antic to and fro. The only thing they did well was the prodigal child's hunger, most of their scholars being hungrily kept; & surely you would have said they had been brought up in hogs' academy to learn to eat acorns, if you had seen how sedulously they fell to them. Not a jest had they to keep their auditors from sleeping but of swill and draff; yes, now and then the servant put his hand into the dish before his master, & almost choked himself, eating slovenly and ravenously to cause sport.

The next day they had solemn disputations, where Luther and Carolostadius[130] scolded level coil.[131] A mass of words I wot well they heaped up against the Mass and the Pope, but farther particulars of their disputations I remember not. I thought verily they would have worried one another with words, they were so earnest and vehement. Luther had the louder voice, Carolostadius went beyond him in beating and bouncing with his fists. *Quae supra nos, nihil ad nos:* [132] they uttered nothing to make a man laugh, therefore I will leave them. Marry, their outward gestures would now and then afford a man a morsel of mirth: of those two I mean not so much as of all the other train of opponents & respondents. One pecked with his forefinger at every half syllable he brought forth, and nodded with his nose like an old singing man teaching a young querister to keep time. Another would be sure to wipe his mouth with his handkercher at the end of every full point, and ever when he thought he has cast a figure so curiously as he dived over head and ears into his auditors' admiration, he would take occasion to stroke up his hair, and twine up his mustachios twice or thrice over, while they might have leisure to applaud him. A third wavered & waggled his head, like a proud horse playing with his bridle, or as I have seen some fantastical swimmer, at every stroke, train his chin sidelong over his left shoulder. A fourth sweat and foamed at the mouth for very anger his adversary had denied that part

of the syllogism which he was not prepared to answer. A fifth
spread his arms like an usher that goes before to make room,
and thripped with his finger and his thumb when he thought
he had tickled it with a conclusion. A sixth hung down his
countenance like a sheep, and stuttered and slavered very pitifully when his invention was stept aside out of the way. A
seventh gasped for wind, & groaned in his pronunciation as
if he were hard-bound with some bad argument. Gross plod-
ders they were all, that had some learning and reading, but
no wit to make use of it. They imagined the Duke took the
greatest pleasure and contentment under heaven to hear them
speak Latin, and as long as they talked nothing but Tully he
was bound to attend them. A most vain thing it is in many
universities at this day, that they count him excellent eloquent,
who stealeth not whole phrases but whole pages out of Tully.
If of a number of shreds of his sentences he can shape an
oration, from all the world he carries it away, although in
truth it be no more than a fool's coat of many colours. No
invention or matter have they of their own, but tack up a
style of his stale gallimaufries. The leaden-headed Germans
first began this, and we Englishmen have surfeited of their
absurd imitation. I pity Nizolius[133] that had nothing to do but
pick threads' ends out of an old overworn garment.

This is but by the way, we must look back to our dis-
putants. One amongst the rest thinking to be more conceited
than his fellows, seeing the Duke have a dog he loved well,
which sat by him on the terrace, converted all his oration to
him, and not a hair of his tail but he combed out with comparisons: so to have courted him if he were a bitch had been
very suspicious. Another commented and descanted on the
Duke's staff, new tipping it with many quaint epithets. Some
cast his nativity, and promised him he should not die until
the day of judgement. Omitting further superfluities of this
stamp, in this general assembly we found intermixed that
abundant scholar Cornelius Agrippa.[134] At that time he bare
the fame to be the greatest conjurer in Christendom. Scoto,
that did the juggling tricks before the Queen, never came near

him one quarter in magic reputation. The doctors of Wittenberg, doting on the rumor that went of him, desired him before the Duke and them to do something extraordinary memorable.

One requested to see pleasant Plautus,[135] and that he would shew them in what habit he went, and with what countenance he looked when he ground corn in the mill. Another had half a month's mind to Ovid and his hook nose. Erasmus, who was not wanting in that honorable meeting, requested to see Tully in that same grace and majesty he pleaded his oration *Pro Roscio Amerino*, affirming that till in person he beheld his importunity of pleading, he would in no wise be persuaded that any man could carry away a manifest case with rhetoric so strangely. To Erasmus' petition he easily condescended, & willing the doctors at such an hour to hold their convocation, and everyone to keep him in his place without moving, at the time prefixed, in entered Tully, ascended his pleading place, and declaimed verbatim the forenamed oration, but with such astonishing amazement, with such fervent exaltation of spirit, with such soul-stirring gestures, that all his auditors were ready to instal his guilty client for a God.

Great was the concourse of glory Agrippa drew to him with this one feat. And indeed he was so cloyed with men which came to behold him, that he was fain, sooner than he would, to return to the Emperor's court from whence he came, and leave Wittenberg before he would. With him we travelled along, having purchased his acquaintance a little before. By the way as we went, my master and I agreed to change names. It was concluded betwixt us, that I should be the Earl of Surrey, and he my man, only because in his own person, which he would not have reproached, he meant to take more liberty of behavior: as for my carriage he knew he was to tune it at a key, either high or low, as he list.

To the Emperor's court we came, where our entertainment was every way plentiful; carouses we had in whole gallons instead of quart pots. Not a health was given us but contained well near a hogshead. The customs of the country we were eager to be instructed in, but nothing we could learn but this, that ever at the Emperor's coronation there is an ox roasted with a stag in the belly, and that stag in his belly hath a kid, and that kid is stuffed full of birds. Some courtiers, to weary out time, would tell us further tales of Cornelius Agrippa, and how when Sir Thomas More, our countryman, was there, he shewed him the whole destruction of Troy in a dream. How the Lord Cromwell [136] being the King's ambassador there, in like case, in a perspective glass he set before his eyes King Henry the Eight with all his lords on hunting in his forest at Windsor, and when he came into his study and was very urgent to be partaker of some rare experiment, that he might report when he came into England, he willed him amongst two thousand great books to take down which he list, and begin to read one line in any place, and without book he would rehearse twenty leaves following. Cromwell did so, and in many books tried him, when in everything he exceeded his promise and conquered his expectation. To Charles the Fifth, then emperor, they reported how he shewed the nine worthies, David, Solomon, Gideon, and the rest, in that similitude and likeness that they lived upon earth. My master and I, having by the highway side gotten some reasonable familiarity with him, upon this access of miracles imputed to him, resolved to request him something in our own behalves. I, because I was his suborned lord and master, desired him to see the lively image of Geraldine, his love, in the glass, and what at that instant she did and with whom she was talking. He shewed her us without any more ado, sick weeping on her bed, and resolved all into devout religion for the absence of her lord. At the sight thereof he could in no wise refrain, though he had took upon him the condition of a servant, but he must forthwith frame this extemporal ditty.

> All soul, no earthly flesh, why dost thou fade?
> All good, no worthless dross, why look'st thou pale?
> Sickness, how dar'st thou one so fair invade?
> Too base infirmity to work her bale.
> > Heaven be distemper'd since she grieved pines,
> > Never be dry these my sad plaintive lines.

Perch thou, my spirit, on her silver breasts,
And with their pain-redoubled music-beatings,
Let them toss thee to world where all toil rests,
Where bliss is subject to no fear's defeatings:
    Her praise I tune whose tongue doth tune the spheres,
    And gets new muses in her hearer's ears.

Stars fall to fetch fresh light from her rich eyes,
Her bright brow drives the sun to clouds beneath,
Her hair's reflex with red streaks paints the skies,
Sweet morn and evening dew flows from her breath:
    Phoebe rules tides, she my tears' tides forth draws,
    In her sickbed love sits and maketh laws.

Her dainty limbs tinsel her silk soft sheets,
Her rose-crowned cheeks eclipse my dazzled sight;
O glass, with too much joy my thoughts thou greets,
And yet thou shewest me day but by twilight.
    I'll kiss thee for the kindness I have felt,
    Her lips one kiss would unto nectar melt.

Though the Emperor's court and the extraordinary edifying company of Cornelius Agrippa might have been arguments of weight to have arrested us a little longer there, yet Italy still stuck as a great mote in my master's eye; he thought he had travelled no farther than Wales till he had took survey of that country which was such a curious molder of wits.

To cut off blind ambages by the highway side, we made a long stride and got to Venice in short time; where having scarce looked about us, a precious supernatural pander, apparelled in all points like a gentleman & having half a dozen several languages in his purse, entertained us in our own tongue very paraphrastically and eloquently, & maugre all other pretended acquaintance, would have us in a violent kind of courtesy to be the guests of his appointment. His name was Petro de Campo Frego, a notable practitioner in the policy of bawdry. The place whither he brought us was a pernicious courtezan's house named Tabitha the Temptress's, a wench that could set as civil a face on it as chastity's first martyr Lucretia. What will you conceit to be in any saint's house that was there to seek? Books, pictures, beads, crucifixes, why, there was a haberdasher's shop of them in every chamber. I warrant you should not see one set of her neckercher perverted or turned awry, not a piece of a hair displaced. On her beds there was not wrinkle of any wallowing to be found, her pillows bare out as smooth as a groaning wife's belly, & yet she was a Turk and an infidel, & had more doings than all her neighbours besides. Us for our money they used like emperors. I was master as you heard before, & my master, the Earl, was but as my chief man whom I made my companion. So it happened (as iniquity will out at one time or other) that she, perceiving my expense had no more vents than it should have, fell in with my supposed servant, my man, and gave him half a promise of marriage, if he would help to make me away, that she and he might enjoy the jewels and wealth that I had.

The indifficulty of the condition thus she explained unto him: her house stood upon vaults, which in two hundred years together were never searched; who came into her house none took notice of; his fellow servants that knew of his master's abode there should be all dispatched by him, as from his master, into sundry parts of the city about business, and when they returned, answer should be made that he lay not there any more, but had removed to Padua since their departure, & thither they must follow him. "Now," quoth she, "if you be disposed to make him away in their absence, you shall have my house at command. Stab, poison, or shoot him through with a pistol, all is one, into the vault he shall be thrown when the deed is done." On my bare honesty it was a crafty quean, for she had enacted with herself, if he had been my legitimate servant, as he was one that served and supplied my necessities, when he had murthered me, to have accused him of the murther, and made all that I had hers (as I carried all my master's wealth, money, jewels, rings, or bills of exchange, continually about me). He very subtilely consented to her stratagem at the first motion; kill me he would, that heavens could not withstand, and a pistol was the predestinate engine which must deliver the parting blow. God wot I was a raw young squire, and my master dealt Judasly with me, for he told me but everything that she and he agreed of. Wherefore I could not possibly prevent it, but as a man would say avoid it. The execution day aspired to his utmost devolution, into my chamber came my honorable attendant with his pistol charged by his side, very suspiciously and sullenly: Lady Tabitha and Petro de Campo Frego, her pander followed him at the hard heels.

At their entrance I saluted them all very familiarly and merrily, & began to impart unto them what disquiet dreams had disturbed me the last night. "I dreamt," quoth I, "that my man Brunquell [137] here (for no better name got he of me) came into my chamber with a pistol charged under his arm to kill me, and that he was suborned by you, Mistress Tabitha, and my very good friend Petro de Campo Frego; God send it turn to good, for it hath affrighted me above measure." As they were ready to enter into a colourable commonplace of the deceitful frivolousness of dreams, my trusty servant Brunquell stood quivering and quaking every joint of him, &, as it was before compacted between us, let his pistol drop from him on the sudden; wherewith I started out of my bed, and drew my rapier, and cried, "Murther, murther," which made good wife Tabitha ready to bepiss her.

My servant, or my master, which you will, I took roughly by the collar, and threatened to run him through incontinent if he confessed not the truth. He, as it were stricken with remorse of conscience, (God be with him, for he could counterfeit most daintily,) down on his knees, asked me forgiveness, and impeached Tabitha and Petro de Campo Frego as guilty of subornation. I very mildly and gravely gave him audience; rail on them I did not after his tale was ended, but said I would try what the law could do. Conspiracy by the custom of their country was a capital offence, and what custom or justice might afford they should be all sure to feel. "I could," quoth I, "acquit myself otherwise, but it is not for a stranger to be his own carver in revenge." Not a word more with Tabitha, but die she would before God or the devil would have her: she sounded [138] and revived, and then sounded again.

and after she revived again, sighed heavily, spoke faintly and pitifully, yea, and so pitifully, as if a man had not known the pranks of harlots before, he would have melted into commiseration. Tears, sighs, and doleful-tuned words could not make any forcible claim to my stony ears; it was the glittering crowns that I hungered and thirsted after, & with them for all her mock holy-day gestures she was fain to come off, before I condescended to any bargain of silence. So it fortuned (fie upon that unfortunate word of fortune) that this whore, this quean, this courtezan, this common of ten thousand, so bribing me not to bewray her, had given me a great deal of counterfeit gold, which she had received of a coiner to make away a little before. Amongst the gross sum of my bribery, I, silly milksop, mistrusting no deceit, under an angel of light[139] took what she gave me, ne'er turned it over, for which (O falsehood in fair shew) my master & I had like to have been turned over. He that is a knight arrant, exercised in the affairs of ladies and gentlewomen, hath more places to send money to than the devil hath to send his spirits to. There was a delicate wench named Flavia Aemilia lodging in Saint Mark's Street at a goldsmith's, which I would fain have had to the grand test, to try whether she were cunning in alchemy or no. Aye me, she was but a counterfeit slip,[140] for she not only gave me the slip, but had well-nigh made me a slipstring.[141] To her I sent my gold to beg an hour of grace: ah, graceless fornicatress, my hostess and she were confederate, who having gotten but one piece of my ill gold in their hands, devised the means to make me immortal. I could drink for anger till my head ached, to think how I was abused. Shall I shame the devil and speak the truth? To prison was I sent as principal, and my master as accessary; nor was it to a prison neither, but to the master of the mint's house, who though partly our judge, and a most severe upright justice in his own nature, extremely seemed to condole our ignorant estate, and without all peradventure a present redress he had ministered, if certain of our countrymen, hearing an English earl was apprehended for coining, had not come to visit us. An ill planet brought them thither, for at the first glance they knew the servant of my secrecies to be the Earl of Surrey, and I (not worthy to be named I) an outcast of his cup or pantofles.[142] Thence, thence sprung the full period of our infelicity. The master of the mint, our whilom refresher and consolation, now took part against us; he thought we had a mint in our heads of mischievous conspiracies against their state. Heavens bear witness with us it was not so, (heavens will not always come to witness when they are called.)

To a straighter ward were we committed: that which we have imputatively transgressed must be answered. O, the heathen high pass and the intrinsical legerdemain of our special approved good pander, Petro de Campo Frego. He, although he dipt in the same dish with us every day, seeming to labour our cause very importunately, & had interpreted for us to the state from the beginning, yet was one of those treacherous Brother Trulies, and abused us most clerkly. He interpreted to us with a pestilence, for whereas we stood obstinately upon it, we were wrongfully detained, and that it was naught but a malicious practise of sinful Tabitha, our late hostess, he, by a fine cony-catching corrupt translation, made us plainly to confess, and cry *Miserere*, ere we had need of our neck-verse.[143]

Detestable, detestable, that the flesh and the devil should deal by their factors. I'll stand to it, there is not a pander but hath vowed paganism. The devil himself is not such a devil as he, so be he perform his function aright. He must have the back of an ass, the snout of an elephant, the wit of a fox, and the teeth of a wolf; he must fawn like a spaniel, crouch like a Jew, leer like a sheepbiter.[144] If he be half a Puritan, and have Scripture continually in his mouth, he speeds the better. I can tell you it is a trade of great promotion, & let none ever think to mount by service in foreign courts, or creep near to some magnifique lord's, if they be not seen in this science. O, it is the art of arts, and ten thousand times goes beyond the intelligencer. None but a staid grave civil man is capable of it; he must have exquisite courtship in him or else he is not old who,[145] he wants the best point in his tables.

God be merciful to our pander (and that were for God to work a miracle), he was seen in all the seven liberal deadly sciences, not a sin but he was as absolute in as Satan himself. Satan could never have supplanted us so as he did. I may say to you, he planted in us the first Italianate wit that we had. During the time we lay close and took physic in this castle of contemplation, there was a magnifico's wife of good calling sent to bear us company. Her husband's name was Castaldo, she hight Diamante: the cause of her committing was an ungrounded jealous suspicion which her doting husband had conceived of her chastity. One Isaac Medicus, a Bergomast,[146] was the man he chose to make him a monster, who being a courtier, and repairing to his house very often, neither for love of him nor his wife, but only with a drift to borrow money of a pawn of wax and parchment, when he saw his expectation deluded, & that Castaldo was too chary for him to close with, he privily, with purpose of revenge, gave out amongst his copesmates[147] that he resorted to Castaldo's house for no other end but to cuckold him, and doubtfully he talked that he had and he had not obtained his suit. Rings which he borrowed of a light courtezan that he used too, he would fain to be taken from her fingers, and, in sum, so handled the matter, that Castaldo exclaimed, "Out, whore, strumpet, sixpenny hackster, away with her to prison."

As glad were we almost as if they had given us liberty, that fortune lent us such a sweet pew-fellow. A pretty round-faced wench was it, with black eyebrows, a high forehead, a little mouth, and a sharp nose, as fat and plump every part of her as a plover, a skin as slick and soft as the back of a swan, it doth me good when I remember her. Like a bird she tript on the ground, and bore out her belly as majestical as an ostrich. With a licorous[148] rolling eye fixt piercing on the earth, and sometimes scornfully darted on the tone side,[149] she figured forth a high discontented disdain; much like a prince puffing and storming at the treason of some mighty subject fled lately out of his power. Her very countenance repiningly wrathful, and yet clear and unwrinkled, would have confirmed the clearness of her conscience to the austerest judge in the world. If in anything she were culpable, it was in being too melancholy chaste, and shewing herself as covetous of her beauty as her husband was of his bags. Many are honest because they know not how to be dishonest: she thought there was no pleasure in stolen bread, because there was no pleasure in an old man's bed. It is almost impossible that any woman should be excellently witty, and not make the utmost penny of her beauty. This age and this country of ours admits of some miraculous exceptions, but former times are my constant informers. Those that have quick motions of wit have quick motions in everything: iron only needs many strokes, only iron wits are not won without a long siege of entreaty. Gold easily bends, the most ingenious minds are easiest moved, *Ingenium nobis molle Thalia dedit*, saith Sappho to Phao.[150] Who hath no merciful mild mistress, I will maintain, hath no witty but a clownish dull phlegmatic puppy to his mistress.

This magnifico's wife was a good loving soul that had metal enough in her to make a good wit of, but being never removed from under her mother's and her husband's wing, it was not molded and fashioned as it ought. Causeless distrust is able to drive deceit into a simple woman's head. I durst pawn the credit of a page, which is worth ams ace[151] at all times, that she was immaculate honest till she met with us in prison. Marry, what temptations she had then, when fire and flax were put together, conceit with yourselves, but hold my master excusable.

Alack, he was too virtuous to make her vicious; he stood upon religion and conscience, what a heinous thing it was to subvert God's ordinance. This was all the injury he would offer her: sometimes he would imagine her in a melancholy humor to be his Geraldine, and court her in terms correspondent; nay, he would swear she was his Geraldine, and take her white hand and wipe his eyes with it, as though the very touch of her might staunch his anguish. Now would he kneel & kiss the ground as holy ground which she vouchsafed to bless from barrenness by her steps. Who would have learned to write an excellent passion, might have been a perfect tragic poet, had he but attended half the extremity of his lament. Passion upon passion would throng one on another's neck, he would praise her beyond the moon and stars, and that so sweetly and ravishingly as I persuade myself he was more in love with his own curious forming fancy than her face; and truth it is, many become passionate lovers only to win praise to their wits.

He praised, he prayed, he desired and besought her to pity him that perished for her. From this his entranced mistaking ecstasy could no man remove him. Who loveth resolutely will include everything under the name of his love. From prose he would leap into verse, and with these or such like rimes assault her.

If I must die, O, let me choose my death:
Suck out my soul with kisses, cruel maid,
In thy breasts' crystal balls embalm my breath,
Dole it all out in sighs when I am laid.
Thy lips on mine like cupping glasses clasp,
Let our tongues meet and strive as they would sting,
Crush out my wind with one strait girting grasp,
Stabs on my heart keep time whilst thou doest sing.
Thy eyes like searing irons burn out mine,
In thy fair tresses stifle me outright,
Like Circes[152] change me to a loathsome swine,
So I may live forever in thy sight.
    Into heaven's joys none can profoundly see,
    Except that first they meditate on thee.

Sadly and verily, if my master said true, I should if I were a wench make many men quickly immortal. What is't, what is't for a maid fair and fresh to spend a little lipsalve on a hungry lover? My master beat the bush and kept a coil and a prattling,[153] but I caught the bird: simplicity and plainness shall carry it away in another world. God wot he was Petro Desperato, when I stepping to her with a dunstable[154] tale made up my market. A holy requiem to their

souls that think to woo a woman with riddles. I had some
cunning plot, you must suppose, to bring this about. Her
husband had abused her, and it was very necessary she should
be revenged. Seldom do they prove patient martyrs who
are punished unjustly: one way or other they will cry
quittance whatsoever it cost them. No other apt means had
this poor she captived Cicely, to work her hoddy-peak[155]
husband a proportionable plague for his jealousy, but to
give his head his full loading of infamy. She thought she
would make him complain for something, that now was so
hard bound with an heretical opinion. How I dealt with
her, guess, gentle reader, *subaudi*[156] that I was in prison, and
she my silly jailor.

Means there was made after a month's or two durance by
M. John Russell,[157] a gentleman of King Henry the Eight's
chamber, who then lay ledger[158] at Venice for England,
that our cause should be favorably heard. At that time was
Monsieur Petro Aretino[159] searcher and chief inquisitor to
the college of courtezans. Diverse and sundry ways was this
Aretine beholding to the King of England, especially for
by this foresaid master John Russell, a little before, he had
sent him a pension of four hundred crowns yearly during
his life. Very forcibly was he dealt withal, to strain the utmost of his credit for our delivery out of prison. Nothing
at his hands we sought, but that the courtezan might be more
narrowly sifted and examined. Such and so extraordinary
was his care and industry herein, that, within few days after,
Mistress Tabitha and her pander cried *Peccavi, confiteor*,[160]
and we were presently discharged, they for example's sake
executed. Most honorably, after our enlargement, of the state
were we used, & had sufficient recompense for all our troubles
& wrongs.

Before I go any further, let me speak a word or two of
this Aretine. It was one of the wittiest knaves that ever
God made. If out of so base a thing as ink there may be
extracted a spirit, he writ with nought but the spirit of ink,
and his style was the spirituality of arts, and nothing else;

whereas all others of his age were but the lay temporalty of inkhorn terms.[161] For indeed they were mere temporizers, and no better. His pen was sharp-pointed like a poniard; no leaf he wrote on but was like a burning glass to set on fire all his readers. With more than musket shot did he charge his quill, where he meant to inveigh. No hour but he sent a whole legion of devils into some herd of swine or other. If Martial had ten Muses (as he saith of himself)[162] when he but tasted a cup of wine, he had tenscore when he determined to tyrannize: ne'er a line of his but was able to make a man drunken with admiration. His sight pierced like lightning into the entrails of all abuses. This I must needs say, that most of his learning he got by hearing the lectures at Florence. It is sufficient that learning he had, and a conceit exceeding all learning, to quintessence every-thing which he heard. He was no timorous servile flatterer of the commonwealth wherein he lived. His tongue & his invention were foreborn;[163] what they thought, they would confidently utter. Princes he spared not, that in the least point transgressed. His life he contemned in comparison of the liberty of speech. Whereas some dull-brain maligners of his accuse him of that treatise, *De tribus impostoribus mundi*,[164] which was never contrived without a general counsel of devils, I am verily persuaded it was none of his; and of my mind are a number of the most judicial Italians. One reason is this, because it was published forty years after his death, and he never in his lifetime wrote anything in Latin. Certainly I have heard that one of Machiavel's followers and disciples was the author of that book, who, to avoid discredit, filched it forth under Aretine's name, a great while after he had sealed up his eloquent spirit in the grave. Too much gall did that wormwood of Ghibelline wits put in his ink, who engraved that rhubarb epitaph on this excellent poet's tombstone.[165] Quite forsaken of all good angels was he, and utterly given over to artless envy. Four universities honoured Aretine with these rich titles, *Il flagello de principi. Il veritiero. Il devino, & L'unico Aretino.*[166]

The French king, Frances the First, he kept in such awe, that to chain his tongue he sent him a huge chain of gold, in the form of tongues fashioned. Singularly hath he commented of the humanity of Christ.[167] Besides, as Moses set forth his *Genesis*, so hath he set forth his *Genesis* also, including the contents of the whole *Bible*. A notable treatise hath he compiled, called, *Il sette Psalmi poenetentiarii*. All the Thomasos have cause to love him, because he hath dilated so magnificently of the life of Saint Thomas. There is a good thing that he hath set forth, *La vita della virgine Maria*, though it somewhat smell of superstition; with a number more, which here for tediousness I suppress. If lascivious he were, he may answer with Ovid, *Vita verecunda est, musa iocosa mea est;* My life is chaste though wanton be my verse. Tell me, who is traveled in histories, what good poet is, or ever was there, who hath not had a little spice of wantonness in his days? Even Beza[168] himself by your leave. Aretine, as long as the world lives shalt thou live. Tully, Virgil, Ovid, Seneca were never such ornaments to Italy as thou hast been. I never thought of Italy more religiously than England till I heard of thee. Peace to thy ghost, and yet methinks so indefinite a spirit should have no peace or intermission of pains, but be penning ditties to the archangels in another world. Puritans, spew forth the venom of your dull inventions. A toad swells with thick troubled poison, you swell with poisonous perturbations; your malice hath not a clear dram of any inspired disposition.

My principal subject plucks me by the elbow. Diamante, Castaldo's the magnifico's wife, after my enlargement proved to be with child, at which instant there grew an unsatiable famine in Venice, wherein, whether it were for mere niggardice or that Castaldo still eat out his heart with jealousy, Saint Anne be our record, he turned up the heels very devoutly. To master Aretine after this, once more very dutifully I appealed, requested him of favour, acknowledged former gratuities: he made no more humming or halting, but, in despite of her husband's kinsfolks, gave her her

Nunc dimittis,[169] and so established her free of my company.

Being out, and fully possessed of her husband's goods, she invested me in the state of a monarch. Because the time of childbirth drew nigh, and she could not remain in Venice but discredited, she decreed to travel whithersoever I would conduct her. To see Italy throughout was my proposed scope, and that way if she would travel, have with her, I had wherewithal to relieve her.

From my master by her full-hand provokement I parted without leave: the state of an earl he had thrust upon me before, & now I would not bate him an ace of it. Through all the cities past I by no other name but the young Earl of Surrey; my pomp, my apparel, train, and expense, was nothing inferior to his, my looks were as lofty, my words as magnifical. Memorandum, that Florence being the principal scope of my master's course, missing me, he journeyed thither without interruption. By the way as he went, he heard of another Earl of Surrey besides himself, which caused him make more haste to fetch me in, whom he little dreamed of had had such art in my budget, to separate the shadow from the body. Overtake me at Florence he did, where, sitting in my pontificalibus[170] with my courtezan at supper, like Anthony and Cleopatra, when they quaffed standing bowls of wine spiced with pearl together, he stole in ere we sent for him, and bade much good it us,[171] and asked us whether we wanted any guests. If he had asked me whether I would have hanged myself, his question had been more acceptable. He that had then ungartered me might have plucked out my heart at my heels.

My soul which was made to soar upward, now sought for passage downward; my blood, as the blushing Sabine maids, surprised on the sudden by the soldiers of Romulus, ran to the noblest of blood amongst them for succour, that were in no less (if not greater) danger, so did it run for refuge to the noblest of his blood about my heart assembled, that stood in more need itself of comfort and refuge. A trembling earthquake or shaking fever assailed either of us; and I think unfeignedly, if he, seeing our faint-heart agony, had not soon cheered and refreshed us, the dogs had gone together by the ears under the table for our fear-dropped limbs.

Instead of menacing or affrighting me with his sword or his frowns for my superlative presumption, he burst out into laughter above e-la,[172] to think how bravely napping he had took us, and how notably we were damped and struck dead in the nest, with the unexpected view of his presence.

"Ah," quoth he, "my noble lord," after his tongue had borrowed a little leave of his laughter, "is it my luck to visit you thus unlooked for? I am sure you will bid me welcome, if it be but for the name's sake. It is a wonder to see two English earls of one house at one time together in Italy." I, hearing him so pleasant, began to gather up my spirits, and replied as boldly as I durst: "Sir, you are welcome, your name which I borrowed I have not abused; some large sums of money this my sweet mistress Diamante hath made me master of, which I knew not how better to employ for the honor of my country, than by spending it munificently under your name. No Englishman would I have renowned for bounty, magnificence, and courtesy but you; under your colours all my meritorious works I was desirous to shroud. Deem it no insolence to add increase to your fame. Had I basely and beggarly, wanting ability to support any part of your royalty, undertook the estimation of this high calling, your allegement of injury had been the greater, and my defence less authorized. It will be thought but a policy of yours thus to send one before you, who, being a follower of yours, shall keep and uphold the estate and port of an earl. I have known many earls myself that in their own persons would go very plain, but delighted to have one that belonged to them (being loaden with jewels, apparelled in cloth of gold and all the rich embroidery that might be) to stand bareheaded unto him; arguing thus much, that if the greatest men went not more sumptuous, how more great than the greatest was he that could command one going so sumptuous. A nobleman's glory appeareth in nothing so much as in the pomp of his attendants. What is the glory of the sun, but that the moon and so many millions of stars borrow their lights from him? If you can reprehend me of any one illiberal licentious action I have disparaged your name with, heap shame on me prodigally, I beg no pardon or pity."

Non veniunt in idem pudor & amor,[173] he was loth to detract from one that he loved so. Beholding with his eyes that I clipped not the wings of his honour, but rather increased them with additions of expense, he intreated me as if I had been an embassador; he gave me his hand and swore he had no more hearts but one, and I should have half of it, in that I so enhanced his obscured reputation. "One thing," quoth he, "my sweet Jack, I will intreat thee, (it shall be but one,) that though I am well pleased thou shouldest be the ape of my birthright, (as what nobleman hath not his ape & his fool?) yet that thou be an ape without a clog,[174] not carry thy courtezan with thee." I told him that a king could do nothing without his treasury; this courtezan was my purse-bearer, my countenance and supporter. "My earldom I would sooner resign than part with such a special benefactor. Resign it I will however, since I am thus challenged of stolen goods by the true owner: Lo, into my former state I return again; poor Jack Wilton and your servant am I, as I was at the beginning, and so will I persevere to my life's ending."

That theme was quickly cut off, & other talk entered in place, of what I have forgot, but talk it was, and talk let it be, & talk it shall be, for I do not mean here to remember it. We supped, we got to bed, rose in the morning, on my master I waited, & the first thing he did after he was up, he went and visited the house where his Geraldine was born, at sight whereof he was so impassioned that in the open street, but for me, he would have made an oration in praise of it. Into it we were conducted, and shewed each several room thereto appertaining. O, but when he came to the chamber where his Geraldine's clear sunbeams first thrust themselves into this cloud of flesh, and acquainted mortality with the purity of angels, then did his mouth overflow with magnificats, his tongue thrust the stars out of heaven, and eclipsed the sun and moon with comparisons; Geraldine was the soul of heaven, sole daughter and heir to *primus motor*.[175] The alchemy of his eloquence, out of the incomprehensible drossy matter of clouds and air, distilled no more quintessence than would make his Geraldine complete fair. In praise of the chamber that was so illuminatively honored with her radiant conception, he penned this sonnet.

> Fair room, the presence of sweet beauty's pride,
> The place the sun upon the earth did hold,
> When Phaeton his chariot did misguide,
> The tower where Jove rain'd down himself in gold,
>   Prostrate, as holy ground I'll worship thee;
> Our lady's chapel henceforth be thou named;
> Here first love's queen put on mortality,
> And with her beauty all the world inflam'd.
>   Heaven's chambers harboring fiery cherubines,
> Are not with thee in glory to compare;
> Lightning it is, not light, which in thee shines,
> None enter thee but straight entranced are.
>   O, if Elysium be above the ground,
>   Then here it is, where nought but joy is found.

Many other poems and epigrams in that chamber's patient alabaster enclosure (which her melting eyes long sithence had softened) were curiously engraved. Diamonds thought themselves *dii mundi*,[176] if they might but carve her name on the naked glass. With them on it did he anatomize these body-wanting mots, *Dulce puella malum est. Quod fugit ipse sequor. Amor est mihi causa sequendi. O infoelix ego. Cur vidi? cur perii? Non patienter amo. Tantum patiatur amari*.[177] After the view of these venereal monuments, he published a proud challenge in the Duke of Florence's court against all comers, (whether Christians, Turks, Jews, or Saracens) in defence of his Geraldine's beauty. More mildly was

it accepted in that she whom he defended was a town-born
child of that city, or else the pride of the Italian would have
prevented him ere he should have come to perform it. The
Duke of Florence nevertheless sent for him, and demanded
him of his estate and the reason that drew him thereto, which
when he was advertised of to the full, he granted all countries
whatsoever, as well enemies and outlaws as friends and con-
federates, free access and regress into his dominions un-
molested, until that insolent trial were ended.

The right honorable and ever-renowned Lord Henry
Howard, Earl of Surrey, my singular good lord and master,
entered the lists after this order. His armour was all intermixed with lilies and roses, and the bases[178] thereof bordered
with nettles and weeds, signifying stings, crosses, and over-
growing incumbrances in his love; his helmet round-propor-
tioned like a gardener's water-pot, from which seemed to
issue forth small threads of water, like cittern strings, that
not only did moisten the lilies and roses, but did fructify as
well the nettles and weeds, and made them overgrow their
liege lord's. Whereby he did import thus much, that the tears
that issued from his brains, as those artificial distillations
issued from the well-counterfeit water-pot on his head,
watered and gave life as well to his mistress' disdain (resembled to nettles and weeds) as increase of glory to her
care-causing beauty (comprehended under the lilies and
roses). The symbol thereto annexed was this, *Ex lachrimis
lachrimae.*[179] The trappings of his horse were pounced and
bolstered out with rough-plumed silver plush, in full proportion and shape of an estrich.[180] On the breast of the horse
were the foreparts of this greedy bird advanced, whence, as
his manner is, he reached out his long neck to the reins of
the bridle, thinking they had been iron, & still seemed to gape
after the golden bit, and ever as the courser did raise or
corvet,[181] to have swallowed it half in. His wings, which
he never useth but running, being spread full sail, made
his lusty steed as proud under him as he had been some other
Pegasus, & so quiveringly and tenderly were these his broad

wings bound to either side of him, that as he paced up and down the tiltyard in his majesty ere the knights were entered, they seemed wantonly to fan in his face and make a flickering sound, such as eagles do, swiftly pursuing their prey in the air. On either of his wings, as the estrich hath a sharp goad or prick wherewith he spurreth himself forward in his sail-assisted race, so this artificial estrich, on the inbent knuckle of the pinion of either wing, had embossed crystal eyes affixed, wherein wheelwise were circularly ingrafted sharp-pointed diamonds, as rays from those eyes derived, that like the rowel of a spur ran deep into his horse's sides, and made him more eager in his course.

Such a fine dim shine did these crystal eyes and these round enranked diamonds make through their bollen[182] swelling bowers of feathers as if it had been a candle in a paper lantern, or a glow-worm in a bush by night, glistering through the leaves & briars. The tail of the estrich, being short and thick, served very fitly for a plume to trick up his horse's tail with, so that every part of him was as naturally coapted[183] as might be. The word to this device was *Aculeo alatus*,[184] I spread my wings only spurred with her eyes. The moral of the whole is this, that as the estrich, the most burning-sighted bird of all others, insomuch as the female of them hatcheth not her eggs by covering them, but by the effectual rays of her eyes, as he, I say, outstrippeth the nimblest trippers of his feathered condition in footmanship, only spurred on with the needle quickening goad under his side, so he, no less burning-sighted than the estrich, spurred on to the race of honor by the sweet rays of his mistress' eyes, persuaded himself he should outstrip all other in running to the goal of glory, only animated and incited by her excellence. And as the estrich will eat iron, swallow any hard metal whatsoever, so would he refuse no iron adventure, no hard task whatsoever, to sit in the grace of so fair a commander. The order of his shield was this: it was framed like a burning glass, beset round with flame-coloured feathers, on the outside whereof was his mistress' picture adorned as beautiful as art could portraiture; on the inside a naked sword tied in a true love knot; the mot, *Militat omnis amans*.[185] Signifying that in a true love knot his sword was tied to defend and maintain the features of his mistress.

Next him entered the Black Knight, whose beaver was pointed [186] all torn & bloody, as though he had new come from combatting with a bear; his headpiece seemed to be a little oven fraught full with smothering flames, for nothing but sulphur and smoke voided out at the clefts of his beaver. His bases were all embroidered with snakes and adders, engendered of the abundance of innocent blood that was shed. His horse's trappings were throughout bespangled with honey spots, which are no blemishes, but ornaments. On his shield he bare the sun full shining on a dial at his going down; the word, *Sufficit tandem*.[187]

After him followed the Knight of the Owl, whose armor was a stubbed tree overgrown with ivy, his helmet fashioned like an owl sitting on the top of this ivy; on his bases were wrought all kind of birds, as on the ground, wandering about him; the word, *Ideo mirum quia monstrum*:[188] his horse's furniture was framed like a cart, scattering whole sheaves of corn amongst hogs; the word, *Liberalitas liberalitate perit*.[189] On his shield a bee entangled in sheep's wool; the mot, *Frontis nulla fides*.[190] The fourth that succeeded was a well-proportioned knight in an armor imitating rust, whose headpiece was prefigured like flowers growing in a narrow pot, where they had not any space to spread their roots or disperse their flourishing. His bases embellished with open-armed hands scattering gold amongst truncheons; the word, *Cura futuri est*.[191] His horse was harnessed with leaden chains, having the outside gilt, or at least saffroned instead of gilt, to decipher a holy or golden pretence of a covetous purpose; the sentence, *Cani capilli mei compedes*:[192] on his target he had a number of crawling worms kept under by a block; the faburthen,[193] *Speramus lucent*.[194] The fifth was the Forsaken Knight, whose helmet was crowned with nothing but cypress and willow garlands: over his armour he had Hymen's nuptial robe, dyed in a dusky yellow, and all to be defaced and discoloured with spots and stains. The enigma, *Nos quoque floruimus*,[195] as who should say, we have been in fashion: his steed was adorned with orange-tawny eyes, such as those have that have the yellow jaundice, that make all things yellow they look upon, with this brief, *Qui invident egent*, those that envy are hungry. The sixth was the Knight of the Storms, whose helmet was round-molded like the moon, and all his armor like waves, whereon the shine of the moon, slightly silvered, perfectly represented moonshine in the water; his bases were the banks or shores that bounded in the streams. The spoke was this, *Frustra pius*, [196] as much to say fruitless service. On his shield he set forth a lion driven from his prey by a dunghill cock. The word, *Non vi sed voce*, not by violence but by voice.

The seventh had, like the giants that sought to scale heaven in despite of Jupiter, a mount overwhelming his head and whole body; his bases outlaid with arms and legs which the skirts of that mountain left uncovered. Under this did he characterize a man desirous to climb to the heaven of honour, kept under with the mountain of his prince's command, and yet had he arms and legs exempted from the suppression of that mountain. The word, *Tu mihi criminis author* (alluding to his prince's command), thou art the occasion of my imputed cowardice. His horse was trapt in the earthy strings of tree roots, which though their increase was stubbed down to the ground, yet were they not utterly deaded, but hoped for an after-resurrection. The word, *Spe alor*,[197] I hope for a spring. Upon his shield he bare a ball, stricken down with a man's hand that it might mount. The word, *Ferior ut efferar*, I suffer myself to be contemned because I will climb. The eighth had all his armor throughout engrailed like a crabbed briary hawthorne bush, out of which notwithstanding sprung (as a good child of an ill father) fragrant blossoms of delightful Mayflowers, that made (according to the nature of May) a most odoriferous smell. In midst of this his snowy curled top, round-wrapped together,

on the ascending of his crest sat a solitary nightingale close
encaged, with a thorn at her breast, having this mot in her
mouth, *Luctus monumenta manebunt.*[198] At the foot of this
bush represented on his bases, lay a number of black swollen
toads gasping for wind, and summer-lived grasshoppers gaping after dew, both which were choked with excessive drouth
for want of shade. The word, *Non sine vulnere viresco*, I
spring not without impediments, alluding to the toads and
such like, that erst lay sucking at his roots, but now were
turned out, and near choked with drought. His horse was
suited in black sandy earth (as adjacent to this bush) which
was here and there patched with short burned grass, and as
thick ink-dropped with toiling ants and emmets as ever
it might crawl, who, in the full of the summer moon (ruddy-
garnished on his horse's forehead), hoarded up their provision
of grain against winter. The word, *Victrix fortunae sapientia*,
providence prevents misfortune. On his shield he set forth the
picture of death doing alms-deeds to a number of poor deso-
late children. The word, *Nemo alius explicat.* No other man
takes pity upon us. What his meaning was herein I cannot
imagine, except death had done him and his brethren some
great good turn in ridding them of some untoward parent
or kinsman that would have been their confusion; for else
I cannot see how death should have been said to do alms-
deeds, except he had deprived them suddenly of their lives,
to deliver them out of some further misery; which could
not in any wise be, because they were yet living.

The ninth was the Infant Knight, who on his armour had
enameled a poor young infant put into a ship without tackling,
masts, furniture, or anything. This weather-beaten or ill-
apparelled ship was shadowed on his bases, and the slender
compass of his body set forth the right picture of an infant.
The waves wherein the ship was tossed were fretted on his
steed's trappings so movingly, that ever as he offered to
bound or stir, they seemed to bounce and toss, and sparkle
brine out of their hoary silver billows; the mot, *Inopem me*

copia fecit,[199] as much to say as the rich prey makes the thief.

On his shield he expressed an old goat that made a young tree to wither only with biting it; the word thereto, *Primo extinguor in aevo*. I am frostbitten ere I come out of the blade.

It were here too tedious to manifest all the discontented or amorous devises that were used in this tournament: the shields only of some few I will touch, to make short work. One bare for his impress the eyes of young swallows coming again after they were plucked out, with this mot, *Et addit et addimit*, your beauty both bereaves and restores my sight. Another, a siren smiling when the sea rageth and ships are overwhelmed, including a cruel woman, that laughs, sings, and scorns at her lover's tears and the tempests of his despair; the word, *Cuncta pereunt*, all my labor is ill employed. A third, being troubled with a curst, a treacherous, and wanton wife, used this similitude. On his shield he caused to be limned Pompey's ordinance for paracides, as namely, a man put into a sack with a cock, a serpent, and an ape, interpreting that his wife was a cock for her crowing, a serpent for her stinging, and an ape for her unconstant wantonness, with which ill qualities he was so beset, that thereby he was thrown into a sea of grief; the word *Extremum malorum mulier*, the utmost of evils is a woman. A fourth, who, being a person of suspected religion, was continually haunted with intelligencers and spies that thought to prey upon him for that he had, he could not devise which way to shake them off but by making away that he had. To obscure this, he used no other fancy but a number of blind flies, whose eyes the cold had closed; the word, *Aurum redit acutissimum*, Gold is the only physic for the eye-sight. A fifth, whose mistress was fallen into a consumption and yet would condescend to no treaty of love, emblazoned for his complaint grapes that withered for want of pressing. The ditty to the mot, *Quid regna sine usu*.[200] I will rehearse no more, but I have an hundred other: let this be the upshot of those shews, they were the admirablest that ever Florence yielded. To particularize their manner of encounter were to describe the whole art of tilting. Some had like to have fallen over their horses' necks and so break their necks in breaking their staves. Others ran at a buckle instead of a button, and peradventure whetted their spears' points, idly gliding on their enemies' sides, but did no other harm. Others ran across at their adversaries' left elbow, yea, and by your leave sometimes let not the lists scape scot-free, they were so eager. Others, because they would be sure not to be unsaddled with the shock, when they came to the spear's utmost proof, they threw it over the right shoulder, and so tilted backward, for forward they durst not. Another had a monstrous spite at the pommel of his rival's saddle, and thought to have thrust his spear twixt his legs without raising any skin, and carried him clean away on it as a coolstaff. Another held his spear to his nose, or his nose to his spear, as though he had been discharging his caliver, and ran at the right foot of his fellow's steed. Only the Earl of Surrey, my master, observed the true measures of honour, and made all his encounterers new scour their armor in the dust: so great was his glory that day as Geraldine was thereby eternally glorified. Never such a bountiful master came amongst the heralds, (not that he did enrich them with any plentiful purse's largesse, but that by his stern assaults he tithed them more rich offals of bases, of helmets, of armor, than the rent of their offices came to in ten years before.)

What would you have more? the trumpets proclaimed him master of the field, the trumpets proclaimed Geraldine the exceptionless fairest of women. Everyone strived to magnify him more than other. The Duke of Florence, whose name (as my memory serveth me) was Paschal de Medicis,[201] offered him such large proffers to stay with him as it were incredible to report. He would not; his desire was, as he had done in Florence, so to proceed throughout all the chief cities in Italy. If you ask why he began not this at Venice first; it was because he would let Florence, his mistress' native city, have the maidenhead of his chivalry. As he came back again he thought to have enacted something there worthy the annals of posterity, but he was debarred both of that and all his other determinations; for, continuing in feasting and banqueting with the Duke of Florence and the princes of Italy there assembled, posthaste letters came to him from the King his master, to return as speedily as he could possible into England; whereby his fame was quite cut off by the shins, and there was no reprieve but *bazelus manus*,[202] he must into England; and I with my courtezan travelled forward in Italy.

What adventures happened him after we parted, I am ignorant, but Florence we both forsook, and I, having a wonderful ardent inclination to see Rome, the queen of the world & metropolitan mistress of all other cities, made thither with my bag and baggage as fast as I could.

Attained thither, I was lodged at the house of one Johannes de Imola,[203] a Roman cavaliero. Who, being acquainted with my courtezan's deceased doting husband, for his sake used us with all the familiarity that might be. He shewed us all the monuments that were to be seen, which are as many as there have been emperors, consuls, orators, conquerors, famous painters or players in Rome. Till this day not a Roman (if he be a right Roman indeed) will kill a rat, but he will have some registered remembrance of it.

There was a poor fellow during my remainder there, that, for a new trick that he had invented of killing cimices[204] and scorpions, had his mountebank banner hung up on a high pillar, with an inscription about it longer than the King of Spain's style. I thought these cimices, like the Cimbrians,[205] had been some strange nation he had brought under, and they were no more but things like lice, which alive have the most venomous sting that may be, and being dead do stink out of measure; Saint Austin[206] compareth heretics unto them. The chiefest thing that my eyes delighted in, was the Church of the Seven Sybils,[207] which is a most miraculous thing; all their prophecies and oracles being there enrolled, as also the beginning and ending of their whole catalogue of the heathen gods, with their manner of worship. There are a number of other shrines and statues dedicated to the emperors, and withal some statues of idolatry reserved for detestation.

I was at Pontius Pilate's house[208] and pissed against it. The name of the place I remember not, but it is as one goes to Saint Paul's Church not far from the iemmes Piazza.[209] There is the prison yet packed up together (an old rotten thing) where the man that was condemned to death, and could have nobody come to him and succour him but was searched, was kept alive a long space by sucking his daughter's breasts.

These are but the shop dust of the sights that I saw, and in truth I did not behold with any care hereafter to report, but contented my eye for the present, & so let them pass: should I memorize half the miracles which they were told me had been done about martyrs' tombs, or the operations of the earth of the sepulchre and other relics brought from Jerusalem, I should be counted the most monstrous liar that ever came in print. The ruins of Pompey's theater, reputed one of the nine wonders[210] of the world, Gregory the Sixth's tomb, Priscilla's grate, or the thousands of pillars areared amongst the razed foundations of old Rome, it were frivolous to specify, since he that hath but once drunk with a traveller talks of them. Let me be a historiographer of my own misfortunes, and not meddle with the continued trophies of so old a triumphing city.

At my first coming to Rome, I, being a youth of the English cut, wore my hair long, went apparelled in light colors, and imitated four or five sundry nations in my attire at once; which no sooner was noted, but I had all the boys of the city in a swarm wondering about me.

I had not gone a little farther, but certain officers crossed the way of me, and demanded to see my rapier: which when they found (as also my dagger) with his point unblunted, they would have hauled me headlong to the strappado,[211] but that with money I appeased them: and my fault was more pardonable in that I was a stranger, altogether ignorant of their customs.

Note, by the way, that it is the use in Rome for all men whatsoever to wear their hair short: which they do not so much for conscience's sake, or any religion they place in it, but because the extremity of the heat is such there that, if they should not do so, they should not have a hair left on their heads to stand upright when they were scared with sprites. And he is counted no gentleman amongst them that goes not in black: they dress their jesters and fools only in fresh colours, and say variable garments do argue unstaidness and unconstancy of affections.

The reason of their strait ordinance for carrying weapons without points is this: The bandettos, which are certain outlaws that lie betwixt Rome and Naples, and besiege the passage, that none can travel that way without robbing. Now and then, hired for some few crowns, they will steal to Rome and do a murther, and betake them to their heels again. Disguised as they go, they are not known from strangers; sometimes they will shroud themselves under the habit of grave citizens. In this consideration, neither citizen or stranger, gentleman, knight, marquess, or any may wear any weapon endamageable upon pain of the strappado. I bought it out; let others buy experience of me better cheap.

To tell you of the rare pleasures of their gardens, their baths, their vineyards, their galleries, were to write a second part of the *Gorgeous Gallery of Gallant Devices*.[212] Why, you should not come into any man's house of account, but he had fish-ponds and little orchards on the top of his leads. If by rain or any other means those ponds were so full they need to be sluiced [213] or let out, even of their superfluities they made melodious use, for they had great wind instruments instead of leaden spouts, that went duly on consort,[214] only with this water's rumbling descent. I saw a summer banqueting house belonging to a merchant, that was the marvel of the world, & could not be matched except God should make another paradise. It was built round of green marble like a theater without: within there was a heaven and earth comprehended both under one roof; the heaven was a clear overhanging vault of crystal, wherein the sun and moon and each visible star had his true similitude, shine, situation, and motion, and, by what enwrapped [215] art I cannot conceive, these spheres in their proper orbs observed their circular wheelings and turnings, making a certain kind of soft angelical murmuring music in their often windings & going about; which music the philosophers say in the true heaven, by reason of the grossness of our senses, we are not capable of. For the earth, it was counterfeited in that likeness that Adam lorded out it before his fall. A wide vast spacious room it was, such as we would conceit Prince Arthur's hall to be, where he feasted all his knights of the round table together every Pentecost. The floor was painted with the beautifullest flowers that ever man's eye admired; which so lineally were delineated that he that viewed them afar off, and had not directly stood poringly over them, would have sworn they had lived indeed. The walls round about were hedged with olives and palm trees, and all other odoriferous fruit-bearing plants; which at any solemn entertainment dropt myrrh and frankincense. Other trees, that bore no fruit, were set in just order one against another, & divided the room into a number of shady lanes, leaving but one overspreading pine tree arbor, where we sat and banqueted. On the well-clothed boughs of this conspiracy of pine trees against the resembled sun beams, were perched as many sorts of shrill breasted birds as the summer hath allowed for singing men in her sylvan chapels. Who though there were bodies without souls, and sweet resembled substances without sense, yet by the mathematical experiments of long silver pipes secretly enrinded in the entrails of the boughs whereon they sat, and undiscernibly conveyed under their bellies into their small throats' sloping, they whistled and freely caroled their natural field note. Neither went those silver pipes straight, but, by many edged unsundered writhings & crankled wanderings aside, strayed from bough to bough into an hundred throats. But into this silver pipe so writhed and wandering aside, if any demand how the wind was breathed; Forsooth the tail of the silver pipe stretched itself into the mouth of a great pair of bellows, where it was close soldered, and baled about with iron, it could not stir or have any vent betwixt. Those bellows with the rising and falling of leaden plummets wound up on a wheel, did beat up and down uncessantly, and so gathered in wind, serving with one blast all the snarled pipes to and fro of one tree at once. But so closely were all those organizing implements obscured in the corpulent trunks of the trees, that every man there present renounced conjectures of art, and said it was done by enchantment.

One tree for his fruit bore nothing but enchained chirping birds, whose throats being conduit-piped with squared narrow shells, & charged syringe-wise with searching sweet water driven in by a little wheel for the nonce, that fed it afar off, made a spurting sound, such as chirping is, in bubbling upwards through the rough crannies of their closed bills.

Under tuition of the shade of every tree that I have signified to be in this round hedge, on delightful leafy cloisters, lay a wild tyrannous beast asleep all prostrate; under some, two together, as the dog nuzzling his nose under the neck of the deer, the wolf glad to let the lamb lie upon him to keep him warm, the lion suffering the ass to cast his leg over him, preferring one honest unmannerly friend before a number of crouching pickthanks. No poisonous beast there reposed, (poison was not before our parent Adam transgressed.) There were no sweet-breathing panthers that would hide their terrifying heads to betray; no men-imitating hyenas that changed their sex to seek after blood. Wolves as now when they are hungry eat earth, so then did they feed on earth only, and abstained from innocent flesh. The unicorn did not put his horn into the stream to chase away venom before he drunk, for then there was no such thing extant in the water or on the earth. Serpents were as harmless to mankind as they are still one to another: the rose had no cankers, the leaves no caterpillars, the sea no sirens, the earth no usurers. Goats then bore wool, as it is recorded in Sicily they do yet. The torrid zone was habitable: only jays loved to steal gold and silver to build their nests withal, and none cared for covetous clientry, or running to the Indies. As the elephant understands his country's speech, so every beast understood what man spoke. The ant did not hoard up against winter, for there was no winter, but a perpetual spring, as Ovid saith. No frosts to make the green almond tree counted rash and improvident, in budding soonest of all other; or the mulberry tree a strange politician, in blooming late and ripening early. The peach tree at the first planting was fruitful and wholesome, whereas now, till it be transplanted, it is poisonous and hateful: young plants for their sap had balm, for their yellow gum glistering amber. The evening dewed not water on flowers, but honey. Such a golden age, such a good age, such an honest age was set forth in this banqueting house.

O Rome, if thou hast in thee such soul-exalting objects, what a thing is heaven in comparison of thee, of which Mercator's globe[216] is a perfecter model than thou art? Yet this I must say to the shame of us Protestants; if good works may merit heaven, they do them, we talk of them. Whether superstition or no makes them unprofitable servants, that let pulpits decide; but there you shall have the bravest ladies, in gowns of beaten gold, washing pilgrims' & poor soldiers' feet, and doing nothing, they and their waiting maids, all the year long, but making shirts and bands for them against they come by in distress. Their hospitals are more like noblemen's houses than otherwise; so richly furnished, clean kept, and hot perfumed, that a soldier would think it a sufficient recompense for all his travail and his wounds, to have such a heavenly retiring place. For the Pope and his pontificalibus I will not deal with; only I will dilate unto you what happened whilst I was in Rome.

So it fell out that it being a vehement hot summer when I was a sojourner there, there entered such a hotspurred plague as hath not been heard of: why, it was but a word and a blow, Lord have mercy upon us, and he was gone. Within three quarters of a year in that one city there died of it a hundred thousand; look in Lanquet's chronicle[217] and you shall find it. To smell of a nosegay that was poisoned, and turn your nose to a house that had the plague, it was all one. The clouds, like a number of cormorants that keep their corn till it stink and is musty, kept in their stinking exhalations, till they had almost stifled all Rome's inhabitants. Physicians' greediness of gold made them greedy of their destiny. They would come to visit those with whose infirmity their art had no affinity; and even as a man with a fee should be hired to hang himself, so would they quietly go home and die presently after they had been with their patients. All day and all night long car-men did nothing but go up and down the streets with their carts and cry, "Have you any dead bodies to bury?" and had many times out of one house their whole loading: one grave was the sepulchre of sevenscore, one bed was the altar whereon whole families were offered.

The walls were hoared and furred with the moist scorching steam of their desolation. Even as before a gun is shot off, a stinking smoke funnels out and prepares the way for him, so before any gave up the ghost, death arrayed in a stinking smoke stopt his nostrils and crammed itself full into his mouth that closed up his fellow's eyes, to give him warning to prepare for his funeral. Some died sitting at their meat, others as they were asking counsel of the physician for their friends. I saw at the house where I was hosted a maid bring her master warm broth for to comfort him, and she sink down dead herself ere he had half eat it up.

During this time of visitation, there was a Spaniard, one Esdras of Granado, a notable bandetto, authorized by the Pope because he had assisted him in some murthers. This villain, colleagued with one Bartol, a desperate Italian, practised to break into those rich men's houses in the night where the plague had most reigned, and if there were none but the mistress and maid left alive, to ravish them both, & bring away all the wealth they could fasten on. In an hundred chief citizens' houses where the hand of God had been, they put this outrage in ure.[218] Though the women so ravished cried out, none durst come near them, for fear of catching their deaths by them, and some thought they cried out only with the tyranny of the malady. Amongst the rest, the house where I lay he invaded, where all being snatched up by sickness but the good wife of the house, a noble & chaste matron called Heraclide, and her zany,[219] and I and my courtezan, he, knocking at the door late in the night, ran in to the matron, and left me and my love to the mercy of his companion. Who finding me in bed (as the time required) ran at me full with his rapier, thinking I would resist him, but, as good luck was, I escaped him and betook me to my pistol in the window uncharged. He, fearing it had been charged, threatened to run her through if I once offered but to aim at him. Forth the chamber he dragged her, holding his rapier at her heart, whilst I cried out, "Save her, kill me, and I'll ransom her with a thousand ducats": but lust prevailed, no prayers would be heard. Into my chamber I was locked, and watchmen charged (as he made semblance when there was none there) to knock me down with their halberds if I stirred but a foot down the stairs. Then threw I myself pensive again on my pallet, and dared all the devils in hell, now I was alone, to come and fight with me one after another in defence of that detestable rape. I beat my head against the walls & called them bawds, because they would see such a wrong committed, and not fall upon him. To return to Heraclide below, whom the ugliest of all bloodsuckers, Esdras of Granado, had under shrift. First he assailed her with rough means, and slew her zany at her foot that stept before her in rescue. Then when all armed resist was put to flight, he assayed her with honey speech, & promised her more jewels and gifts than he was able to pilfer in an hundred years after. He discoursed unto her how he was countenanced and born out by the Pope, and how many execrable murders with impunity he had executed on them that displeased him. "This is the eightscore house," quoth he, "that hath done homage unto me, & here I will prevail, or I will be torn in pieces." "Ah," quoth Heraclide (with a heart-rending sigh), "art thou ordained to be a worse plague to me than the plague itself? Have I escaped the hands of God to fall into the hands of man? Hear me, Jehovah, & be merciful

in ending my misery. Dispatch me incontinent, dissolute homicide, death's usurper. Here lies my husband stone-cold on the
dewy floor. If thou beest of more power than God to strike
me speedily, strike home, strike deep, send me to heaven with
my husband. Aye me, it is the spoil of my honor thou seekest
in my soul's troubled departure; thou art some devil sent to
tempt me. Avoid from me, Satan, my soul is my saviour's; to
him I have bequeathed it, from him can no man take it. Jesu,
Jesu, spare me undefiled for thy spouse; Jesu, Jesu, never fail
those that put their trust in thee." With that she fell in a
swoon, and her eyes in their closing seemed to spawn forth
in their outward sharp corners new-created seed pearl, which
the world before never set eye on. Soon he rigorously revived
her, & told her that he had a charter above Scripture; she must
yield, she should yield, see who durst remove her out of his
hands. Twixt life and death thus she faintly replied. "How
thinkest thou, is there a power above thy power? if there be,
he is here present in punishment, and on thee will take present
punishment if thou persistest in thy enterprise. In the time of
security every man sinneth, but when death substitutes one
friend his special baily[220] to arrest another by infection, and
disperseth his quiver into ten thousand hands at once, who is
it but looks about him? A man that hath an unevitable huge
stone hanging only by a hair over his head, which he looks,
every paternoster while,[221] to fall and pash[222] him in pieces,
will not he be submissively sorrowful for his transgressions,
refrain himself from the least thought of folly, and purify his
spirit with contrition and penitence? God's hand like a huge
stone hangs inevitably over thy head: what is the plague but
death playing the provost marshal, to execute all those that
will not be called home by any other means? This my dear
knight's body is a quiver of his arrows, which already are shot
into thee invisibly. Even as the age of goats is known by the
knots on their horns, so think the anger of God apparently
visioned or shown unto thee in the knitting of my brows. A
hundred have I buried out of my house, at all whose departures I have been present: a hundred's infection is mixed with

my breath: lo, now I breathe upon thee, a hundred deaths come upon thee. Repent betimes, imagine there is a hell though not a heaven: that hell thy conscience is thoroughly acquainted with, if thou hast murdered half so many as thou unblushingly braggest. As Maecenas[223] in the latter end of his days was seven years without sleep, so these seven weeks have I took no slumber, my eyes have kept continual watch against the devil, my enemy: death I deemed my friend (friends fly from us in adversity), death, the devil, and all the ministering spirits of temptation are watching about thee to entrap thy soul (by my abuse) to eternal damnation. It is thy soul thou mayst save, only by saving mine honour. Death will have thy body infallibly for breaking into my house, that he had selected for his private habitation. If thou ever cam'st of a woman, or hopest to be saved by the seed of a woman, pity a woman. Deers oppressed with dogs, when they cannot take soil, run to men for succour: to whom should women in their disconsolate and desperate estate run but to men (like the deer) for succour and sanctuary? If thou be a man, thou wilt succour me, but if thou be a dog and a brute beast, thou wilt spoil me, defile me, and tear me: either renounce God's image, or renounce the wicked mind thou bearest."

These words might have moved a compound heart of iron and adamant, but in his heart they obtained no impression: for he sitting in his chair of state against the door all the while that she pleaded, leaning his overhanging gloomy eyebrows on the pommel of his unsheathed sword, he never looked up or gave her a word: but when he perceived she expected his answer of grace or utter perdition, he start[224] up and took her currishly by the neck, asking how long he should stay for her ladyship. "Thou tell'st me," quoth he, "of the plague, & the heavy hand of God, and thy hundred infected breaths in one: I tell thee I have cast the dice an hundred times for the galleys in Spain, and yet still missed the ill chance. Our order of casting is this, If there be a general or captain new come home from the wars, & hath some 4. or 500. crowns overplus of the King's in his hand, and his soldiers all paid, he makes proclamation that whatsoever two resolute men will go to dice for it, and win the bridle or lose the saddle, to such a place let them repair, and it shall be ready for them. Thither go I, and find another such needy squire resident. The dice run, I win, he is undone. I winning have the crowns, he losing is carried to the galleys. This is our custom, which a hundred times and more hath paid me custom of crowns, when the poor fellows[225] have gone to Gehenna had coarse bread and whipping cheer all their life after. Now thinkest thou that I who so oft have escaped such a number of hellish dangers, only depending upon the turning of a few pricks, can be scare-bugged with the plague? what plague canst thou name worse than I have had? whether diseases, imprisonment, poverty, banishment, I have past through them all. My own mother gave I a box of the ear too, and broke her neck down a pair of stairs, because she would not go in to a gentleman when I bade her: my sister I sold to an old leno,[226] to make his best of her: any kinswoman that I have, knew I she were not a whore, myself would make her one: thou art a whore, thou shalt be a whore, in spite of religion or precise ceremonies."

Therewith he flew upon her, and threatened her with his sword, but it was not that he meant to wound her with. He grasped her by the ivory throat, and shook her as a mastiff would shake a young bear, swearing and staring he would tear out her weasand if she refused. Not content with that savage constraint, he slipped his sacrilegious hand from her lily lawn-skinned neck, and inscarfed it in her long silver locks, which with struggling were unrolled. Backward he dragged her, even as a man backward would pluck a tree down by the twigs, and then, like a traitor that is drawn to execution on a hurdle, he traileth her up and down the chamber by those tender untwisted braids, and setting his barbarous foot on her bare snowy breast, bade her yield or have her wind stamped out. She cried, "Stamp, stifle me in my hair, hang me up by it on a beam, and so let me die, rather than I should go to heaven with a beam in my eye." "No," quoth he, "nor stamped, nor stifled, nor hanged, nor to heaven shalt thou go, till I have had my will of thee; thy busy arms in these silken fetters I'll enfold." Dismissing her hair from his fingers, and pinioning her elbows therewithal, she struggled, she wrested, but all was in vain. So struggling and so resisting, her jewels did sweat, signifying there was poison coming towards her.[227] On the hard boards he threw her, and used his knee as an iron ram to beat ope the two-leaved gate of her chastity. Her husband's dead body he made a pillow to his abomination. Conjecture the rest, my words stick fast in the mire and are clean tired; would I had never undertook this tragical tale. Whatsoever is born, is born to have an end. Thus ends my tale: his whorish lust was glutted, his beastly desire satisfied; what in the house of any worth was carriageable, he put up, and went his way.

Let not your sorrow die, you that have read the proem and narration of this elegiacal history. Shew you have quick wits in sharp conceit of compassion. A woman that hath viewed all her children sacrificed before her eyes, & after the first was slain, wiped the sword with her apron to prepare it for the cleanly murther of the second, and so on forward till it came to the empiercing of the seventeenth of her loins, will you not give her great allowance of anguish? This woman, this matron, this forsaken Heraclide, having buried fourteen children in five days, whose eyes she howlingly closed, & caught many wrinkles with funeral kisses; besides having her husband within a day after laid forth as a comfortless corse, a carrionly block, that could neither eat with her, speak with her, nor weep with her; is she not to be borne withal though her body swell with a tympany of tears, though her speech be as impatient as unhappy Hecuba's, though her head raves and her brain dote? Devise with yourselves that you see a corse rising from his hearse after he is carried to church, & such another suppose Heraclide to be, rising from the couch of enforced adultery.

Her eyes were dim, her cheeks bloodless, her breath smelt earthy, her countenance was ghastly. Up she rose after she was deflowered, but loath she arose, as a reprobate soul rising to the day of judgement. Looking on the tone side as she rose, she spied her husband's body lying under her head: ah, then she bewailed, as Cephalus[228] when he had killed Procris unwittingly, or Oedipus when ignorantly he had slain his father, & known his mother incestuously: this was her subdued reason's discourse.

"Have I lived to make my husband's body the bier to carry me to hell? had filthy pleasure no other pillow to lean upon but his spreaded limbs? On thy flesh my fault shall be imprinted at the day of resurrection. O beauty, the bait ordained to ensnare the irreligious: rich men are robbed for their wealth, women are dishonested for being too fair. No blessing is beauty, but a curse: cursed be the time that ever I was begotten; cursed be the time that my mother brought me forth to tempt. The serpent in paradise did no more; the serpent in paradise is damned sempiternally: why should not I hold myself damned (if predestination's opinions be true) that am predestinate to this horrible abuse? The hog dieth presently if he loseth an eye: with the hog have I wallowed in the mire, I have lost my eye of honesty, it is clean plucked out with a strong hand of unchastity: what remaineth but I die? Die I will, though life be unwilling: no recompense is there for me to redeem my compelled offence, but with a rigorous compelled death. Husband, I'll be thy wife in heaven: let not thy pure deceased spirit despise me when we meet, because I am tyrannously polluted. The devil, the belier of our frailty, and common accuser of mankind, cannot accuse me, though he would, of unconstrained submitting. If any guilt be mine, this is my fault, that I did not deform my face, ere it should so impiously allure." Having passioned thus awhile, she hastily ran and looked herself in her glass, to see if her sin were not written on her forehead: with looking she blusht, though none looked upon her but her own reflected image.

Then began she again. "*Heu quam difficile est crimen non prodere vultu;* How hard is it not to bewray a man's fault by his forehead. Myself do but behold myself, and yet I blush: then, God beholding me, shall not I be ten times more ashamed? The angels shall hiss at me, the saints and martyrs

fly from me: yea, God himself shall add to the devil's damnation, because he suffered such a wicked creature to come before him. Agamemnon, thou wert an infidel, yet when thou
went'st to the Trojan War, thou left'st a musician at home
with thy wife, who by playing the foot *spondaeus* till thy
return, might keep her in chastity.[229] My husband going to
war with the devil and his enticements, when he surrendered
left no musician with me, but mourning and melancholy: had
he left any, as Aegistus killed Agamemnon's musician ere he
could be successful, so surely would he have been killed ere
this Aegistus surceased. My distressed heart, as the hart when
as he loseth his horns is astonied, and sorrowfully runneth
to hide himself, so be thou afflicted and distressed; hide thyself under the Almighty's wings of mercy: sue, plead, intreat;
grace is never denied to them that ask. It may be denied; I may
be a vessel ordained to dishonor.

"The only repeal we have from God's undefinite chastisement is to chastise ourselves in this world: and I will; nought
but death be my penance, gracious and acceptable may it be:
my hand and my knife shall manumit me out of the horror of
mind I endure. Farewell, life, that hast lent me nothing but
sorrow. Farewell, sin-sowed flesh, that hast more weeds than
flowers, more woes than joys. Point, pierce, edge, enwiden, I
patiently afford thee a sheath: spur forth my soul to mount
post to heaven. Jesu, forgive me, Jesu, receive me."

So (throughly stabbed) fell she down, and knocked her
head against her husband's body: wherewith he, not having
been aired his full four and twenty hours, start as out of a
dream: whiles I, through a cranny of my upper chamber un-
sealed, had beheld all this sad spectacle. Awaking, he rubbed
his head to and fro, and wiping his eyes with his hand, began
to look about him. Feeling something lie heavy on his breast
he turned it off, and getting upon his legs, lighted a candle.

Here beginneth my purgatory. For he, good man, coming
into the hall with the candle, and spying his wife with her
hair about her ears, defiled and massacred, and his simple zany
Capestrano run through, took a halberd in his hand, and run-

ning from chamber to chamber to search who in his house was likely to do it, at length found me lying on my bed, the door locked to me on the outside, and my rapier unsheathed in the window: wherewith he straight conjectured it was I, and calling the neighbours hard by, said I had caused myself to be locked into my chamber after that sort, sent away my courtezan whom I called my wife, and made clean my rapier, because I would not be suspected.

Upon this was I laid in prison, should have been hanged, was brought to the ladder, had made a ballad for my farewell in a readiness, called "Wilton's Wantonness," and yet for all that scaped dancing in a hempen circle. He that hath gone through many perils and returned safe from them, makes but a merriment to dilate them. I had the knot under my ear, there was fair play, the hangman had one halter, another about my neck was fastened to the gallows, the riding device was almost thrust home, and his foot on my shoulder to press me down, when I made my saint-like confession as you have heard before, that such and such men at such an hour brake into the house, slew the zany, took my courtezan, locked me into my chamber, ravished Heraclide, and finally how she slew herself.

Present at the execution was there a banished English earl, who hearing that a countryman of his was to suffer for such a notable murder, came to hear his confession, and see if he knew him. He had not heard me tell half of that I have recited but he craved audience, and desired the execution might be stayed.

"Not two days since it is, gentlemen and noble Romans," said he, "since, going to be let blood in a barber's shop against the infection, all on sudden in a great tumult and uproar was there brought in one Bartol, an Italian, grievously wounded and bloody. I, seeming to commiserate his harms, courteously questioned him with what ill debtors he had met, or how or by what casualty he came to be so arrayed. 'O,' quoth he, 'long have I lived sworn brothers in sensuality with one Esdras of Granado: five hundred rapes and murders have we committed betwixt us. When our iniquities were grown to the height, and God had determined to countercheck our amity, we came to the house of Johannes de Imola' (whom this young gentleman hath named); there did he justify all those rapes in manner and form as the prisoner here hath confessed. But lo, an accident after, which neither he nor this audience is privy to. Esdras of Granado, not content to have ravished the matron Heraclide and robbed her, after he had betook him from thence to his heels, lighted on his companion Bartol with his courtezan: whose pleasing face he had scarce winkingly glanced on, but he picked a quarrel with Bartol to have her from him. On this quarrel they fought, Bartol was wounded to the death, Esdras fled, and the fair dame left to go whither she would. This, Bartol in the barber's shop freely acknowledged, as both the barber and his man and other here present can amply depose."

Deposed they were; their oaths went for current; I was quit by proclamation: to the banished earl I came to render thanks, when thus he examined and schooled me.

"Countryman, tell me, what is the occasion of thy straying so far out of England to visit this strange nation? If it be languages, thou mayst learn them at home; nought but lasciviousness is to be learned here. Perhaps, to be better accounted of than other of thy condition, thou ambitiously undertakest this voyage: these insolent fancies are but Icarus' feathers, whose wanton wax, melted against the sun, will betray thee into a sea of confusion.

"The first traveller was Cain, and he was called a vagabond runagate on the face of the earth. Travel (like the travail wherein smiths put wild horses when they show them) is good for nothing but to tame and bring men under.

"God had no greater curse to lay upon the Israelites, than by leading them out of their own country to live as slaves in a strange land. That which was their curse, we Englishmen count our chief blessedness; he is nobody that hath not traveled: we had rather live as slaves in another land, crouch and cap, and be servile to every jealous Italian's and proud Spaniard's humor, where we may neither speak, look, nor do anything, but what pleaseth them, than live as freemen and lords in our own country.

"He that is a traveler must have the back of an ass to bear all, a tongue like the tail of a dog to flatter all, the mouth of a hog to eat what is set before him, the ear of a merchant to hear all and say nothing: and if this be not the highest step of thraldom, there is no liberty or freedom.

"It is but a mild kind of subjection to be the servant of one master at once: but when thou hast a thousand thousand masters, as the veriest butcher, tinker, or cobbler freeborn will domineer over a foreigner, and think to be his better or master in company; then shalt thou find there is no such hell as to leave thy father's house (thy natural habitation) to live in the land of bondage.

"If thou doest but lend half a look to a Roman's or Italian's wife, thy porridge shall be prepared for thee, and cost thee nothing but thy life. Chance some of them break a bitter jest on thee, and thou retort'st it severely, or seemest discontented: go to thy chamber, and provide a great banquet, for thou shalt be sure to be visited with guests in a mask the next night, when in kindness and courtship thy throat shall be cut, and the doers return undiscovered. Nothing so long of memory as a dog; these Italians are old dogs, & will carry an injury a whole age in memory: I have heard of a box on the ear that hath been revenged thirty year after. The Neapolitan carrieth the blood-iest mind, and is the most secret fleering murderer: where-upon it is grown to a common proverb, I'll give him the Neapolitan shrug, when one intends to play the villain and make no boast of it.

"The only precept that a traveller hath most use of, and shall find most ease in, is that of Epicharchus,[230] *Vigila, & memor sis ne quid credas:* Believe nothing, trust no man; yet seem thou as thou swallowed'st all, suspected'st none, but wert easy to be gulled by everyone. *Multi fallere docuerunt* (as Seneca saith) *dum timent falli:* Many by showing their jealous suspect of deceit have made men seek more subtile means to deceive them.

"Alas, our Englishmen are the plainest-dealing souls that ever God put life in: they are greedy of news, and love to be fed in their humors and hear themselves flattered the best that may be. Even as Philemon,[231] a comic poet, died with extreme laughter at the conceit of seeing an ass eat figs; so have the Italians no such sport as to see poor English asses, how soberly they swallow Spanish figs, devour any hook baited for them. He is not fit to travel, that cannot, with the Candians, live on serpents, make nourishing food even of poison. Rats and mice engender by licking one another; he must lick, he must crouch, he must cog, lie, and prate, that either in the court or a foreign country will engender and come to preferment. Be his feature what it will, if he be fair-spoken he winneth friends: *Non formosus erat, sed erat facundus Ulysses:* Ulysses, the long traveler, was not amiable, but eloquent. Some allege they travel to learn wit, but I am of this opinion, that as it is not possible for any man to learn the art of memory, whereof Tully, Quintilian, Seneca, and Hermannus Buschius[232] have written so many books, except he have a natural memory before: so is it not possible for any man to attain any great wit by travel, except he have the grounds of it rooted in him before. That wit which is thereby to be perfected or made staid, is nothing but *Experientia longa malorum*, the experience of many evils: The experience that such a man lost his life by this folly, another by that: such a young gallant consumed his substance on such a courtezan: these courses of revenge a merchant of Venice took against a merchant of Ferrara; and this point of justice was shewed by the Duke upon the murtherer. What is here but we may read in books, and a great deal more too, without stirring our feet out of a warm study?

> *Vobis alii ventorum praelia narrent*, (saith Ovid)
> *Quasque Scilla infestat, quasque Charybdis aquas.*

> Let others tell you wonders of the wind,
> How Scylla or Charybdis is inclined.

> —*vos quod quisque loquetur*
> *Credite*. Believe you what they say, but never try.

So let others tell you strange accidents, treasons, poisonings, close packings in France, Spain, and Italy: it is no harm for you to hear of them, but come not near them.

"What is there in France to be learned more than in England, but falsehood in fellowship, perfect slovenry, to love no man but for my pleasure, to swear *Ah par la mort Dieu*,[233] when a man's hams are scabbed. For the idle traveller, (I mean not for the soldier,) I have known some that have continued there by the space of half a dozen years, and when they come home, they have hid a little weerish[234] lean face under a broad French hat, kept a terrible coil with the dust in the street in their long cloaks of gray paper, and spoke English strangely. Nought else have they profited by their travel, save learned to distinguish of the true Bordeaux grape, and know a cup of neat Gascogne wine from wine of Orleans: yea, and peradventure this also, to esteem of the pox as a pimple, to wear a velvet patch on their face, and walk melancholy with their arms folded.

"From Spain what bringeth our traveller? a skull-crowned hat of the fashion of an old deep porringer, a diminutive alderman's ruff with short strings like the droppings of a man's nose, a close-bellied doublet coming down with a peak behind as far as the crupper, and cut off before by the breastbone like a partlet or neckercher, a wide pair of gascoynes[235] which ungathered would make a couple of women's riding kirtles, huge hangers[236] that have half a cowhide in them, a rapier that is lineally descended from half a dozen dukes at the least. Let his cloak be as long or as short as you will: if long, it is faced with turkey grogram raveled; if short, it hath a cape like a calf's tongue, and is not so deep in his whole length, nor hath so much cloth in it, I will justify, as only the standing cape of a Dutchman's cloak. I have not yet touched all, for he hath in either shoe as much taffety for his tyings as would serve for an ancient; which serveth him (if you will have the mystery of it) of the own accord for a shoe-rag. A soldier & a braggart he is (that's concluded); he jetteth strutting, dancing on his toes with his hands under his sides. If you talk with him, he makes a dishcloth of his own country in comparison of Spain, but if you urge him more particularly wherein it exceeds, he can give no instance but in Spain they have better bread than any we have; when (poor hungry slaves) they may crumble it into water well enough, & make misers[237] with it, for they have not a good morsel of meat except it be salt pilchers to eat with it all the year long: and, which is more, they are poor beggars, and lie in fowl straw every night.

"Italy, the paradise of the earth and the epicure's heaven, how doth it form our young master? It makes him to kiss his hand like an ape, cringe his neck like a starveling, and play at hey passe repass[238] come aloft, when he salutes a man. From thence he brings the art of atheism, the art of epicurizing, the art of whoring, the art of poisoning, the art of sodomitry. The only probable good thing they have to keep us from utterly condemning it is that it maketh a man an excellent courtier, a curious carpet-knight:[239] which is, by interpretation, a fine close lecher, a glorious hypocrite. It is now a privy note amongst the better sort of men, when they would set a singular mark or brand on a notorious villain, to say, he hath been in Italy.

"With the Dane and the Dutchman I will not encounter, for they are simple honest men, that, with Danaus' daughters,[240] do nothing but fill bottomless tubs, & will be drunk & snort in the midst of dinner: he hurts himself only that goes thither, he cannot lightly be damned, for the vintners, the brewers, the maltmen, and alewives pray for him. Pitch and pay, they will pray all day: score & borrow, they will wish him much sorrow. But lightly a man is ne'er the better for their prayers, for they commit all deadly sin for the most part of them in mingling their drink, the vintners in the highest degree.

"Why jest I in such a necessary persuasive discourse? I am a banished exile from my country, though ne'er linked in consanguinity to the best: an earl born by birth, but a beggar now as thou seest. These many years in Italy have I lived an outlaw. A while I had a liberal pension of the Pope, but that lasted not, for he continued not: one succeeded him in his chair that cared neither for Englishmen nor his own countrymen. Then was I driven to pick up my crumbs among the cardinals, to implore the benevolence & charity of all the dukes of Italy, whereby I have since made a poor shift to live, but so live as I wish myself a thousand times dead.

Cum patriam amisi, tunc me perisse putato:
When I was banished, think I caught my bane.

The sea is the native soil to fishes; take fishes from the sea, they take no joy, nor thrive, but perish straight. So likewise the birds removed from the air (the abode whereto they were born), the beasts from the earth, and I from England. Can a lamb take delight to be suckled at the breasts of a she-wolf? I am a lamb nourished with the milk of wolves, one that, with the Ethiopians inhabiting over against Meroë,[241] feed on nothing but scorpions: use is another nature, yet ten times more contentive were nature, restored to her kingdom from whence she is excluded. Believe me, no air, no bread, no fire, no water doth a man any good out of his own country. Cold fruits never prosper in a hot soil, nor hot in a cold. Let no man for any transitory pleasure sell away the inheritance he hath of breathing in the place where he was born. Get thee home, my young lad, lay thy bones peaceably in the sepulcher of thy fathers, wax old in overlooking thy grounds, be at hand to close the eyes of thy kindred. The devil and I am desperate, he of being restored to heaven, I of being recalled home."

Here he held his peace and wept. I, glad of any opportunity of a full point to part from him, told him I took his counsel in worth; what lay in me to requite in love should not be lacking. Some business that concerned me highly called me away very hastily, but another time I hoped we should meet. Very hardly he let me go, but I earnestly overpleading my occasions, at length he dismissed me, told me where his lodging was, and charged me to visit him without excuse very often.

Here's a stir, thought I to myself after I was set at liberty, that is worse than an upbraiding lesson after a breeching; certainly if I had bethought me like a rascal as I was, he should have had an Ave Mary of me for his cynic exhortation. God plagued me for deriding such a grave fatherly advertiser. List the worst throw of ill lucks. Tracing up and down the city to seek my courtezan till the evening began to grow very well in age, it thus fortuned: the element, as if it had drunk too much in the afternoon, poured down so profoundly, that I was forced to creep like one afraid of the watch close under the pentices,[242] where the cellar door of a Jew's house called Zadoch (over which in my direct way I did pass) being unbarred on the inside, over head and ears I fell into it, as a man falls in a ship from the orlop into the hold, or as in an earthquake the ground should open, and a blind man come feeling pad pad over the open gulf with his staff, should tumble on a sudden into hell. Having worn out the anguish of my fall a little with wallowing up & down, I cast up mine eyes to see under what continent I was: and lo, (O destiny,) I saw my courtezan kissing very lovingly with a prentice.

My back and my sides I had hurt with my fall, but now my head swelled and ached worse than both. I was even gathering wind to come upon her with a full blast of contumely, when the Jew (awaked with the noise of my fall) came hastily bustling down the stairs, and, raising his other tenants, attached both the courtezan and me for breaking his house, and conspiring with his prentice to rob him.

It was then the law in Rome, that if any man had a felon fallen into his hands, either by breaking into his house, or robbing him by the highway, he might choose whether he would make him his bondman, or hang him. Zadoch, (as all Jews are covetous,) casting with himself he should have no benefit by casting me off the ladder, had another policy in his head: he went to one Doctor Zachary, the Pope's physician, that was a Jew and his countryman likewise, and told him he had the finest bargain for him that might be. "It is not concealed from me," saith he, "that the time of your accustomed yearly anatomy is at hand, which it behooves you under forfeiture of the foundation of your college very carefully to

provide for. The infection is great, & hardly will you get a
sound body to deal upon: you are my countryman, therefore
I come to you first. Be it known unto you, I have a young
man at home fallen to me for my bondman, of the age of
eighteen, of stature tall, straight-limbed, of as clear a complexion as any painter's fancy can imagine: go to, you are an
honest man, and one of the scattered children of Abraham;
you shall have him for five hundred crowns." "Let me see
him," quoth Doctor Zachary, "and I will give you as much as
another." Home he sent for me; pinioned and shackled I was
transported alongst the street: where passing under Juliana's,
the Marquess of Mantua's wife's, window, that was a lusty
Bona Roba,[243] one of the Pope's concubines, as she had her
casement half open, she looked out and spied me. At the first
sight she was enamoured with my age and beardless face, that
had in it no ill sign of physiognomy fatal to fetters: after me
she sent to know what I was, wherein I had offended, and
whither I was going? My conducts resolved them all. She having received this answer, with a lustful collachrymation lamenting my Jewish praemunire,[244] that body and goods I
should light into the hands of such a cursed generation, invented the means of my release.

But first I'll tell you what betided me after I was brought to
Doctor Zachary's. The purblind doctor put on his spectacles
and looked upon me: and when he had throughly viewed my
face, he caused me to be stript naked, to feel and grope
whether each limb were sound & my skin not infected. Then
he pierced my arm to see how my blood ran: which assays
and searchings ended, he gave Zadoch his full price and sent
him away; then locked me up in a dark chamber till the day
of anatomy.

O, the cold sweating cares which I conceived after I knew
I should be cut like a French summer doublet. Methought already the blood began to gush out at my nose: if a flea on the
arm had but bit me, I deemed the instrument had pricked me.
Well, well, I may scoff at a shrewd turn, but there's no such
ready way to make a man a true Christian, as to persuade him-

self he is taken up for an anatomy. I'll depose I prayed then more than I did in seven years before. Not a drop of sweat trickled down my breast and my sides, but I dreamt it was a smooth-edged razor tenderly slicing down my breast and sides. If any knocked at door, I supposed it was the beadle of Surgeons' Hall come for me. In the night I dreamed of nothing but phlebotomy, bloody fluxes, incarnatives,[245] running ulcers. I durst not let out a wheal, for fear through it I should bleed to death. For meat in this distance I had plum porridge of purgations ministered me one after another to clarify my blood, that it should not lie cloddered [246] in the flesh. Nor did he it so much for clarifying physic, as to save charges. Miserable is that mouse that lives in a physician's house; Tantalus lives not so hunger-starved in hell, as she doth there. Not the very crumbs that fall from his table, but Zachary sweeps together, and of them molds up a manna.[247] Of the ashy pairings of his bread, he would make conserve of chippings. Out of bones, after the meat was eaten off, he would alchemize an oil, that he sold for a shilling a dram. His snot and spittle a hundred times he hath put over to his apothecary for snow water. Any spider he would temper to perfect mithridate. His rheumatic eyes when he went in the wind, or rose early in a morning, dropt as cool alum water as you would request. He was Dame Niggardize's sole heir & executor. A number of old books had he, eaten with the moths and worms: now all day would not he study a dodkin,[248] but pick those worms and moths out of his library, and of their mixture make a preservative against the plague. The liquor out of his shoes he would wring, to make a sacred balsamum[249] against barrenness.

Spare we him a line or two, and look back to Juliana, who, conflicted in her thoughts about me very doubtfully, adventured to send a messenger to Doctor Zachary in her name, very boldly to beg me of him, and if she might not beg me, to buy me with what sums of money soever he would ask. Zachary Jewishly and churlishly denied both her suits, and said if there were no more Christians on the earth, he would thrust his incision knife into his[250] throat-bowl immediately. Which reply she taking at his hands most despitefully, thought to cross him over the shins with as sore an overwhart[251] blow ere a month to an end. The Pope (I know not whether at her entreaty or no) within two days after fell sick; Doctor Zachary was sent for to minister unto him, who, seeing a little danger in his water, gave him a gentle comfortive for the stomach, and desired those near about him to persuade His Holiness to take some rest, & he doubted not but he would be forthwith well. Who should receive this mild physic of him but the concubine Juliana, his utter enemy? she, being not unprovided of strong poison at that instant, in the Pope's outward chamber so mingled it, that when his grand-sublimity-taster came to relish it, he sunk down stark dead on the pavement. Herewith the Pope called Juliana, and asked her what strong concocted broth she had brought him. She kneeled down on her knees, & said it was such as Zachary the Jew had delivered her with his own hands, and therefore if it misliked His Holiness she craved pardon. The Pope, without further sifting into the matter, would have had Zachary and all the Jews in Rome put to death, but she hung about his knees, and with crocodile tears desired him the sentence might be lenified,[252] and they be all but banished at the most. "For Doctor Zachary," quoth she, "your ten-times ungrateful physician, since notwithstanding his treacherous intent, he hath much art, and many sovereign simples, oils, gargarisms,[253] and syrups in his closet and house that may stand Your Mightiness in stead, I beg all his goods only for Your Beatitude's preservation and good." This request at the first was sealed with a kiss, and the Pope's edict without delay proclaimed throughout Rome, namely, that all foreskin clippers, whether male or female, belonging to the Old Jewry,[254] should depart and avoid upon pain of hanging, within twenty days after the date thereof.

Juliana (two days before the proclamation came out) sent her servants to extend upon Zachary's territories, his goods, his moveables, his chattels, and his servants: who performed their commission to the utmost title,[255] and left him not so much as master of an old urinal case or a candle-box. It was about six o'clock in the evening when those boot-halers[256] entered: into my chamber they rushed, when I sat leaning on my elbow, and my left hand under my side, devising what a kind of death it might be, to be let blood till a man die. I called to mind the assertion of some philosophers, who said the soul was nothing but blood: then thought I, what a thing were this, if I should let my soul fall and break his neck into a basin. I had but a pimple rose with heat in that part of the vein where they use to prick, and I fearfully misdeemed it was my soul searching for passage. Fie upon it, a man's breath to be let out at a back door, what a villainy it is! To die bleeding is all one as if a man should die pissing. Good drink makes good blood, so that piss is nothing but blood under age. Seneca and Lucan[257] were lobcocks[258] to choose that death of all other: a pig or a hog or any edible brute beast a cook or a butcher deals upon dies bleeding. To die with a prick, wherewith the faintest-hearted woman under heaven would not be killed; O God, it is infamous.

In this meditation did they seize upon me, in my cloak they muffled me, that no man might know me, nor I see which way I was carried. The first ground I touched after I was out of Zachary's house was the Countess Juliana's chamber: little did I surmise that fortune reserved me to so fair a death. I made no other reckoning all the while they had me on their shoulders, but that I was on horseback to heaven, and carried to church on a bier, excluded forever for[259] drinking any more ale or beer. Juliana scornfully questioned them thus (as if I had fallen into her hands beyond expectation): "What proper apple squire[260] is this you bring so suspiciously into my chamber? what hath he done? or where had you him?" They answered likewise afar off, that in one of Zachary's chambers they found him close prisoner, and thought themselves guilty of the breach of her ladyship's commandment if they should have left him. "O," quoth she, "ye love to be double diligent, or thought peradventure that I, being a lone woman, stood in need of a love. Bring you me a princox[261] beardless boy (I know not whence he is, nor whether he would) to call my name in suspense? I tell you, you have abused me, and I can hardly brook it at your hands. You should have led him to the magistrate; no commission received you of me but for his goods & his servants." They besought her to excuse their error, proceeding of duteous zeal, no negligent default. "But why should not I conjecture the worst?" quoth she. "I tell you troth, I am half in a jealousy he is some fantastic youngster, who hath hired you to dishonor me. It is a likely matter that such a man as Zachary should make a prison of his house. By your leave, Sir Gallant, under lock and key shall you stay with me, till I have enquired farther of you; you shall be sifted thoroughly ere you and I part. Go, maid, shew him to the farther chamber at the end of the gallery that looks into the garden: you, my trim panders, I pray guard him thither as you took pains to bring him hither: when you have so done, see the doors be made fast, and come your way." Here was a wily wench had her liripoop[262] without book, she was not to seek in her knacks and shifts: such are all women, each of them hath a cloak for the rain, and can blear her husband's eyes as she list. Not too much of this madam marquess at once; let me dilate a little what Zadoch did with my courtezan, after he had sold me to Zachary. Of an ill tree I hope you are not so ill-sighted in grafting to expect good fruit: he was a Jew, and intreated her like a Jew. Under shadow of enforcing her to tell how much money she had of his prentice so to be trained to his cellar, he stripped her, and scourged her from top to toe tantara.[263] Day by day he digested his meat with leading her the measures.[264] A diamond Delphinical[265] dry lecher it was.

The ballad of the whipper[266] of late days here in England was but a scoff in comparison of him. All the colliers of Romford, who hold their corporation by yarking the blind bear at Paris Garden,[267] were but bunglers to him; he had the right agility of the lash, there were none of them could make the cord come aloft with a twang half like him. Mark the ending, mark the ending. The tribe of Judah is adjudged from Rome to be trudging, they may no longer be lodged there, all the Albumazers, Rabisacks, Gedions, Tebiths, Benhadads, Benrodans, Zedechiaes, Halies[268] of them were bankrupts and turned out of house and home. Zachary came running to Zadoch's in sackcloth and ashes presently after his goods were confiscated, and told him how he was served, and what decree was coming out against them all. Descriptions, stand by, here is to be expressed the fury of Lucifer when he was turned over heaven bar for a wrangler. There is a toad fish, which taken out of the water swells more than one would think his skin could hold, and bursts in his face that toucheth him. So swelled Zadoch, and was ready to burst out of his skin and shoot his bowels like chain-shot full at Zachary's face for bringing him such baleful tidings; his eyes glared & burnt blue like brimstone and aqua vitae set on fire in an eggshell, his very nose lightened glowworms, his teeth crashed and grated together, like the joints of a high building cracking and rocking like a cradle, whenas a tempest takes her full butt against his broad side. He swore, he cursed, and said, "These be they that worship that crucified God of Nazareth, here's the fruits of their new-found Gospel; sulphur and gunpowder carry them all quick to Gehenna. I would spend my soul willingly, to have that triple-headed Pope with all his sin-absolved whores and oil-greased priests borne with a black sant[269] on the devil's backs in procession to the pit of perdition. Would I might sink presently into the earth, so I might blow up this Rome, this whore of Babylon, into the air with my breath. If I must be banished, if those heathen dogs will needs rob me of my goods, I will poison their springs & conduit heads, whence they receive all their water round about the city; I'll tice[270] all the young children into my house that I can get, and cutting their throats barrel them up in powdering beef tubs, and so send them to victual the Pope's galleys. Ere the officers come to extend, I'll bestow an hundred pound on a dole of bread, which I'll cause to be kneaded with scorpion's oil that will kill more than the plague. I'll hire them that make their wafers or sacramentary gods, to ming[271] them after the same sort, so in the zeal of their superstitious religion shall they languish and droop like carrion. If there be ever a blasphemous conjurer that can call the winds from their brazen caves, and make the clouds travel before their time, I'll give him the other hundred pounds to disturb the heavens a whole week together with thunder and lightning, if it be for nothing but to sour all the wines in Rome, and turn them to vinegar. As long as they have either oil or wine, this plague feeds but pinglingly[272] upon them."

"Zadoch, Zadoch," said Doctor Zachary (cutting him off), "thou threatenest the air, whilst we perish here on earth. It is the Countess Juliana, the Marquess of Mantua's wife, and no other, that hath complotted our confusion. Ask not how, but insist in my words, and assist in revenge."

"As how? as how?" said Zadoch, shrugging and shrubbing. "More happy than the patriarchs were I, if, crushed to death with the greatest torments Rome's tyrants have tried, there might be quintessenced out of me one quart of precious poison. I have a leg with an issue, shall I cut it off, & from his fount of corruption extract a venom worse than any serpent's? If thou wilt, I'll go to a house that is infected, where catching the plague, and having got a running sore upon me, I'll come and deliver her a supplication, and breathe upon her. I know my breath stinks so already, that it is within half a degree of poison. I'll pay her home, if I perfect it with any more putrefaction."

"No, no, brother Zadoch," answered Zachary, "that is not the way. Canst thou provide me e'er a bondmaid, endued with singular & divine qualified beauty, whom as a present from our synagogue thou mayst commend unto her, desiring her to be good and gracious unto us?"

"I have, I am for you," quoth Zadoch: "Diamante, come forth. Here's a wench," said he, "of as clean a skin as Susanna,[273] she hath not a wem[274] on her flesh from the sole of the foot to the crown of the head: how think you, Master Doctor, will she not serve the turn?"

"She will," said Zachary; "and therefore I'll tell you what charge I would have committed to her. But I care not if I disclose it only to her. Maid (if thou beest a maid), come hither to me; thou must be sent to the Countess of Mantua's about a small piece of service, whereby, being now a bond-woman, thou shalt purchase freedom and gain a large dowry to thy marriage. I know thy master loves thee dearly, though he will not let thee perceive so much; he intends after he is dead to make thee his heir, for he hath no children: please him in that I shall instruct thee and thou art made forever. So it is, that the Pope is far out of liking with the Countess of Mantua, his concubine, and hath put his trust in me, his physician, to have her quietly and charitably made away. Now, I cannot intend it, for I have many cures in hand which call upon me hourly: thou, if thou beest placed with her as her waiting maid or cup-bearer, mayst temper poison with her broth, her meat, her drink, her oils, her syrups, and never be bewrayed. I will not say whether the Pope hath heard of thee, and thou mayst come to be his leman in her place if thou behave thyself wisely. What, hast thou the heart to go through with it or no?" Diamante, deliberating with herself in what hellish servitude she lived with the Jew, & that she had no likelihood to be released of it, but fall from evil to worse if she omitted this opportunity, resigned herself over wholly to be disposed and employed as seemed best unto them. Thereupon, without further consultation, her wardrobe was richly rigged, her tongue smooth filed & new edged on the whetstone, her drugs delivered her, and presented she was by Zadoch, her master, to the Countess, together with some other slight newfangles, as from the whole congregation, desiring her to stand their merciful mistress, and solicit the Pope for them, that through one man's ignorant offence were all generally in disgrace with him, and had incurred the cruel sentence of loss of goods and of banishment.

Juliana, liking well the pretty round face of my black-browed Diamante, gave the Jew better countenance than otherwise she would have done, and told him for her own part she was but a private woman, and could promise nothing confidently of His Holiness: for though he had suffered himself to be overruled by her in some humors, yet in this that touched him so nearly, she knew not how he would be inclined: but what lay in her, either to pacify or persuade him, they should be sure of, and so craved his absence.

His back turned, she asked Diamante what countrywoman she was, what friends she had, and how she fell into the hands of that Jew? She answered that she was a magnifico's daughter of Venice, stolen when she was young from her friends, and sold to this Jew for a bondwoman, "who," quoth she, "hath used me so Jewishly and tyrannously, that forever I must celebrate the memory of this day, wherein I am delivered from his jurisdiction. Alas," quoth she, deep sighing, "why did I enter into any mention of my own misusage? It will be thought that that which I am now to reveal proceeds of malice, not truth. Madam, your life is sought by these Jews that sue to you. Blush not, nor be troubled in your mind, for with warning I shall arm you against all their intentions. Thus and thus," quoth she, "said Doctor Zachary unto me, this poison he delivered me. Before I was called in to them, such & such consultation through the crevice of the door hard locked did I hear betwixt them. Deny it if they can, I will justify it: only I beseech you to be favorable lady unto me, and let me not fall again into the hands of those vipers."

Juliana said little, but thought unhappily; only she thanked her for detecting it, and vowed though she were her bondwoman to be a mother unto her. The poison she took of her, and set it up charily on a shelf in her closet, thinking to keep it for some good purposes: as, for example, when I was consumed and worn to the bones through her abuse, she would give me but a dram too much, and pop me into a privy. So she had served some of her paramours ere that, and if God had not sent Diamante to be my redeemer, undoubtedly I had drunk of the same cup.

In a leaf or two before was I locked up: here in this page the foresaid goodwife Countess comes to me; she is no longer a judge but a client. How she came, in what manner of attire, with what immodest and uncomely words she courted me, if I should take upon me to enlarge, all modest ears would abhor me. Some inconvenience she brought me too by her harlot-like behavior, of which enough I can never repent me.

Let that be forgiven and forgotten, fleshly delights could not make her slothful or slumbering in revenge against Zadoch. She set men about him to incense and egg him on in courses of discontentment, and other supervising espials to ply, follow, and spur forward those suborning incensers. Both which played their parts so, that Zadoch, of his own nature violent, swore by the ark of Jehovah to set the whole city on fire ere he went out of it. Zachary, after he had furnished the wench with the poison, and given her instructions to go to the devil, durst not stay one hour for fear of disclosing, but fled to the Duke of Bourbon,[275] that after sacked Rome, and there practised with his bastardship all the mischief against the Pope & Rome that envy could put into his mind. Zadoch was left behind for the hangman. According to his oath, he provided balls of wild fire in a readiness, and laid trains of gunpowder in a hundred several places of the city to blow it up, which he had set fire to, & also bandied his balls abroad, if his attendant spies had not taken him with the manner. To the straitest prison in Rome he was dragged, where from top to toe he was clogged with fetters and manacles. Juliana informed the Pope of Zachary's and his practice: Zachary was sought for, but *Non est inventus,*[276] he was packing long before. Commandment was given, that Zadoch, whom they had under hand and seal of lock and key, should be executed with all the fiery torments that could be found out.

I'll make short work, for I am sure I have wearied all my readers. To the execution place was he brought, where first and foremost he was stript, then on a sharp iron stake fastened in the ground he had his fundament pitched, which stake ran up along into the body like a spit; under his armholes two of like sort; a great bonfire they made round about him, wherewith his flesh roasted, not burned: and ever as with the heat his skin blistered, the fire was drawn aside, and they basted him with a mixture of aqua fortis,

alum water, and mercury sublimatum,[277] which smarted to
the very soul of him, and searched him to the marrow. Then
did they scourge his back parts so blistered and basted,
with burning whips of red hot wire: his head they nointed
over with pitch and tar, and so inflamed it. To his privy
members they tied streaming fireworks: the skin from the
crest of the shoulder, as also from his elbows, his huckle-
bones, his knees, his ankles, they plucked and gnawed off with
sparkling pincers: his breast and his belly with sealskins they
grated over, which as fast as they grated and rawed, one
stood over & laved with smith's sundry water[278] & aqua
vitae: his nails they half raised up, and then under-propt
them with sharp pricks, like a tailor's shop window half
open on a holy day: every one of his fingers they rent up
to the wrist: his toes they broke off by the roots, and let
them still hang by a little skin. In conclusion, they had a
small oil fire, such as men blow light bubbles of glass with,
and beginning at his feet, they let him lingeringly burn up
limb by limb, till his heart was consumed, and then he died.
Triumph, women, this was the end of the whipping Jew,
contrived by a woman, in revenge of two women, herself
and her maid.

I have told you or should tell you in what credit Diamante
grew with her mistress. Juliana never dreamed but she was
an authentical maid: she made her the chief of her bed-
chamber; she appointed none but her to look in to me, &
serve me of such necessaries as I lacked. You must suppose
when we met there was no small rejoicing on either part,
much like the three brothers that went three several ways
to seek their fortunes,[279] & at the year's end at those three
crossways met again, and told one another how they sped:
so after we had been long asunder seeking our fortunes,
we commented one to another most kindly, what cross haps
had encountered us. Ne'er a six hours but the Countess cloyed
me with her company. It grew to this pass, that either I
must find out some miraculous means of escape, or drop
away in a consumption, as one pined for lack of meat:

I was clean spent and done, there was no hope of me.

The year held on his course to doomsday, when Saint Peter's Day[280] dawned. That day is a day of supreme solemnity in Rome, when the Embassador of Spain comes and presents a milk-white jennet to the Pope, that kneels down upon his own accord in token of obeisance and humility before him, and lets him stride on his back as easy as one strides over a block: with this jennet is offered a rich purse of a yard length, full of Peter pence. No music that hath the gift of utterance, but sounds all the while: copes and costly vestments deck the hoarsest and beggarliest singing-man, not a clerk or sexton is absent, no, nor a mule nor a foot-cloth belonging to any cardinal but attends on the tail of the triumph. The Pope himself is borne in his pontificalibus through the Burgo (which is the chief street in Rome) to the Embassador's house to dinner, and thither resorts all the assembly: where if a poet should spend all his lifetime in describing a banquet, he could not feast his auditors half so well with words, as he doth his guests with junkets.

To this feast Juliana addressed herself like an angel; in a litter of green needlework wrought like an arbour and open on every side was she borne by four men, hidden under cloth rough-plushed and woven like eglantine and woodbine. At the four corners it was topt with four round crystal cages of nightingales. For footmen, on either side of her went four virgins clad in lawn, with lutes in their hands, playing. Next before her, two and two in order, a hundred pages in suits of white cypress and long horse-men's coats of cloth of silver: who, being all in white, advanced every one of them her picture, enclosed in a white round screen of feathers, such as is carried over great princesses' heads when they ride in summer, to keep them from the heat of the sun. Before them went a fourscore bead women she maintained, in green gowns, scattering strewing herbs and flowers. After her followed the blind, the halt, and the lame, sumptuously apparelled like lords; and thus passed she on to S. Peter's.

Interea quid agitur domi, how is't at home all this while? My courtezan is left my keeper, the keys are committed unto her, she is mistress factotum.[281] Against our countess we conspire, pack up all her jewels, plate, money that was extant, and to the waterside send them: to conclude, courageously rob her, and run away. *Quid non auri sacra fames?* what defame will not gold salve? He mistook himself that invented the proverb, *Dimicandum est pro aris & focis:* for it should have been *pro auro & fama:* not for altars and fires we must contend, but for gold and fame.

Oars nor wind could not stir nor blow faster, than we toiled out of Tiber; a number of good fellows would give size ace and the dice,[282] that with as little toil they could leave Tyburn behind them. Out of ken we were, ere the Countess came from the feast. When she returned and found her house not so much pestered [283] as it was wont, her chests, her closets, and her cupboards broke open to take air, and that both I and my keeper was missing; O, then she fared like a frantic bacchanal, she stamped, she stared, she beat her head against the walls, scratched her face, bit her fingers, and strewed all the chamber with her hair. None of her servants durst stay in her sight, but she beat them out in heaps, and bade them go seek, search they knew not where, and hang themselves, and never look her in the face more, if they did not hunt us out. After her fury had reasonably spent itself, her breast began to swell with the mother, caused by her former fretting & chafing, and she grew very ill at ease. Whereupon she knocked for one of her maids, and bade her run into her closet, and fetch her a little glass that stood on the upper shelf, wherein there was *spiritus vini*.[284] The maid went, & mistaking took the glass of poison which Diamante had given her, and she kept in store for me. Coming with it as fast as her legs could carry her, her mistress at her return was in a sound, and lay for dead on the floor, whereat she shrieked out, and fell a rubbing & chafing her very busily. When that would not serve, she took a key and opened her mouth, and having heard that *spiritus vini* was a thing of mighty operation, able to call a man from death to life, she took the poison, and verily thinking it to be *spiritus vini* (such as she was sent for), poured a large quantity of it into her throat, and jogged on her back to digest it. It revived her with a very vengeance, for it killed her outright; only she awakened & lift[285] up her hands, but spake ne'er a word. Then was the maid in my grandame's beans,[286] and knew not what should become of her: I heard the Pope took pity on her, & because her trespass was not voluntary but chance-medley, he assigned her no other punishment but this, to drink out the rest of the poison in the glass that was left, and so go scot-free. We, careless of these mischances, held on our flight, and saw no man come after us but we thought had pursued us. A thief, they say, mistakes every bush for a true man; the wind rattled not in any bush by the way as I rode, but I straight drew my rapier. To Bologna with a merry gale we posted, where we lodged ourselves in a blind street out of the way, and kept secret many days: but when we perceived we sailed in the haven, that the wind was laid, and no alarum made after us, we boldly came abroad: & one day hearing of a more desperate murtherer than Cain that was to be executed, we followed the multitude, and grudged not to lend him our eyes at his last parting.

Who should it be but one Cutwolfe, a wearish dwarfish writhen-faced cobbler, brother to Bartol the Italian, that was confederate with Esdras of Granado, and at that time stole away my courtezan, when he ravished Heraclide?

It is not so natural for me to epitomize his impiety, as to hear him in his own person speak upon the wheel where he was to suffer.

Prepare your ears and your tears, for never till this thrust I any tragical matter upon you. Strange and wonderful are God's judgements, here shine they in their glory. Chaste Heraclide, thy blood is laid up in heaven's treasury, not one drop of it was lost, but lent out to usury: water poured forth sinks down quietly into the earth, but blood spilt on the ground sprinkles up to the firmament. Murder is wide-mouthed and will not let God rest till he grant revenge. Not only the blood of the slaughtered innocent, but the soul, ascendeth to his throne, and there cries out & exclaims for justice and recompense. Guiltless souls that live every hour subject to violence, and with your despairing fears do much impair God's providence, fasten your eyes on this spectacle that will add to your faith. Refer all your oppressions, afflictions, & injuries to the even-balanced eye of the Almighty; He it is, that when your patience sleepeth, will be most exceeding mindful of you.

This is but a gloze upon the text: thus Cutwolfe begins his insulting oration.

"Men and people that have made holy day to behold my pained flesh toil on the wheel, expect not of me a whining penitent slave, that shall do nothing but cry and say his prayers, and so be crushed in pieces. My body is little, but my mind is as great as a giant's: the soul which is in me is the very soul of Julius Caesar by reversion. My name is Cutwolfe, neither better nor worse by occupation than a poor cobbler of Verona; cobblers are men, and kings are no more. The occasion of my coming hither at this present is to have a few of my bones broken (as we are all born to die) for being the death of the emperor of homicides, Esdras of Granado. About two years since in the streets of Rome he slew the only and eldest brother I had, named Bartol, in quarrelling about a courtezan. The news brought to me as I was sitting in my shop under a stall, knocking in of tacks, I think I raised up my bristles, sold pritch-awl,[287] sponge, blacking tub, and punching iron, bought me rapier and pistol, and to go I went. Twenty months together I pursued him, from Rome to Naples, from Naples to Chieti, passing over the river, from Chieti to Siena, from Siena to Florence, from Florence to Parma, from Parma to Pavia, from Pavia to Sion, from Sion to Geneva, from Geneva back again towards Rome: where in the way it was my chance to meet him in the nick here at Bologna, as I will tell you how. I saw a great fray in the streets as I past along, and many swords walking, whereupon drawing nearer, and enquiring who they were, answer was returned me it was that notable bandetto, Esdras of Granado. O, so I was tickled in the spleen with that word, my heart hopped and danced, my elbows itched, my fingers frisked, I wist not what should become of my feet, nor knew what I did for joy. The fray parted, I thought it not convenient to single him out (being a sturdy knave) in the street, but to stay till I had got him at more advantage. To his lodging I dogged him, lay at the door all night where he entered, for fear he should give me the slip any way. Betimes in the morning I rung the bell and craved to speak with him: now to his chamber door I was brought, where knocking, he rose in his shirt and let me in, and when I was entered, bade me lock the door and declare my errand,[288] and so he slipped to bed again.

" 'Marry this,' quoth I, 'is my errand. Thy name is Esdras of Granado, is it not? Most treacherously thou slew'st my brother Bartol about two years ago in the streets of Rome: his death am I come to revenge. In quest of thee ever since, above three thousand miles have I traveled. I have begged to maintain me the better part of the way, only because I would intermit no time from my pursuit in going back for money. Now have I got thee naked in my power; die thou shalt, though my mother and my grandmother dying did intreat for thee. I have promised the devil thy soul within this hour, break my word I will not; in thy breast I intend to bury a bullet. Stir not, quinch[289] not, make no noise: for if thou dost it will be worse for thee.'

"Quoth Esdras, 'Whatever thou beest at whose mercy I lie, spare me, and I will give thee as much gold as thou wilt ask. Put me to any pains, my life reserved, and I willingly will sustain them: cut off my arms and legs, and leave me as a lazar to some loathsome spital, where I may but live a year to pray and repent me. For thy brother's death the despair of mind that hath ever since haunted me, the guilty gnawing worm of conscience I feel may be sufficient penance. Thou canst not send me to such a hell as already there

is in my heart. To dispatch me presently is no revenge, it
will soon be forgotten: let me die a lingering death, it will
be remembered a great deal longer. A lingering death may
avail my soul, but it is the illest of ills that can befortune
my body. For my soul's health I beg my body's torment:
be not thou a devil to torment my soul, and send me to
eternal damnation. Thy overhanging sword hides heaven from
my sight, I dare not look up, lest I embrace my death's
wound unawares. I cannot pray to God and plead to thee
both at once. Aye me, already I see my life buried in the
wrinkles of thy brows: say but I shall live, though thou
meanest to kill me. Nothing confounds like to sudden terror, it thrusts every sense out of office. Poison wrapped
up in sugared pills is but half a poison: the fear of death's
looks are more terrible than his stroke. The whilst I view
death, my faith is deaded: where a man's fear is, there his
heart is. Fear never engenders hope: how can I hope that
heaven's Father will save me from the hell everlasting, when
he gives me over to the hell of thy fury?

" 'Heraclide, now think I on thy tears sown in the dust,
(thy tears, that my bloody mind made barren). In revenge
of thee, God hardens this man's heart against me: yet I did
not slaughter thee, though hundreds else my hand hath
brought to the shambles. Gentle sir, learn of me what it is
to clog your conscience with murther, to have your dreams,
your sleeps, your solitary walks troubled and disquieted with
murther: your shadow by day will affright you, you will
not see a weapon unsheathed, but immediately you will
imagine it is predestinate for your destruction.

" 'This murther is a house divided within itself: it sub-
orns a man's own soul to inform against him: his soul (being
his accuser) brings forth his two eyes as witnesses against
him; and the least eyewitness is unrefutable. Pluck out my
eyes if thou wilt, and deprive my traitorous soul of her
two best witnesses. Dig out my blasphemous tongue with
thy dagger, both tongue and eyes will I gladly forgo, to have
a little more time to think on my journey to heaven.

" 'Defer a while thy resolution, I am not at peace with the world, for even but yesterday I fought, and in my fury threatened further vengeance: had I a face to ask forgiveness, I should think half my sins were forgiven. A hundred devils haunt me daily for my horrible murthers: the devils when I die will be loth to go to hell with me, for they desired of Christ He would not send them to hell before their time: if they go not to hell, into thee they will go, and hideously vex thee for turning them out of their habitation. Wounds I contemn, life I prize light, it is another world's tranquility which makes me so timorous; everlasting damnation, everlasting howling and lamentation. It is not from death I request thee to deliver me, but from this terror of torment's eternity. Thy brother's body only I pierced unadvisedly, his soul meant I no harm to at all: my body & soul both shalt thou cast away quite, if thou doest at this instant what thou mayst. Spare me, spare me, I beseech thee; by thy own soul's salvation I desire thee, seek not my soul's utter perdition: in destroying me, thou destroyest thyself and me.'

"Eagerly I replied after this long suppliant oration: 'Though I knew God would never have mercy upon me except I had mercy on thee, yet of thee no mercy would I have. Revenge in our tragedies is continually raised from hell: of hell do I esteem better than heaven, if it afford me revenge. There is no heaven but revenge. I tell thee, I would not have undertook so much toil to gain heaven, as I have done in pursuing thee for revenge. Divine revenge, of which (as of the joys above) there is no fullness or satiety. Look how my feet are blistered with following thee from place to place. I have riven my throat with overstraining it to curse thee. I have ground my teeth to powder with grating & grinding them together for anger when any hath named thee. My tongue with vain threats is bolne,[290] and waxen too big for my mouth: my eyes have broken their strings with staring and looking ghastly, as I stood devising how to frame or set my countenance when I met thee. I have ne'er spent my strength in imaginary acting on stone walls, what I determined to execute on thee: intreat not, a miracle may not reprieve thee: villain, thus march I with my blade into thy bowels.'

" 'Stay, stay,' exclaimed Esdras, 'and hear me but one word further. Though neither for God nor man thou carest, but placest thy whole felicity in murther, yet of thy felicity learn how to make a greater felicity. Respite me a little from thy sword's point, and set me about some execrable enterprise, that may subvert the whole state of Christendom, and make all men's ears tingle that hear of it. Command me to cut all my kindreds' throats, to burn men, women, and children in their beds in millions, by firing their cities at midnight. Be it pope, emperor, or Turk that displeaseth thee, he shall not breathe on the earth. For thy sake will I swear and forswear, renounce my baptism, and all the interest I have in any other sacrament. Only let me live how miserable soever, be it in a dungeon amongst toads, serpents, and adders, or set up to the neck in dung. No pains I will refuse however prorogued; to have a little respite to purify my spirit: oh, hear me, hear me, & thou canst not be hardened against me.'

"At this his importunity I paused a little, not as retiring from my wreakful resolution, but going back to gather more forces of vengeance. With myself I devised how to plague him double for his base mind: my thoughts traveled in quest of some notable new Italianism, whose murderous platform might not only extend on his body, but his soul also. The groundwork of it was this: that whereas he had promised for my sake to swear and forswear, and commit Julian-like[291] violence on the highest seals of religion; if he would but this far satisfy me, he should be dismissed from my fury. First and foremost, he should renounce God and his laws, and utterly disclaim the whole title or interest he had in any covenant of salvation. Next, he should curse him to his face, as Job was willed by his wife, and write an absolute firm obligation of his soul to the devil, without condition or exception. Thirdly and lastly, (having done this,) he should pray to God fervently never to have mercy upon him, or pardon him.

"Scarce had I propounded these articles unto him, but he was beginning his blasphemous abjurations. I wonder the earth opened not and swallowed us both, hearing the bold terms he blasted forth in contempt of Christianity: heaven hath thundered when half less contumelies against it have been uttered. Able they were to raise saints and martyrs from their graves, and pluck Christ Himself from the right hand of his father. My joints trembled & quaked with attending them, my hair stood upright, & my heart was turned wholly to fire. So affectionately and zealously did he give himself over to infidelity, as if Satan had gotten the upper hand of our High Maker. The vein in his left hand that is derived from the heart with no faint blow he pierced, & with the full blood that flowed from it, writ a full obligation of his soul to the devil: yea, he more earnestly prayed unto God never to forgive his soul, than many Christians do to save their souls. These fearful ceremonies brought to an end, I bade him ope his mouth and gape wide. He did so, (as what will not slaves do for fear?); therewith made I no more ado, but shot him full into the throat with my pistol: no more spake he after; so did I shoot him that he might never speak after, or repent him. His body being dead looked as black as a toad: the devil presently branded it for his own. This is the fault that hath called me hither; no true Italian but will honor me for it. Revenge is the glory of arms, & the highest performance of valour: revenge is whatsoever we call law or justice. The farther we wade in revenge, the nearer come we to the throne of the Almighty. To his scepter it is properly ascribed; his scepter he lends unto man, when he lets one man scourge another. All true Italians imitate me in revenging constantly and dying valiantly. Hangman, to thy task, for I am ready for the utmost of thy rigor." Herewith all the people (outrageously incensed) with one conjoined outcry yelled mainly, "Away with him, away with him. Executioner, torture him, tear him, or we will tear thee in pieces if thou spare him."

The executioner needed no exhortation hereunto, for of his own nature was he hackster good enough: old excellent he was at a bone-ache. At the first chop with his wood-knife would he fish for a man's heart, and fetch it out as easily as a plum from the bottom of a porridge pot. He would crack necks as fast as a cook cracks eggs: a fiddler cannot turn his pin so soon as he would turn a man of the ladder. Bravely did he drum on this Cutwolfe's bones, not breaking them outright, but, like a saddler knocking in of tacks, jarring on them quaveringly[292] with his hammer a great while together. No joint about him but with a hatchet he had for the nonce he disjointed half, and then with boiling lead soldered up the wounds from bleeding: his tongue he pulled out, lest he should blaspheme in his torment: venomous stinging worms he thrust into his ears, to keep his head ravingly occupied: with cankers scruzed[293] to pieces he rubbed his mouth and his gums: no limb of his but was lingeringly splintered in shivers. In his horror left they him on the wheel as in hell; where, yet living, he might behold his flesh legacied amongst the fowls of the air. Unsearchable is the book of our destinies. One murder begetteth another: was never yet bloodshed barren from the beginning of the world to this day. Mortifiedly abjected and daunted was I with this truculent tragedy of Cutwolfe and Esdras. To such straight life did it thenceforward incite me that ere I went out of Bologna I married my courtezan, performed many alms-deeds; and hasted so fast out of the Sodom of Italy, that within forty days I arrived at the King of England's camp twixt Ardes and Guines[294] in France, where he with great triumphs met and entertained the Emperor and the French king, and feasted many days. And so as my story began with the king at Turney and Turwin, I think meet here to end it with the King at Ardes and Guines. All the conclusive epilogue I will make is this: that if herein I have pleased any, it shall animate me to more pains in this kind. Otherwise I will swear upon an English chronicle never to be outlandish chronicler more while I live. Farewell as many as wish me well.

FINIS.

THOMAS DELONEY

JACK OF NEWBURY

1597

Thomas Deloney (1543?–1600)

By the middle of the sixteenth century the bourgeoisie was well on the way to economic domination of England, but the new tradesmen were so busy with production and distribution that they had little time for literary expression. Artistic creation and appreciation were still almost the exclusive possession of the feudal aristocracy and its patronized writers, but during the reign of Elizabeth this condition changed rapidly. Thomas Deloney was one of the first conspicuous voices of the recently articulate middle class.

Deloney himself was an artisan. A 1586 baptismal entry in the church register of the parish of St. Giles Cripplegate, London, referred to one Richard Deloney as the "son of Thomas Deloney silk-weaver," and ten years later Nashe, in HAVE WITH YOU TO SAFFRON-WALDON, described Deloney as "the ballading silk-weaver of Norwich." Flemish and Huguenot refugees had come to England in the fifteenth and early sixteenth centuries in search of a Protestant haven; some of them had settled around Norwich, where they continued their crafts and trades, including weaving and the making of clothes. Deloney, with his apparently French name, his occupation of weaving, and his professed anti-Catholic sympathies, was probably descended from these immigrants.

The details of the first three or four decades of Deloney's life are largely a matter of conjecture. The classical and historical allusions in his verse and in his prose point to his having attended an Elizabethan grammar school, open to the sons of tradesmen, or at least to his having received an equivalent education, formal or not. He was somewhat familiar with Latin authors, or certainly with source books which quoted them, and he apparently knew some French, whether from study, from his own family background, or from his association with foreign merchants and artisans. But Deloney is not known to have written anything until the early 1580's; he must have devoted the early years of his maturity almost entirely to his trade.

The latter half of his life can be pieced together from isolated allusions. References later than Nashe's epithet of 1596 mention Deloney as "ballad-maker" or "chronicler" without designating his early craft. By the beginning of the final decade of the century, Deloney's reputation as a composer of ballads was so firmly and widely established that he was considered the successor to Elderton, the famous London song maker who died in 1592. JACK OF NEWBURY, THE GENTLE CRAFT, and THOMAS OF READING, Deloney's prose tales, came a few years later, perhaps at the commission of the companies of clothiers and shoemakers, in whose praise he wrote, though there is no specific evidence of this support. In any case, Deloney seems to have given up weaving altogether in order to join the traveling fraternity of ballad makers; his works show that he knew well all of London and the specific geography of many English towns.

Two incidents suggest that Deloney became a kind of political spokesman for his class, as well as an entertainer with songs and stories. In 1595 Deloney wrote with some lesser collaborators COMPLAINT OF THE YEOMAN WEAVERS AGAINST THE IMMIGRANT WEAVERS, a prose piece describing the plight of English silk weavers trying to compete with alien craftsmen who would not respect the agreed-upon practices and prices. This pamphlet was distributed among the immigrants and sent to the alderman and lord mayor. The lord mayor was sufficiently disturbed to send Deloney and eleven others to Newgate Prison and to order the burning of the pamphlet. Deloney was released only after a petition to the lord justice. The very next year Deloney was again in difficulty. An "abusive ballad" in complaint of "great want and scarcity of corn within the realm," attributed to Deloney by the historian John Strype, resulted in its printer's arrest. The charge was that the ballad aroused discontent among the poor and showed disrespect for Queen Elizabeth by presenting her as "speaking with her people dialogue-wise in very fond and undecent sort" and sympathetically ordering that the famine be remedied. Someone had complained to the lord mayor, who in turn had complained to Elizabeth's powerful advisor, Lord Burleigh, a man known for his strong identification with the aristocracy and his consistent opposition to middle-class interests. Deloney certainly intended his characterization of Elizabeth as praise of a ruler interested in the commonalty rather than in her own wealth and power. Similarly, in JACK OF NEWBURY, written in the very next year, Deloney pictured Henry VIII, Elizabeth's father, as a jovial ruler more sympathetic to the desires of the clothiers for free trade than to the advice of his counselor, Cardinal Wolsey, for further taxes and restrictions.

A final contemporary mention of Deloney appeared in NINE DAYS' WONDER (1600), by William Kemp, the comic actor and dancer. The ballad makers as a group were frequently criticized by public figures whom they satirized in song, and Kemp added his voice, more jokingly than not, to the upbraiding of "the impudent generations of balladmakers" who invented stories about their subjects. He accused "the great ballad-maker, T. D., alias Thomas Deloney," of being the chief offender against him, and he concluded with good-humored respect: "But I was since given to understand, your late general, Thomas, died poorly (as ye all must do) and was honestly buried, which is much to be doubted of some of you."

Deloney had died in the first year of the seventeenth century, but even in the few known events of his life he was already a conscious part of the economic conflict around which the English Revolution was to center less than half a century later. Despite the scarcity of biographical material about Deloney, the clear and comprehensive attitudes implicit in his works have made him significant among Elizabethan writers: at a time when most writers, conditioned and supported by the feudal framework, were fearfully satirizing bourgeois values, Deloney revealed an optimistic belief in the importance and efficacy of middle-class endeavor.

The standard edition of Deloney is F. O. Mann's THE WORKS OF THOMAS DELONEY, The Clarendon Press (Oxford), 1912. Mann's introduction includes a careful biographical study of Deloney and a pioneering essay on the contribution of Deloney to English fiction, and his notes on Deloney's separate works are complete and useful. Important additions to Mann's biographical study are G. W. Kuehn's "Thomas Deloney: Two Notes," MODERN LANGUAGE NOTES, LII, 103–105, and H. E. Rollins' "Thomas Deloney's Euphuistic Learning," PMLA, L, 679–686. The most extensive study of Deloney and his background is Abel Chevalley's THOMAS DELONEY, Gallimard (Paris), 1926. A special study of interest is Llewelyn Powys' "Thomas Deloney," VIRGINIA QUARTERLY REVIEW, IX, 578–594.

The text is taken from a 1626 printing of JACK OF NEWBURY in Mann's edition of Deloney's WORKS.

THE MOST PLEASANT AND DELECTABLE HISTORY OF JOHN WINCHCOMBE, *OTHERWISE CALLED JACK OF NEWBURY: AND FIRST OF HIS LOVE AND PLEASANT LIFE*

CHAP. I

IN THE DAYS of King Henry the eight, that most noble and victorious prince, in the beginning of his reign, John Winchcombe, a broadcloth weaver, dwelt in Newbury, a town in Berkshire: who for that he was a man of a merry disposition, & honest conversation, was wondrous well-beloved of rich and poor, specially, because in every place where he came, he would spend his money with the best, and was not at any time found a churl of his purse. Wherefore being so good a companion, he was called of old and young Jack of Newbury: a man so generally well known in all his country for his good fellowship, that he could go in no place but he found acquaintance; by means whereof, Jack could no sooner get a crown, but straight he found means to spend it: yet had he ever this care, that he would always keep himself in comely and decent apparel: neither at any time would he be overcome in drink, but so discreetly behave himself with honest mirth, and pleasant conceits, that he was every gentleman's companion.

After that Jack had long led this pleasant life, being (though he were but poor) in good estimation: it was his master's chance to die, and his dame to be a widow, who was a very comely ancient woman, and of reasonable wealth. Wherefore she, having a good opinion of her man John, committed unto his government the guiding of all her workfolks for the space of three years together: In which time she found him so careful and diligent, that all things came forward and prospered wondrous well. No man could entice him for his business all the week, by all the entreaty they could use: Insomuch that in the end some of the wild youths of the town began to deride and scoff at him.

"Doubtless," quoth one, "I think some female spirit hath enchanted Jack to his treadles, and conjured him within the compass of his loom, that he can stir no further."

"You say true," quoth Jack, "and if you have the leisure to stay till the charm be done, the space of six days and five nights, you shall find me ready to put on my holy-day apparel, and on Sunday morning for your pains I will give you a pot of ale over against the maypole."

"Nay," quoth another, "I'll lay my life, that as the salamander cannot live without the fire, so Jack cannot live without the smell of his dame's smock."

"And I marvel," quoth Jack, "that you being of the nature of a herring (which so soon as he is taken out of the sea, presently dies) can live so long with your nose out of the pot."

"Nay Jack, leave thy jesting," quoth another, "and go along with us, thou shalt not stay a jot."

"And because I will not stay; nor make you a liar," quoth Jack, "I'll keep me here still: and so farewell."

Thus then they departed: and after they had for half a score times tried him to this intent, and saw he would not be led by their lure, they left him to his own will. Nevertheless, every Sunday in the afternoon, and every holy-day, Jack would keep them company, and be as merry as a pie,[1] and having still good store of money in his purse, one or other would ever be borrowing of him, but never could he get penny of it again: which when Jack perceived, he would never after carry above twelve pence at once in his purse: and that being spent, he would straight return home merrily, taking his leave of the company in this sort.

My masters, I thank you, it's time to pack home,
For he that wants money is counted a mome:[2]
And twelve pence a Sunday being spent in good cheer,
To fifty-two shillings amounts in the year;
Enough for a craftsman that lives by his hands:
And he that exceeds it, shall purchase no lands.
For that I spend this day, I'll work hard tomorrow.
For woe is that party that seeketh to borrow.
My money doth make me full merry to be;
And without my money none careth for me:
Therefore wanting money, what should I do here?
But haste home, and thank you for all my good cheer?

Thus was Jack's good government and discretion noted of the best and substantialest men of the town: so that it wrought his great commendations, and his dame thought herself not a little blest to have such a servant, that was so obedient unto her, and so careful for her profit: for she had never a prentice that yielded her more obedience than he did, or was more dutiful: so that by his good example, he did as much good as by his diligent labour and painful travail: which his singular virtue being noted by the widow, she began to cast a very good countenance to her man John, and to use very much talk with him in private: and first by way of communication, she would tell unto him what suitors she had, as also the great offers they made her, what gifts they sent her, and the great affection they bore her, craving his opinion in the matter.

When Jack found the favour to be his dame's secretary, he thought it an extraordinary kindness: and guessing by the yarn it would prove a good web, began to question with his dame in this sort. "Although it becometh not me your servant to pry into your secrets, nor to be busy about matters of your love: yet for so much as it hath pleased you to use conference with me in those causes, I pray you let me intreat you to know their names that be your suitors, and of what profession they be."

"Marry John," saith she, "that you shall, and I pray thee take a cushion and sit down by me."

"Dame," quoth he, "I thank you: but there is no reason I should sit on a cushion till I have deserved it."

"If thou hast not thou mightest have done," said she: "but some soldiers never find favour."

John replied, "That maketh me indeed to want favour: for I never durst try maidens because they seem coy, nor wives for fear of their husbands, nor widows doubting their disdainfulness."

"Tush John," quoth she, "he that fears and doubts womankind, cannot be counted mankind: and take this for a principle, All things are not as they seem. But let us leave this, and proceed to our former matter. My first suitor dwells at Wallingford, by trade a tanner, a man of good wealth, and his name is Crafts, of comely personage and very good behaviour, a widower, well thought of among his neighbours: he hath proper land, a fair house well furnished, and never a child in the world, and he loves me passing well."

"Why then dame," quoth John, "you were best to have him."

"Is that your opinion?" quoth she. "Now trust me, so it is not mine: for I find two special reasons to the contrary: the one is, that he being overworn in years, makes me overloth to love him: and the other, that I know one nearer hand."

"Believe me dame," quoth Jack, "I perceive store is no sore, & proffered ware is worse by ten in the hundred than that which is sought: but I pray who is your second suitor?"

"John," quoth she, "it may seem immodesty in me to bewray my lovers' secrets: yet seeing thy discretion, and being persuaded of thy secrecy, I will shew thee: the other is a man of middle years, but yet a bachelor, by occupation a tailor, and dwelling at Hungerford: by report a very good husband, such a one as hath crowns good store, and to me he professes much good will: for his person, he may please any woman."

"Aye dame," quoth John, "because he pleaseth you."

"Not so," said she, "for my eyes are unpartial judges in that case: and albeit my opinion may be contrary to others, if his art deceive not my eyesight, he is worthy of a good wife, both for his person and conditions."

"Then trust me dame," quoth John, "for so much as you are without doubt of yourself that you will prove a good wife, and so well persuaded of him, I should think you could make no better a choice."

"Truly John," quoth she, "there be also two reasons that move me not to like of him: the one, that being so large a ranger, he would at home be a stranger: and the other, that I like better of one nearer hand."

"Who is that?" quoth Jack.

Saith she, "The third suitor is the parson of Speenhamland, who hath a proper living, he is of holy conversation and good estimation, whose affection to me is great."

"No doubt dame," quoth John, "you may do wondrous well with him, where you shall have no care but to serve God, and to make ready his meat."

"O John," quoth she, "the flesh and the spirit agrees not: for he will be so bent to his book, that he will have little mind of his bed: for one month's studying for a sermon, will make him forget his wife a whole year."

"Truly dame," quoth John, "I must needs speak in his behalf and the rather, for that he is a man of the church, and your near neighbour, to whom (as I guess) you bear the best affection: I do not think that he will be so much bound to his book, or subject to the spirit, but that he will remember a woman at home or abroad."

"Well John," quoth she, "I wis[3] my mind is not that way: for I like better of one nearer hand."

"No marvel," quoth Jack, "you are so peremptory, seeing you have so much choice: but I pray ye dame," quoth he, "let me know this fortunate man that is so highly placed in your favour?"

"John," quoth she, "they are worthy to know nothing, that cannot keep something: that man (I tell thee) must go nameless: for he is lord of my love, and king of my desires: there is neither tanner, tailor, nor parson may compare with him, his presence is a preservative to my health, his sweet smiles my heart's solace, and his words heavenly music to my ears."

"Why then dame," quoth John, "for your body's health, your heart's joy, and your ears' delight, delay not the time, but entertain him with a kiss, make his bed next yours, and chop up the match in the morning."

"Well," quoth she, "I perceive thy consent is quickly got to any, having no care how I am matched so I be matched: I wis, I wis I could not let thee go so lightly, being loth that anyone should have thee, except I could love her as well as myself."

"I thank you for your kindness and good will, good dame," quoth he, "but it is not wisdom for a young man that can scantly keep himself, to take a wife: therefore I hold it the best way to lead a single life: for I have heard say, that many sorrows follow marriage, especially where want remains: and beside, it is a hard matter to find a constant woman: for as young maids are fickle, so are old women jealous: the one a grief too common, the other a torment intolerable."

"What John," quoth she, "consider that maidens' fickleness proceeds of vain fancies, but old women's jealousy of superabounding love: and therefore the more to be borne withal."

"But dame," quoth he, "many are jealous without cause: for is it sufficient for their mistrusting natures to take exceptions at a shadow, at a word, at a look, at a smile, nay at the twinkle of an eye, which neither man nor woman is able to expel? I knew a woman that was ready to hang herself, for seeing but her husband's shirt hang on a hedge with her maid's smock."

"I grant that this fury may haunt some," quoth she, "yet there be many other that complain not without great cause."

"Why, is there any cause that should move jealousy?" quoth John.

"Aye by S. Mary is there," quoth she: "for would it not

grieve a woman (being one every way able to delight her husband) to see him forsake her, despise and contemn her, being never so merry as when he is in other company, sporting abroad from morning till noon, from noon till night, and when he comes to bed, if he turns to his wife, it is in such solemnness, and wearisome drowsy lameness, that it brings rather lothsomeness than any delight? can you then blame a woman in this case to be angry and displeased? I'll tell you what, among brute beasts it is a grief intolerable: for I heard my grandame tell, that the bellwether of her flock fancying one of the ewes above the rest, and seeing Gratis the shepherd abusing her in abominable sort (subverting the law of nature) could by no means bear that abuse; but watching opportunity for revenge, on a time found the said shepherd sleeping in the field, and suddenly ran against him in such violent sort, that by the force of his wreathen horns, he beat the brains out of the shepherd's head and slew him. If then a sheep could not endure that injury, think not that women are so sheepish to suffer it."

"Believe me," quoth John, "if every horn-maker should be so plagued by a horned beast, there should be less horns made in Newbury by many in a year. But dame," quoth he, "to make an end of this prattle, because it is an argument too deep to be discussed between you and I, you shall hear me sing an old song, and so we will depart to supper.

> A maiden fair I dare not wed,
> For fear to have Acteon's head.[4]
> A maiden black is often proud:
> A maiden little will be loud.
> A maiden that is high of growth,
> They say is subject unto sloth.
> Thus fair or foul, little or tall,
> Some faults remain among them all:
> But of all the faults that be,
> None is so bad as jealousy.
> For jealousy is fierce and fell,
> And burns as hot as fire in hell:

It breeds suspicion without cause,
And breaks the bonds of reason's laws.
To none it is a greater foe,
Than unto those where it doth grow.
And God keep me both day and night,
From that fell, fond and ugly sprite:
For why? of all the plagues that be,
The secret plague is jealousy.
Therefore I wish all women kind,
Never to bear a jealous mind."

"Well said John," quoth she, "thy song is not so sure, but thy voice is as sweet: but seeing the time agrees with our stomachs, though loth, yet will we give over for this time, and betake ourselves to our suppers." Then calling the rest of her servants, they fell to their meat merrily, and after supper, the goodwife went abroad for her recreation, to walk a while with one of her neighbours. And in the mean space John got him up into his chamber, and there began to meditate on this matter, bethinking with himself what he were best to do: for well he perceived that his dame's affection was great towards him: knowing therefore the woman's disposition, and withal, that her estate was reasonable good, and considering beside, that he should find a house ready furnished, servants ready taught, and all other things for his trade necessary, he thought it best not to let slip that good occasion, lest he should never come to the like. But again, when he considered her years to be unfitting to his youth, and that she that sometime had been his dame, would (perhaps) disdain to be governed by him that had been her poor servant, and that it would prove but a bad bargain, doubting many inconveniencies that might grow thereby, he therefore resolved to be silent, rather than to proceed further: wherefore he got him straight to bed, and the next morning settled himself close to his business.

His dame coming home, and hearing that her man was gone to bed, took that night but small rest, and early in the morning hearing him up at his work, merrily singing, she by and by arcse, and in seemly sort attiring herself, she came into the workshop, and sat her down to make quills.

Quoth John, "Good morrow dame, how do you today?"

"God a mercy John," quoth she, "even as well as I may: for I was sore troubled in my dreams. Methought two doves walked together in a corn field, the one (as it were) in communication with the other, without regard of picking up anything to sustain themselves: and after they had with many nods spent some time to their content, they both fell hard with their pretty bills to peck up the scattered corn, left by the weary reaper's hand. At length (finding themselves satisfied) it chanced another pigeon to light in that place, with whom, one of the first pigeons at length kept company: and after, returning to the place where she left her first companion, perceived he was not there: she kindly[5] searching up and down the high stubble to find him, lights at length on a hog fast asleep, wherewith methought, the poor dove was so dismayed that presently she fell down in a trance. I seeing her legs fail, and her wings quiver, yielding herself to death, moved with pity ran unto her, and thinking to take up the pigeon, methought, I had in my hands my own heart, wherein methought an arrow stuck so deep, that the blood trickled down the shaft, and lay upon the feathers like the silver pearled dew on the green grass, which made me to weep most bitterly. But presently, methought there came one to me crowned like a queen, who told me my heart would die in time, except I got some of that sleeping hog's grease to heal the wounds thereof. Whereupon I ran in all haste to the hog with my heart bleeding in my hand, who (methought) grunted at me in most churlish sort, and vanished out of my sight. Whereupon coming straight home, methought, I found this hog rustling among the looms, wherewith I presently awaked, suddenly after midnight, being all in a sweat and very ill: and I am sure you could not choose but hear me groan."

"Trust me dame, I heard you not," quoth John, "I was so sound asleep."

"And thus," quoth she, "a woman may die in the night before you will have the care to see what she ails, or ask what she lacks. But truly John," quoth she, "all is one: for if thou shouldest have come, thou couldest not have got in, because my chamber door was locked: but while I live this shall teach me wit: for henceforth I will have no other lock but a latch, till I am married."

"Then dame," quoth he, "I perceive though you be curious in your choice, yet at length you will marry."

"Aye truly," quoth she, "so thou wilt not hinder me."

"Who I?" quoth John. "On my faith dame, not for a hundred pounds, but rather will further you to the uttermost of my power."

"Indeed," quoth she, "thou hast no reason to shew any discourtesy to me in that matter, although some of our neighbours do not stick to say, that I am sure to thee already."

"If it were so," quoth John, "there is no cause to deny it, or to be ashamed thereof, knowing myself far unworthy of so high a favour."

"Well, let this talk rest," quoth she, "and take there thy quills, for it is time for me to go to market."

Thus the matter rested for two or three days, in which space she daily devised which way she might obtain her desire, which was to marry her man. Many things came in her head, and sundry sleights in her mind, but none of them did fit her fancy, so that she became wondrous sad, and as civil as the nine sibyls;[6] and in this melancholy humour continued three weeks or a month, till at last it was her luck upon a Bartholomew Day[7] (having a fair in the town) to spy her man John give a pair of gloves to a proper maid for a fairing,[8] which the maiden with a bashful modesty kindly accepted, and requited it with a kiss: which kindled in her an inward jealousy: but notwithstanding very discreetly she covered it, and closely past along unspied of her man or the maid.

She had not gone far, but she met with one of her suitors, namely the tailor who was very fine and brisk in his apparel, and needs he would bestow the wine upon the widow: and after some faint denial, meeting with a gossip of hers, to the tavern they went, which was more courtesy than the tailor could ever get of her before, shewing herself very pleasant and merry; and finding her in such a pleasing humour, the tailor after a new quart of wine, renewed his old suit: the widow with patience heard him, and gently answered, that in respect of his great good will long time borne unto her, as also in regard of his gentleness, cost, and courtesy at that present bestowed, she would not flatly deny him. "Therefore," quoth she, "seeing this is not a place to conclude of such matters, if I may intreat you to come to my poor house on Thursday next, you shall be heartily welcome, and be further satisfied of my mind:" and thus preferred to a touch of her lips, he paid the shot[9] and departed.

The tailor was scant out of sight, when she met with the tanner: who albeit he was aged, yet lustily he saluted her, and to the wine she must, there was no nay. The widow seeing his importunacy, calls her gossip, and along they walked together. The old man called for wine plenty, and the best cheer in the house: and in an hearty manner he bids the widow welcome. They had not sitten long, but in comes a noise of musicians in tawny coats, who (putting off their caps) asked if they would have any music. The widow answered no, they were merry enough.

"Tut," quoth the old man, "let us hear good fellows what you can do, and play me *The Beginning of the World*." [10]

"Alas," quoth the widow, "you had more need to hearken to the ending of the world."

"Why widow," quoth he, "I tell thee the beginning of the world was the begetting of children: and if you find me faulty in that occupation, turn me out of thy bed for a bungler, and then send for the sexton."

He had no sooner spoken the word, but the parson of Speen with his corner cap, popped in at the door, who seeing the widow sitting at the table, craved pardon, and came in.

Quoth she, "For want of the sexton, here is the priest if you need him."

"Marry," quoth the tanner, "in good time, for by this means we need not go far to be married."

"Sir," quoth the parson, "I shall do my best in convenient place."

"Wherein?" quoth the tanner.

"To wed her myself," quoth the parson.

"Nay soft," said the widow, "one swallow makes not a summer, nor one meeting a marriage: as I lighted on you unlooked for, so came I hither unprovided for the purpose."

"I trust," quoth the tanner, "you came not without your eyes to see, your tongue to speak, your ears to hear, your hands to feel, nor your legs to go."

"I brought my eyes," quoth she, "to discern colours, my tongue to say no to questions I like not, my hands to thrust from me the things that I love not, my ears to judge twixt flattery and friendship, & my feet to run from such as would wrong me."

"Why then," quoth the parson, "by your gentle abiding in this place, it is evident that here are none but those you like & love."

"God forbid I should hate my friends," quoth the widow, "whom I take all these in this place to be."

"But there be divers sorts of loves," quoth the parson.

"You say truth," quoth the widow. "I love yourself for your profession, and my friend the tanner, for his courtesy and kindness, and the rest for their good company."

"Yet," quoth the parson, "for the explaining of your love, I pray you drink to them you love best in the company."

"Why," quoth the tanner, "have you any hope in her love?"

"Believe me," saith the parson, "as much as another."

"Why then parson sit down," said the tanner: "for you that are equal with me in desire, shall surely be half with me in the shot: and so widow, on God's name fulfill the parson's request."

"Seeing," quoth the widow, "you are so pleasantly bent, if my courtesy might not breed contention between you, and that I may have your favour to shew my fancy, I will fulfill your request."

Quoth the parson, "I am pleased howsoever it be."

"And I," quoth the tanner.

"Why then," quoth she, "with this cup of claret wine and sugar, I heartily drink to the minstrel's boy."

"Why, is it he you love best?" quoth the parson.

"I have reason," said she, "to like and love them best, that will be least offended with my doings."

"Nay, widow," quoth they, "we meant you should drink to him whom you loved best in the way of marriage."

Quoth the widow, "You should have said so at first: but to tell you my opinion, it is small discretion for a woman to disclose her secret affection in an open assembly: therefore, if to that purpose you spake, let me intreat you both to come home to my house on Thursday next, where you shall be heartily welcome, and there be fully resolved of my mind: and so, with thanks at this time, I'll take my leave."

The shot being paid, and the musicians pleased, they all departed, the tanner to Wallingford, the parson to Speen, and the widow to her own house: where in her wonted solemnness she settled herself to her business.

Against Thursday she drest her house fine and brave, and set herself in her best apparel: the tailor nothing forgetting his promise, sent to the widow a good fat pig, and a goose. The parson being as mindful as he, sent to her house a couple of fat rabbits and a capon: and the tanner came himself, and brought a good shoulder of mutton, and half a dozen chickens, beside he brought a good gallon of sack, and half a pound of the best sugar. The widow receiving this good meat, set her maid to dress it incontinent, and when dinner time drew near, the table was covered, and every other thing provided in convenient and comely sort.

At length the guests being come, the widow bade them all heartily welcome. The priest and the tanner seeing the tailor, mused what he made there: the tailor on the other side, mar-

velled as much at their presence. Thus looking strangely one
at another, at length the widow came out of the kitchen, in a
fair train gown stuck full of silver pins, a fine white cap on
her head, with cuts of curious needle work under the same,
and an apron before her as white as the driven snow: then
very modestly making curtsy to them all, she requested them
to sit down. But they straining courtesy the one with the
other, the widow with a smiling countenance took the parson
by the hand, saying, "Sir, as you stand highest in the church,
so it is meet you should sit highest at the table: and therefore
I pray you sit down there on the bench side. And sir," said she
to the tanner, "as age is to be honoured before youth for their
experience, so are they to sit above bachelors for their gravity:" and so she set him down on this side the table, over
against the parson. Then coming to the tailor, she said, "Bachelor, though your lot be the last, your welcome is equal with
the first, and seeing your place points out itself, I pray you
take a cushion and sit down. And now," quoth she, "to make
the board equal, and because it hath been an old saying, that
three things are to small purpose, if the fourth be away: if
so it may stand with your favour, I will call in a gossip of mine
to supply this void place."

"With a good will," quoth they.

With that she brought in an old woman with scant ever a
good tooth in her head, and placed her right against the bachelor. Then was the meat brought to the board in due order by
the widow's servants, her man John being chiefest servitor.
The widow sat down at the table's end, between the parson
and the tanner, who in very good sort carved meat for them
all, her man John waiting on the table.

After they had sitten awhile, and well refreshed themselves,
the widow, taking a crystal glass filled with claret wine, drunk
unto the whole company, and bade them welcome. The parson pledged her, and so did all the rest in due order: but still
in their drinking, the cup past over the poor old woman's
nose; insomuch that at length the old woman (in a merry
vein) spake thus unto the company: "I have had much good

meat among you, but as for the drink I can nothing commend it."

"Alas, good gossip," quoth the widow, "I perceive no man
hath drunk to thee yet."

"No truly," quoth the old woman: "for churchmen have
so much mind of young rabbits, old men such joy in young
chickens, and bachelors in pig's flesh take such delight, that
an old sow, a tough hen, or a gray cony are not accepted:
and so it is seen by me, else I should have been better remembered."

"Well old woman," quoth the parson, "take here the leg of
a capon to stop thy mouth."

"Now by S. Anne, I dare not," quoth she.

"No, wherefore?" said the parson.

"Marry, for fear lest you should go home with a crutch,"
quoth she.

The tailor said, "Then taste here a piece of a goose."

"Now God forbid," said the old woman, "let goose go to
his kind: you have a young stomach, eat it yourself, and much
good may it do your heart, sweet young man."

"The old woman lacks most of her teeth," quoth the tanner: "and therefore a piece of a tender chick is fittest for her."

"If I did lack as many of my teeth," quoth the old woman,
"as you lack points of good husbandry, I doubt I should starve
before it were long."

At this the widow laughed heartily, and the men were
stricken into such a dump, that they had not a word to say.

Dinner being ended, the widow with the rest rose from the
table, and after they had sitten a pretty while merrily talking,
the widow called her man John to bring her a bowl of fresh
ale, which he did. Then said the widow: "My masters, now
for your courtesy and cost I heartily thank you all, and in
requital of all your favour, love and good will, I drink to you,
giving you free liberty when you please to depart."

At these words her suitors looked so sourly one upon another, as if they had been newly champing of crabs. Which
when the tailor heard, shaking up himself in his new russet

jerkin, and setting his hat on one side, he began to speak thus. "I trust sweet widow," quoth he, "you remember to what end my coming was hither today: I have long time been a suitor unto you, and this day you promised to give me a direct answer."

" 'Tis true," quoth she, "and so I have: for your love I give you thanks, and when you please you may depart."

"Shall I not have you?" said the tailor.

"Alas," quoth the widow, "you come too late."

"Good friend," quoth the tanner, "it is manners for young men to let their elders be served before them: to what end should I be here if the widow should have thee? A flat denial is meet for a saucy suitor: but what sayest thou to me, fair widow?" quoth the tanner.

"Sir," said she, "because you are so sharp set, I would wish you as soon as you can to wed."

"Appoint the time yourself," quoth the tanner.

"Even as soon," quoth she, "as you can get a wife, and hope not after me, for I am already promised."

"Now tanner, you may take your place with the tailor," quoth the parson: "for indeed the widow is for no man but myself."

"Master parson," quoth she, "many have run near the goal, and yet have lost the game, and I cannot help it though your hope be in vain: besides, parsons are but newly suffered to have wives,[11] and for my part I will have none of the first head."

"What," quoth the tailor, "is your merriment grown to this reckoning? I never spent a pig and a goose to so bad a purpose before: I promise you, when I came in, I verily thought, that you were invited by the widow to make her and I sure together, and that this jolly tanner was brought to be a witness to the contract, and the old woman fetched in for the same purpose, else I would never have put up so many dry bobs[12] at her hands."

"And surely," quoth the tanner, "I knowing thee to be a

tailor, did assuredly think, that thou wast appointed to come and take measure for our wedding apparel."

"But now we are all deceived," quoth the parson: "and therefore as we came fools, so we may depart hence like asses."

"That is as you interpret the matter," said the widow: "for I ever doubting that a concluding answer would breed a jar in the end among you every one, I thought it better to be done at one instant, and in mine own house, than at sundry times, and in common taverns: and as for the meat you sent, as it was unrequested of me, so had you your part thereof, and if you think good to take home the remainder, prepare your wallets and you shall have it."

"Nay widow," quoth they, "although we have lost our labours, we have not altogether lost our manners: that which you have, keep; and God send to us better luck, and to you your heart's desire." And with that they departed.

The widow being glad she was thus rid of her guests, when her man John with all the rest sat at supper, she sitting in a chair by, spake thus unto them. "Well my masters, you saw, that this day your poor dame had her choice of husbands, if she had listed to marry, and such as would have loved and maintained her like a woman."

" 'Tis true," quoth John, "and I pray God you have not withstood your best fortune."

"Trust me," quoth she, "I know not, but if I have, I may thank mine own foolish fancy."

Thus it past on from Bartolomewtide, till it was near Christmas, at what time the weather was so wonderful cold, that all the running rivers round about the town were frozen very thick. The widow being very loth any longer to lie without company, in a cold winter's night made a great fire, and sent for her man John, having also prepared a chair and a cushion, she made him sit down therein, and sending for a pint of good sack, they both went to supper.

In the end, bedtime coming on, she caused her maid in a merriment to pluck off his hose and shoes, and caused him to be laid in his master's best bed, standing in the best chamber, hung round about with very fair curtains. John being thus preferred, thought himself a gentleman, and lying soft, after his hard labour and a good supper, quickly fell asleep.

About midnight, the widow being cold on her feet, crept into her man's bed to warm them. John feeling one lift up the clothes, asked who was there? "O good John it is I," quoth the widow; "the night is so extreme cold, and my chamber walls so thin, that I am like to be starved in my bed, wherefore rather than I would any way hazard my health, I thought it much better to come hither and try your courtesy, to have a little room beside you."

John being a kind young man, would not say her nay, and so they spent the rest of the night both together in one bed. In the morning betime she arose up and made herself ready, and willed her man John to run and fetch her a link with all speed: "For," quoth she, "I have earnest business to do this morning." Her man did so. Which done, she made him to carry the link before her, until she came to Saint Bartholomew's Chapel, where Sir John the priest with the clerk and sexton, stood waiting for her.

"John," quoth she, "turn into the chapel: for before I go further, I will make my prayers to S. Bartholomew, so shall I speed the better in my business."

When they were come in, the priest according to his order, came to her, and asked where the bridegroom was?

Quoth she, "I thought he had been here before me. Sir," quoth she, "I will sit down and say over my beads, and by that time he will come."

John mused at this matter, to see that his dame should so suddenly be married, and he hearing nothing thereof before. The widow rising from her prayers, the priest told her that the bridegroom was not yet come.

"Is it true?" quoth the widow. "I promise you I will stay no longer for him, if he were as good as George a Green:[13] and therefore dispatch," quoth she, "and marry me to my man John."

"Why dame," quoth he, "you do but jest."

"I trow, John," quoth she, "I jest not: for so I mean it shall be, and stand not strangely, but remember that you did promise me on your faith, not to hinder me when I came to the church to be married, but rather to set it forward: therefore set your link aside, and give me your hand: for none but you shall be my husband."

John seeing no remedy, consented, because he saw the matter could not otherwise be amended; and married they were presently.

When they were come home, John entertained his dame with a kiss, which the other servants seeing, thought him somewhat saucy. The widow caused the best cheer in the house to be set on the table, and to breakfast they went, causing her new husband to be set in a chair at the table's end, with a fair napkin laid on his trencher: then she called out the rest of her servants, willing them to sit down and take part of their good cheer. They wondering to see their fellow John sit at the table's end in their old master's chair, began heartily to smile, and openly to laugh at the matter, especially because their dame so kindly sat by his side: which she perceiving, asked if that were all the manners they could shew before their master? "I tell you," quoth she, "he is my husband: for this morning we were married, and therefore henceforward look you acknowledge your duty towards him."

The folks looked one upon another, marvelling at this strange news. Which when John perceived, he said: "My masters, muse not at all: for although by God's providence, and your dame's favour, I am preferred from being your fellow to be your master, I am not thereby so much puffed up in pride, that any way I will forget my former estate: Notwithstanding, seeing I am now to hold the place of a master, it shall be wisdom in you to forget what I was, and to take me as I am, and in doing your diligence, you shall have no cause to repent that God made me your master."

The servants hearing this, as also knowing his good government before time, past their years with him in dutiful manner.

The next day, the report was over all the town, that Jack of Newbury had married his dame: so that when the woman walked abroad, everyone bade God give her joy: some said that she was matched to her sorrow, saying, that so lusty a young man as he, would never love her being so ancient. Whereupon the woman made answer, that she would take him down in his wedding shoes, and would try his patience in the prime of his lustiness: whereunto, many of her gossips did likewise encourage her. Every day therefore for the space of a month after she was married, it was her ordinary custom, to go forth in the morning among her gossips and acquaintance to make merry, and not to return home till night, without any regard of her household. Of which, at her coming home her husband did very oftentimes admonish her in very gentle sort, shewing what great inconvenience would grow thereby: the which sometime she would take in gentle part, and sometime in disdain, saying.

"I am now in very good case, that he that was my servant but the other day, will now be my master: this it is for a woman to make her foot her head. The day hath been, when I might have gone forth when I would, and come in again when it had pleased me without controlment, and now I must be subject to every Jack's check. I am sure," quoth she, "that by my gadding abroad, and careless spending, I waste no goods of thine. I, pitying thy poverty, made thee a man, and master of the house, but not to the end I would become thy slave. I scorn, I tell thee true, that such a youngling as thyself, should correct my conceit, and give me instructions, as if I were not able to guide myself: but yfaith, yfaith,[14] you shall not use me like a babe nor bridle me like an ass: and seeing my going abroad grieves thee, where I have gone forth one day, I will go abroad three; and for one hour, I will stay five."

"Well," quoth her husband, "I trust you will be better advised:" and with that he went from her about his business, leaving her sweating in her fustian furies.

Thus the time past on, till on a certain day she had been abroad in her wonted manner, and staying forth very late, he shut the doors and went to bed. About midnight she comes to the door, and knocks to come in: to whom he looking out of the window, answered in this sort:

"What? is it you that keeps such a knocking? I pray you get hence, and request the constable to provide you a bed, for this night you shall have no lodging here."

"I hope," quoth she, "you will not shut me out of doors like a dog, or let me lie in the streets like a strumpet."

"Whether like a dog or drab," quoth he, "all is one to me, knowing no reason, but that as you have stayed out all day for your delight, so you may lie forth all night for my pleasure. Both birds and beasts at the night's approach repair to their rest, and observe a convenient time to return to their habitation. Look but upon the poor spider, the frog, the fly, and every other silly worm, and you shall see all these observe time to return to their home: and if you, being a woman, will not do the like, content yourself to bear the brunt of your own folly: and so farewell."

The woman hearing this, made piteous moan, and in very humble sort intreated him to let her in, and to pardon this offence, and while she lived vowed never to do the like. Her husband at length being moved with pity towards her, slipt on his shoes, and came down in his shirt: the door being opened, in she went quaking, and as he was about to lock it again, in very sorrowful manner she said, "Alack husband, what hap have I? my wedding ring was even now in my hand, and I have let it fall about the door: good sweet John come forth with the candle, and help me to seek it."

The man incontinent did so, and while he sought for that which was not there to be found, she whipt into the house, and quickly clapping to the door, she locked her husband out. He stood calling with the candle in his hand to come in, but she made as if she heard not. Anon she went up into her chamber, and carried the key with her: but when he saw she would not answer, he presently began to knock as loud as he could at the door. At last she thrust her head out at the window, saying: "Who is there?"

" 'Tis I," quoth John, "what mean you by this? I pray you come down and open the door that I may come in."

"What sir," quoth she, "is it you? have you nothing to do but dance about the streets at this time of night, and like a sprite of the buttery[15] hunt after crickets, are you so hot that the house cannot hold you?"

"Nay, I pray thee sweetheart," quoth he, "do not gibe no longer, but let me in."

"O sir, remember," quoth she, "how you stood even now at the window, like a judge on the bench, and in taunting sort kept me out of mine own house. How now Jack, am I even with you? What, John my man, were you so lusty to lock your dame out of doors? Sirra, remember you bade me go to the constable to get lodging, now you have leisure to try if his wife will prefer you to a bed. You sir sauce, that made me stand in the cold, till my feet did freeze, and my teeth chatter, while you stood preaching of birds and beasts, telling me a tale of spiders, flies, and frogs: go try now if any of them will be so friendly to let thee have lodging. Why go you not man? fear not to speak with them; for I am sure you shall find them at home: think not they are such ill husbands as you, to be abroad at this time of night."

With this John's patience was greatly moved, insomuch, that he deeply swore, that if she would not let him in, he would break down the door.

"Why John," quoth she, "you need not be so hot, your clothing is not so warm, and because I think this will be a warning for you against another time, how you shut me out of my house, catch, there is the key, come in at thy pleasure, and look thou go to bed to thy fellows, for with me thou shalt not lie tonight."

With that she clapt to the casement, and got her to bed, locking the chamber door fast. Her husband that knew it was in vain to seek to come into her chamber, and being no longer able to endure the cold, got him a place among his prentices, and there slept soundly. In the morning his wife rose betime, and merrily made him a caudle, and bringing it up to his bedside, asked him how he did?

Quoth John, "Troubled with a shrew, who the longer she lives, the worse she is: and as the people of Illyris[16] kill men with their looks, so she kills her husband's heart with untoward conditions. But trust me wife," quoth he, "seeing I find you of such crooked qualities, that (like the spider) ye turn the sweet flowers of good counsel into venomous poison, from henceforth I will leave you to your own wilfulness, and neither vex my mind, nor trouble myself to restrain you: the which if I had wisely done last night, I had kept the house in quiet, and myself from cold."

"Husband," quoth she, "think that women are like starlings, that will burst their gall before they will yield to the fowler: or like the fish *scolopendra*,[17] that cannot be touched without danger. Notwithstanding, as the hard steel doth yield to the hammer's stroke, being used to his kind, so will women to their husbands, where they are not too much crossed. And seeing ye have sworn to give me my will, I vow likewise that my wilfulness shall not offend you. I tell you husband, the noble nature of a woman is such, that for their loving friends they will not stick (like the pelican) to pierce their own hearts to do them good. And therefore forgiving each other all injuries past, having also tried one another's patience, let us quench these burning coals of contention, with the sweet juice of a faithful kiss, and shaking hands, bequeath all our anger to the eating up of this caudle."

Her husband courteously consented: and after this time, they lived long together, in most godly, loving and kind sort, till in the end she died, leaving her husband wondrous wealthy.

CHAP. II

Of Jack of Newbury his great wealth, and number of servants: and also how he brought the Queen Katharine two hundred and fifty men prepared for the war at his own cost against the King of Scots at Flodden Field.

Now Jack of Newbury being a widower, had the choice of many wives, men's daughters of good credit, and widows of great wealth. Notwithstanding he bent his only like to

one of his own servants, whom he had tried in the guiding of
his house a year or two: and knowing her carefulness in her
business, faithful in her dealing, an excellent good housewife,
thought it better to have her with nothing, than some other
with much treasure. And beside as her qualities were good,
so was she of very comely personage, of a sweet favour, and
fair complexion. In the end, he opened his mind unto her, and
craved her good will. The maid (though she took this motion
kindly) said, she would do nothing without consent of her
parents. Whereupon a letter was writ to her father, being a
poor man dwelling at Aylesbury in Buckinghamshire: who
being joyful of his daughter's good fortune, speedily came to
Newbury, whereof her master he was friendly entertained:
who after he had made him good cheer, shewed him all his
servants at work, and every office in his house.

> Within one room being large and long,
> There stood two hundred looms full strong:
> Two hundred men the truth is so,
> Wrought in these looms all in a row.
> By every one a pretty boy,
> Sat making quills with mickle joy;
> And in another place hard by,
> An hundred women merrily,
> Were carding hard with joyful cheer,
> Who singing sat with voices clear.
> And in a chamber close beside,
> Two hundred maidens did abide,
> In petticoats of stammel [18] red,
> And milk-white kerchers on their head:
> Their smock-sleeves like to winter snow,
> That on the western mountains flow,
> And each sleeve with a silken band,
> Was featly tied at the hand.
> These pretty maids did never lin,[19]
> But in that place all day did spin:
> And spinning so with voices meet,
> Like nightingales they sung full sweet.
> Then to another room came they,

Where children were in poor array:
And every one sat picking wool,
The finest from the coarse to cull:
The number was seven score and ten,
The children of poor silly men:
And these their labours to requite,
Had every one a penny at night,
Beside their meat and drink all day,
Which was to them a wondrous stay.
Within another place likewise,
Full fifty proper men he spies,
And these were shearmen every one,
Whose skill and cunning there was shown:
And hard by them there did remain,
Full fourscore rowers taking pain.
A dye-house likewise had he then,
Wherein he kept full forty men:
And likewise in his fulling mill,
Full twenty persons kept he still.
Each week ten good fat oxen he
Spent in his house for certainty:
Beside good butter, cheese, and fish,
And many another wholesome dish.
He kept a butcher all the year,
A brewer eke for ale and beer:
A baker for to bake his bread,
Which stood his household in good stead.
Five cooks within his kitchen great,
Were all the year to dress his meat.
Six scullion boys unto their hands,
To make clean dishes, pots, and pans,
Beside poor chidren that did stay,
To turn the broaches every day.
The old man that did see this sight,
Was much amaz'd, as well he might:
This was a gallant clothier sure,
Whose fame forever shall endure.

When the old man had seen this great household and family, then was he brought into the warehouses, some being filled with wool, some with flocks, some with woad and madder, and some with broadcloths and kerseys ready died and dressed, beside a great number of others, some stretched on the tenters, some hanging on poles, and a great many more lying wet in other places. "Sir," quoth the old man, "I wis che zee you be bominable rich, and cham content you shall have my daughter, and God's blessing and mine light on you both." [20]

"But Father," quoth Jack of Newbury, "what will you bestow with her?"

"Marry hear you," quoth the old man, "I vaith cham but a poor man, but I thong God, cham of good exclamation among my neighbours, and they will as zoon take my vice for anything as a richer man's: thick[21] I will bestow, you shall have with a good will, because che hear very good condemnation of you in every place, therefore chil give you twenty nobles and a weaning calf, and when I die and my wife, you shall have the revelation of all my goods."

When Jack heard his offer, he was straight content, making more reckoning of the woman's modesty, than her father's money. So the marriage day being appointed, all things was prepared meet for the wedding, and royal cheer ordained, most of the lords, knights, and gentlemen thereabout, were invited thereunto: the bride being attired in a gown of sheep's russet, and a kirtle of fine worsted, her head attired with a biliment[22] of gold, and her hair as yellow as gold, hanging down behind her, which was curiously combed and plaited, according to the manner in those days: she was led to church between two sweet boys, with bride-laces and rosemary tied about their silken sleeves: the one of them was son to Sir Thomas Parry, the other to Sir Francis Hungerford.[23] Then was there a fair bride-cup of silver and gilt carried before her, wherein was a goodly branch of rosemary gilded very fair, hung about with silken ribands of all colours: next was there a noise of musicians that played all the way before her: after her came all the chiefest maidens of the country, some bearing great bride-cakes, and some garlands of wheat finely gilded, and so she passed unto the church.

It is needless for me to make any mention here of the bridegroom, who being a man so well beloved, wanted no company, and those of the best sort, beside divers merchant strangers of the Stillyard,[24] that came from London to the wedding. The marriage being solemnized, home they came in order as before, and to dinner they went, where was no want of good cheer, no lack of melody: Rhenish wine at this wedding was as plentiful as beer or ale: for the merchants had sent thither ten tuns of the best in the Stillyard.

This wedding endured ten days, to the great relief of the poor that dwelt all about: and in the end, the bride's father and mother came to pay their daughter's portion: which when the bridegroom had received, he gave them great thanks: Notwithstanding he would not suffer them yet to depart, and against they should go home, their son-in-law came unto them saying; "Father and Mother, all the thanks that my poor heart can yield, I give you for your good will, cost, and courtesy, and while I live make bold to use me in anything that I am able, and in requital of the gift you gave me with your daughter, I give you here twenty pound to bestow as you find occasion, and for your loss of time, and charges riding up and down, I give you here as much broadcloth as shall make you a cloak, and my mother a holiday gown, and when this is worn out, come to me and fetch more."

"O my good zon," quoth the old woman, "Christ's benizon be with thee evermore: for to tell thee true, we had zold all our kine to make money for my daughter's marriage, and this zeaven year we should not have been able to buy more: Notwithstanding we should have zold all that ever we had, before my poor wench should have lost her marriage."

"Aye," quoth the old man, "chud have zold my coat from my back, and my bed from under me, before my girl should have gone without you."

"I thank you good father and mother," said the bride, "and I pray God long to keep you in health:" then the bride kneeled down and did her duty to her parents, who weeping for very joy, departed.

Not long after this, it chanced while our noble king was

making war in France, that James King of Scotland, falsely breaking his oath,[25] invaded England with a great army, and did much hurt upon the borders: whereupon on the sudden, every man was appointed according to his ability, to be ready with his men and furniture, at an hour's warning, on pain of death. Jack of Newbury was commanded by the justices to set out six men, four armed with pikes, and two calivers,[26] and to meet the Queen in Buckinghamshire, who was there raising a great power to go against the faithless King of Scots.

When Jack had received this charge, he came home in all haste, & cut out a whole broadcloth for horsemen's coats, and so much more as would make up coats for the number of a hundred men: in short time he had made ready fifty tall men well mounted in white coats, and red caps with yellow feathers, demilances in their hands, and fifty armed men on foot with pikes, and fifty shot in white coats also, every man so expert in the handling of his weapon, as few better were found in the field. Himself likewise in complete armour on a goodly barbed horse, rode foremost of the company, with a lance in his hand, and a fair plume of yellow feathers in his crest, and in this sort he came before the justices: who at the first approach did not a little wonder what he should be.

At length when they had discovered what he was, the justices and most of the gentlemen gave him great commendations for this his good and forward mind shewed in this action: but some other envying hereat, gave out words that he shewed himself more prodigal than prudent, and more vainglorious than well advised, seeing that the best nobleman in the country would scarce have done so much: "And no marvel," quoth they, "for such a one would call to his remembrance, that the King had often occasions to urge his subjects to such charges; and therefore would do at one time as they might be able to do at another: but Jack of Newbury like the stork in the springtime, thinks the highest cedar too low for him to build his nest in, and ere the year be half done may be glad to have his bed in a bush."

These disdainful speeches being at last brought to Jack of

Newbury's ear, though it grieved him much, yet patiently put them up till time convenient. Within a while after, all the soldiers of Berkshire, Hampshire, and Wiltshire, were commanded to shew themselves before the Queen at Stony Stratford, where Her Grace, with many lords, knights, and gentlemen were assembled, with ten thousand men. Against Jack should go to the Queen, he caused his face to be smeared with blood, and his white coat in like manner.

When they were come before Her Highness, she demanded (above all the rest) what those white coats were? Whereupon, Sir Henry Englefield (who had the leading of the Berkshire men) made answer.

"May it please Your Majesty to understand, that he which rideth foremost there, is called Jack of Newbury, and all those gallant men in white, are his own servants, who are maintained all the year by him: whom he at his own cost hath set out in this time of extremity, to serve the King against his vaunting foe: and I assure Your Majesty, there is not, for the number, better soldiers in the field."

"Good Sir Henry," quoth the Queen, "bring the man to me, that I may see him:" which was done accordingly. Then Jack with all his men alighted, and humbly on their knees fell before the Queen.

Her Grace said, "Gentleman arise;" and putting forth her lily-white hand, gave it him to kiss.

"Most gracious Queen," quoth he, "gentleman I am none, nor the son of a gentleman, but a poor clothier, whose lands are his looms, having no other rents but what I get from the backs of little sheep: nor can I claim any cognizance but a wooden shuttle. Nevertheless, most gracious Queen, these my poor servants and myself, with life and goods, are ready at Your Majesty's command, not only to spend our bloods, but also to lose our lives in defence of our King and country."

"Welcome to me Jack of Newbury," said the Queen, "though a clothier by trade, yet a gentleman by condition, and a faithful subject in heart: and if thou chance to have any suit in court, make account the Queen will be thy friend, and would to God the King had many such clothiers. But tell me, how came thy white coat besmeared with blood, and thy face so bescratched?"

"May it please Your Grace," quoth he, "to understand that it was my chance to meet with a monster, who like the people Cynomolgy,[27] had the proportion of a man, but headed like a dog, the biting of whose teeth was like the poisoned teeth of a crocodile, his breath like the basilisk's, killing afar off. I understand, his name was Envy, who assailed me invisibly, like the wicked spirit of Mogunce,[28] who flung stones at men, & could not be seen: and so I come by my scratched face, not knowing when it was done."

"What was the cause this monster should afflict thee above the rest of thy company, or other men in the field?"

"Although, most sovereign Queen," quoth he, "this poisoned cur snarleth at many, and that few can escape the hurt of his wounding breath, yet at this time he bent his force against me, not for any hurt I did him, but because I surpassed him in hearty affection to my sovereign lord, and with the poor widow, offered all I had to serve my prince and country."

"It were happy for England," said the Queen, "if in every market town there were a gibbet to hang up curs of that kind, who like Aesop's dog lying in the manger, will do no good himself, nor suffer such as would to do any."

This speech being ended, the Queen caused her army to be set in order, and in warlike manner to march toward Flodden, where King James had pitched his field. But as they passed along with drum and trumpet, there came a post from the valiant Earl of Surrey,[29] with tidings to Her Grace, that now she might dismiss her army, for that it had pleased God to grant the noble Earl victory over the Scots: whom he had by his wisdom and valiancy vanquished in fight, and slain their king in battle. Upon which news, Her Majesty discharged her forces, and joyfully took her journey to London, with a pleasant countenance, praising God for her famous victory, and yielding thanks to all the noble gentlemen and soldiers for their readiness in the action, giving many gifts to the nobility, and great rewards to the soldiers: among whom, she nothing forgot Jack of Newbury, about whose neck she put a rich chain of gold: at what time he with all the rest gave a great shout, saying, "God save Katharine the noble Queen of England."

Many noble men of Scotland were taken prisoners at this battle, and many more slain: so that there never came a greater foil to Scotland than this: for you shall understand, that the Scottish king made full account to be lord of this land, watching opportunity to bring to pass his faithless and traitorous practise: which was when our king was in France, at Turney, and Turwin:[30] in regard of which wars the Scots vaunted there was none left in England, but shepherds and ploughmen who were not able to lead an army, having no skill in martial affairs. In consideration of which advantage, he invaded the country, boasting of victory before he had won: which was no small grief to Queen Margaret, his wife, who was eldest sister to our noble king. Wherefore in disgrace of the Scots, and in remembrance of the famous achieved victory, the commons of England made this song: which to this day is not forgotten of many.[31]

THE SONG

King Jamie had made a vow,
    keep it well if he may:
That he will be at lovely London,
    upon Saint James his day.

"Upon Saint James his day at noon,
    at fair London will I be;
And all the Lords in merry Scotland,
    they shall dine there with me."

Then bespake good Queen Margaret,
    the tears fell from her eyes:
"Leave off these wars most noble King,
    keep your fidelity.

"The water runs swift and wondrous deep,
   from bottom unto the brim:
My brother Henry hath men good enough,
   England is hard to win."

"Away," quoth he, "with this silly fool,
   in prison fast let her lie:
For she is come of the English blood,
   and for these words she shall die."

With that bespake Lord Thomas Howard,
   the Queen's chamberlain that day:
"If that you put Queen Margaret to death,
   Scotland shall rue it alway."

Then in a rage King Jamie did say,
   "Away with this foolish mome:
He shall be hanged, and the other be burned,
   so soon as I come home."

At Flodden Field the Scots came in,
   which made our Englishmen fain,
At Bramstone-green this battle was seen:
   there was King Jamie slain.

Then presently the Scots did fly,
   their cannons they left behind,
Their ensigns gay were won all away,
   our soldiers did beat them blind.

To tell you plain, twelve thousand were slain,
   that to the fight did stand;
And many prisoners took that day,
   the best in all Scotland.

That day made many a fatherless child,
   and many a widow poor;
And many a Scottish gay lady
   sat weeping in her bower.

Jack with a feather[32] was lapped all in leather,
   his boastings were all in vain:
He had such a chance with a new morris dance,
   he never went home again.

CHAP. III

How Jack of Newbury went to receive the King, as he went in progress into Berkshire: and how he made him a banquet in his own house.

About the tenth year of the King's reign, His Grace made his progress into Berkshire, against which time Jack of Newbury, clothed 30. tall fellows, being his household servants, in blue coats, faced with sarcenet, everyone having a good sword & buckler on his shoulder, himself in a plain russet coat, a pair of white kersey breeches without welt or guard,[33] and stockings of the same piece sewed to his slops, which had a great codpiece, whereon he stuck his pins: who knowing the King would come over a certain meadow, near adjoining to the town, got himself thither with all his men; and repairing to a certain ant-hill, which was in the field, took up his seat there, causing his men to stand round about the same with their swords drawn.

The King coming near the place with the rest of his nobility, and seeing them stand with their drawn weapons, sent to know the cause. Garret King at Arms[34] was the messenger, who spake in this sort. "Good fellows, the King's Majesty would know to what end you stand here with your swords and bucklers prepared to fight."

With that, Jack of Newbury started up, and made this answer. "Herald," quoth he, "return to His Highness, it is poor Jack of Newbury, who being scant marquess of a mole-hill, is chosen Prince of Ants: and here I stand with my weapons and guard about me, to defend and keep these my poor and painful subjects, from the force of the idle butterflies, their sworn enemies, lest they should disturb this quiet commonwealth, who this summer season are making their winter's provision."

The messenger returning, told His Grace that it was one Jack of Newbury, that stood there with his men about him, to guard (as they say) a company of ants, from the furious wrath of the Prince of Butterflies. With this news the King heartily laughed, saying: "Indeed it is no marvel he stands so well prepared, considering what a terrible tyrant he hath to deal withal. Certainly my lords," quoth he, "this seems to be a pleasant fellow: and therefore we will send to talk with him."

The messenger being sent, told Jack he must come speak with the King. Quoth he, "His Grace hath a horse and I am on foot; therefore will him to come to me: beside that, while I am away, our enemies might come and put my people in hazard, as the Scots did England, while our King was in France."

"How dares the lamb be so bold with the lion?" quoth the herald.

"Why," quoth he, "if there be a lion in the field, here is never a cock to fear him: and tell His Majesty, he might think me a very bad governor, that would walk aside upon pleasure, and leave my people in peril. Herald," quoth he, "it is written, He that hath a charge must look to it, and so tell thy lord my king."

The message being done, the King said: "My lords, seeing it will be no other, we will ride up to the Emperor of Ants, that is so careful in his government."

At the King's approach, Jack of Newbury and his servants put up all their weapons, and with a joyful cry flung up their caps in token of victory. "Why how now my masters," quoth the King, "is your wars ended: Let me see, where is the lord general of this great camp?"

With that, Jack of Newbury with all his servants fell on their knees, saying: "God save the King of England, whose sight hath put our foes to flight, and brought great peace to the poor labouring people."

"Trust me," quoth our King, "here be pretty fellows to fight against butterflies: I must commend your courage, that dares withstand such mighty giants."

"Most dread sovereign," quoth Jack, "not long ago, in my conceit, I saw the most provident nation of the ants, summoned their chief peers to a parliament, which was held in the famous city Dry Dusty, the one and twentieth day of September: whereas, by their wisdoms, I was chosen their king, at what time also many bills of complaint were brought in against divers ill members in the commonwealth: among whom, the mole was attainted of high treason to their state: and therefore was banished forever from their quiet kingdom: so was the grasshopper and the caterpillar, because they were not only idle, but also lived upon the labours of other men, amongst the rest, the butterfly was very much misliked, but few durst say anything to him, because of his golden apparel: who through sufferance grew so ambitious and malapert, that the poor ant could no sooner get an egg into her nest, but he would have it away, and especially against Easter,[35] which at length was misliked. This painted ass took snuff in the nose,[36] and assembled a great many other of his own coat, by windy wars to root this painful people out of the land, that he himself might be seated above them all." ("These were proud butterflies," quoth the King.) "Whereupon I with my men," quoth Jack, "prepared ourselves to withstand them, till such time as Your Majesty's royal presence put them to flight."

"Tush," said the King, "thou must think that the force of flies is not great."

"Notwithstanding," quoth Jack, "their gay gowns make poor men afraid."

"I perceive," quoth Cardinal Wolsey, "that you being a king of ants do carry a great grudge to the butterflies."

"Aye," quoth Jack, "we be as great foes, as the fox and the snake are friends: for the one of them being subtle, loves the other for his craft: but now I intend to be no longer a prince, because the majesty of a king hath eclipsed my glory: so that looking like the peacock on my black feet makes me abase my vainglorious feathers, and humbly yield unto His Majesty all my sovereign rule and dignity, both of life and goods, casting my weapons at his feet, to do any service wherein His Grace shall command me."

"God a mercy good Jack," quoth the King, "I have often heard of thee, and this morning, I mean to visit thy house."

Thus the King with great delight rode along until he came to the town's end, where a great multitude of people attended to see His Majesty: where also Queen Katharine with all her train met him. Thus with great rejoicing of the commons, the King and Queen passed along to this jolly clothier's house, where the good wife of the house with threescore maidens attending on her, presented the King with a beehive, most richly gilt with gold, & all the bees therein were also made of gold curiously by art, and out of the top of the same hive, sprung a flourishing green tree, which bore golden apples, and at the root thereof lay divers serpents, seeking to destroy it, whom Prudence and Fortitude trod under their feet, holding this inscription in their hands:

Lo here presented to your royal sight,
The figure of a flourishing commonwealth:
Where virtuous subjects labour with delight,
And beat the drones to death which live by stealth:
  Ambition, Envy, Treason, loathsome serpents be,
  Which seek the downfall of this fruitful tree.

But Lady Prudence with deep searching eye,
Their ill intended purpose doth prevent,
And noble Fortitude standing always nigh,
Dispersed their power prepared with bad intent.
  Thus are they foiled that mount with means unmeet,
  And so like slaves are trodden under feet.

The King favourably accepted this emblem, and receiving it at the women's hands, willed Cardinal Wolsey to look thereon, commanding it should be sent to Windsor Castle. This cardinal was at that time Lord Chancellor of England, and a wonderful proud prelate, by whose means great variance was set betwixt the King of England and the French king, the Emperor of Almaine,[37] and divers other princes of Christendom, whereby the traffic of those merchants was utterly forbidden, which bred a general woe through England, especially among clothiers: insomuch, that having no sale for their cloth, they were fain to put away many of their people which wrought for them, as hereafter more at large shall be declared.

Then was His Majesty brought into a great hall, where four long tables stood ready covered: and passing through that place, the King and Queen came into a fair and large parlour, hung about with goodly tapestry, where was a table prepared for His Highness and the Queen's Grace. All the floor where the King sat was covered with broadcloths instead of green rushes: these were choice pieces of the finest wool, of an azure colour, valued at an hundred pound a cloth, which afterward was given to His Majesty. The King being set with the chiefest of the Council about him, after a delicate dinner, a sumptuous banquet was brought in, served all in glass: the description whereof were too long for me to write, and you to read. The great hall was also filled with lords, knights, and gentlemen, who were attended by no other but the servants of the house. The ladies of honour and gentlewomen of the court were all seated in another parlour by themselves: at whose table the maidens of the house did wait in decent sort. The servingmen by themselves, and the pages & footmen by themselves, upon whom the prentices did attend most diligently. During the King's abiding in this place, there was no want of delicates: Rhenish wine, claret wine & sack, was as plentiful as small ale. Thus from the highest to the lowest, they were served in such sort, as no discontent was found any way, so that great commendations redounded unto the goodman of the house.

The Lord Cardinal that of late found himself galled by the allegory of the ants, spake in this wise to the King. "If it should please Your Highness," quoth he, "but to note the vainglory of these artificers, you should find no small cause of dislike in many of their actions. For an instance, the fellow of this house, he hath not stuck this day to undo himself, only to become famous by receiving of Your Majesty: like Hero-stratus[38] the shoemaker that burned the Temple of Diana, only to get himself a name, more than for any affection he bears to Your Grace, as may well be proved by this: Let there be but a simple subsidy levied upon them for the assistance of Your Highness' wars, or any other weighty affairs of the commonwealth and state of the realm, though it be not the twentieth part of their substance, they will so grudge and repine, that it is wonderful: and like people desperate cry out, they be quite undone."

"My Lord Cardinal," quoth the Queen, "(under correction of my lord the King) I durst lay an hundred pound Jack of Newbury was never of that mind, nor is not at this instant: if ye ask him, I warrant he will say so. Myself also had a proof thereof at the Scottish invasion, at what time this man being seased [39] but at six men, brought (at his own cost) an hundred and fifty into the field."

"I would I had more such subjects," said the King, "and many of so good a mind."

"Ho, ho, Harry," quoth Will Summers,[40] "then had not Empson and Dudley[41] been chronicled for knaves, nor sent to the Tower for treason."

"But then they had not known the pain of imprisonment," quoth our King, "who with their subtilty grieved many others."

"But their subtilty was such that it broke their necks," quoth Will Summers.

Whereat the King and Queen laughing heartily, rose from the table. By which time Jack of Newbury had caused all his folks to go to their work, that His Grace and all the nobility might see it: so indeed the Queen had requested. Then came His Highness where he saw an hundred looms, standing in one room, and two men working in every one, who pleasantly sung on this sort.

THE WEAVERS' SONG

When Hercules did use to spin,
    and Pallas wrought upon the loom,

Our trade to flourish did begin,
  while conscience went not selling broom.[42]
    Then love and friendship did agree,
    To keep the band of amity.

When princes' sons kept sheep in field,
  and queens made cakes of wheaten flour,
Then men to lucre did not yield,
  which brought good cheer in every bower.
    Then love and friendship did agree,
    To hold the bands of amity.

But when that giants huge and high,
  did fight with spears like weavers' beams,
Then they in iron beds did lie,
  and brought poor men to hard extremes.
    Yet love and friendship did agree,
    To hold the bands of amity.

Then David took his sling and stone,
  not fearing great Goliath's strength,
He pierced his brain, and broke the bone,
  though he were fifty foot of length.
    For love and friendship, &c.

But while the Greeks besieged Troy,
  Penelope apace did spin,
And weavers wrought with mickle joy,
  though little gains were coming in.
    For love and friendship, &c.

Had Helen then sat carding wool,
  (whose beauteous face did breed such strife)
She had not been Sir Paris' trull,
  nor caus'd so many lose their life,
    Yet we by love did still agree, &c.

Or had King Priam's wanton son
  been making quills with sweet content.
He had not then his friends undone,
  when he to Greece a gadding went.
    For love and friendship did agree, &c.

The cedar tree endures more storms,
　　than little shrubs that sprout not high:
The weaver lives more void of harms,
　　than princes of great dignity.
　　　　While love and friendship doth agree, &c.

The shepherd sitting in the field,
　　doth tune his pipe with heart's delight:
When princes march with spear and shield,
　　the poor man soundly sleeps all night.
　　　　While love and friendship doth agree, &c.

Yet this by proof is daily tried,
　　For God's good gifts we are ingrate:
And no man through the world so wide,
　　lives well contented with his state.
　　　　No love nor friendship we can see,
　　　　to hold the bands of amity.

"Well sung good fellows," said our King: "Light hearts and merry minds live long without gray hairs."

"But," quoth Will Summers, "seldom without red noses."

"Well," said the King, "there is a hundred angels to make cheer withal: and look that every year once you make a feast among yourselves, and frankly (every year) I give you leave to fetch four bucks out of Donnington Park, without any man's let or controlment."

"O I beseech Your Grace," quoth Will Summers, "let it be with a condition."

"What is that?" said our King.

"My liege," quoth he, "that although the keeper will have the skins, that they may give their wives the horns."

"Go to," said the Queen, "thy head is fuller of knavery, than thy purse is of crowns."

The poor workmen humbly thanked His Majesty for his bountiful liberality: and ever since, it hath been a custom among the weavers, every year presently after Bartholmew-tide, in a remembrance of the King's favour, to meet together, and make a merry feast.

His Majesty came next among the spinsters and carders,

who were merrily aworking: whereat Will Summers fell into a great laughter.

"What ails the fool to laugh?" said the King.

"Marry," quoth Will Summers, "to see these maidens get their living as bulls do eat their meat."

"How is that?" said the Queen.

"By going still backward," quoth Will Summers: "and I will lay a wager, that they that practise so well being maids to go backward, will quickly learn ere long to fall backward."

"But sirra," said the Cardinal, "thou didst fall forward when thou brokest thy face in Master Kingsmill's cellar." [43]

"But you my lord sat forward," quoth Will Summers, "when you sat in the stocks at Sir Amie Paulet's." [44] Whereat there was greater laughing than before.

The King and Queen, and all the nobility heedfully beheld these women, who for the most part were very fair and comely creatures, and were all attired alike from top to toe. Then (after due reverence) the maidens in dulcet manner chanted out this song, two of them singing the ditty, and all the rest bearing the burden.

THE MAIDENS' SONG [45]

It was a knight in Scotland born,
   follow my love, leap over the strand:
Was taken prisoner and left forlorn,
   even by the good Earl of Northumberland.

Then was he cast in prison strong,
   follow my love, leap over the strand:
Where he could not walk nor lie along,
   even by the good Earl of Northumberland.

And as in sorrow thus he lay,
   follow my love, come over the strand:
The Earl's sweet daughter walked that way,
   and she the fair flower of Northumberland.

And passing by, like an angel bright,
   follow my love, come over the strand:
This prisoner had of her a sight,
   and she the fair flower of Northumberland.

And loud to her this knight did cry,
  follow my love, come over the strand:
The salt tears standing in his eye,
  and she the fair flower of Northumberland.

"Fair lady," he said, "take pity on me,
  follow my love, come over the strand:
And let me not in prison die,
  and you the fair flower of Northumberland."

"Fair, sir, how should I take pity on thee,
  follow my love, come over the strand:
Thou being a foe to our country,
  and I the fair flower of Northumberland."

"Fair lady, I am no foe," he said,
  "follow my love, come over the strand:
Through thy sweet love here was I stayed,
  for thee the fair flower of Northumberland."

"Why shouldst thou come here for love of me,
  follow my love, come over the strand:
Having wife and children in thy country,
  and I the fair flower of Northumberland."

"I swear by the blessed Trinity,
  follow my love, come over the strand:
I have no wife nor children I,
  nor dwelling at home in merry Scotland.

"If courteously you will set me free,
  follow my love, come over the strand:
I vow that I will marry thee,
  so soon as I come in merry Scotland.

"Thou shalt be lady of castles and towers,
  follow my love, come over the strand:
And sit like a queen in princely bowers,
  when I am at home in fair Scotland."

Then parted hence this lady gay,
  follow my love, come over the strand:
And got her father's ring away,
  to help this sad knight into fair Scotland.

Likewise much gold she got by sleight,
  follow my love, come over the strand:
And all to help this forlorn knight,
  To wend from her father to fair Scotland.

Two gallant steeds both good and able,
  follow my love, come over the strand:
She likewise took out of the stable,
  To ride with this knight into fair Scotland.

And to the jailor she sent this ring,
  follow my love, come over the strand:
The knight from prison forth to bring,
  to wend with her into fair Scotland.

This token set this prisoner free,
  follow my love, come over the strand:
Who straight went to this fair lady,
  to wend with her into fair Scotland.

A gallant steed he did bestride,
  follow my love, come over the strand:
And with the lady away did ride,
  and she the fair flower of Northumberland.

They rode till they came to a water clear,
  follow my love, come over the strand:
"Good sir how should I follow you here,
  and I the fair flower of Northumberland.

"The water is rough and wonderful deep,
  follow my love, come over the strand:
And on my saddle I shall not keep,
  and I the fair flower of Northumberland."

"Fear not the ford, fair lady," quoth he,
  "follow my love, come over the strand:
For long I cannot stay for thee,
  and thou the fair flower of Northumberland."

The lady pricked her wanton steed,
  follow my love, come over the strand:
And over the river swam with speed,
  and she the fair flower of Northumberland.

From top to toe all wet was she,
  follow my love, come over the strand:
"This have I done for love of thee,
  and I the fair flower of Northumberland."

Thus rode she all one winter's night,
  follow my love, come over the strand:
Till Edinburgh they saw in sight,
  the chiefest town in all Scotland.

"Now choose," quoth he, "thou wanton flower,
  follow my love, come over the strand:
Whether thou wilt be my paramour,
  or get thee home to Northumberland.

"For I have wife and children five,
  follow my love, come over the strand:
In Edinburgh they be alive,
  then get thee home to fair England.

"This favour shalt thou have to boot,
  follow my love, come over the strand:
I'll have thy horse, go thou a foot,
  go get thee home to Northumberland."

"O false and faithless knight," quoth she,
  "follow my love, come over the strand:
And canst thou deal so bad with me,
  and I the fair flower of Northumberland?

"Dishonour not a lady's name,
  follow my love, come over the strand:
But draw thy sword, and end my shame,
  and I the fair flower of Northumberland."

He took her from her stately steed,
  follow my love, come over the strand:
And left her there in extreme need,
  and she the fair flower of Northumberland.

Then sat she down full heavily,
  follow my love, come over the strand:
At length two knights came riding by,
  two gallant knights of fair England.

She fell down humbly on her knee,
    follow my love, come over the strand:
Saying, "Courteous knights take pity on me,
    and I the fair flower of Northumberland.

"I have offended my father dear,
    follow my love, come over the strand:
And by a false knight that brought me here,
    from the good Earl of Northumberland."

They took her up behind him then,
    follow my love, come over the strand:
And brought her to her father's again,
    And he the good Earl of Northumberland.

All you fair maidens be warned by me,
    follow my love, come over the strand:
Scots were never true, nor never will be,
    to lord, nor lady, nor fair England.

FINIS

After the King's Majesty and the Queen had heard this song sweetly sung by them, he cast them a great reward: and so departing thence, went to the fulling-mills, and dye-house, where a great many were also hard at work: and His Majesty perceiving what a great number of people were by this one man set on work, both admired, and commended him, saying further, that no trade in all the land was so much to be cherished and maintained as this, "which," quoth he, "may well be called, The life of the poor." And as the King returned from this place with intent to take horse and depart, there met him a great many of children in garments of white silk, fringed with gold, their heads crowned with golden bays, and about their arms each one had a scarf of green sarcenet fast tied, in their hands they bore silver bows, and under their girdles golden arrows.

The foremost of them represented Diana, Goddess of Chastity, who was attended on by a train of beautiful nymphs, and they presented to the King four prisoners:

The first was a stern and grisly woman, carrying a frowning countenance, and her forehead full of wrinkles, her hair as black as pitch, and her garments all bloody, a great sword she had in her hand all stained with purple gore: they called her name Bellona, Goddess of Wars, who had three daughters: the first of them was a tall woman, so lean and ill-favoured, that her cheekbones were ready to start out of the skin, of a pale and deadly colour: her eyes sunk into her head: her legs so feeble, that they could scantly carry the body; all along her arms & hands through the skin you might tell the sinews, joints and bones: her teeth were very strong and sharp withal: she was so greedy, that she was ready with her teeth to tear the skin from her own arms: her attire was black, and all torn and ragged, she went barefooted, and her name was Famine.

The second was a strong and lusty woman, with a look pitiless, and unmerciful countenance: her garments were all made of iron and steel, and she carried in her hand a naked weapon, and she was called the Sword.

The third was also a cruel creature, her eyes did sparkle like burning coals: her hair was like a flame, and her garments like burning brass: she was so hot, that none could stand near her, and they called her name Fire.

After this they retired again, and brought unto His Highness two other personages, their countenance was princely and amiable, their attire most rich and sumptuous: the one carried in his hand a golden trumpet, and the other a palm tree: and these were called Fame & Victory, whom the Goddess of Chastity charged to wait upon this famous prince forever. This done, each child after other with due reverence, gave unto His Majesty a sweet smelling gilliflower, after the manner of the Persians,[46] offering something in token of loyalty and obedience.

The King and Queen beholding the sweet favour and countenance of these children, demanded of Jack of Newbury whose children they were?

Who answered: "It shall please Your Highness to understand, that these are the children of poor people, that do get their living by picking of wool, having scant a good meal once in a week."

With that the King began to tell his gilliflowers, whereby he found that there was 96. children.

"Certainly," said the Queen, "I perceive God gives as fair children to the poor as to the rich, and fairer many times: and though their diet and keeping be but simple, the blessing of God doth cherish them. Therefore," said the Queen, "I will request to have two of them to wait in my chamber."

"Fair Katharine," said the King, "thou and I have jumped in one opinion,[47] in thinking these children fitter for the court than the country:" whereupon he made choice of a dozen more, four he ordained to be pages to his royal person, and the rest he sent to the universities, allotting to everyone a gentleman's living. Divers of the noblemen did in like sort entertain some of those children into their services, so that (in the end) not one was left to pick wool, but were all so provided for, that their parents never needed to care for them: and God so blessed them, that each of them came to be men of great account and authority in the land, whose posterities remain to this day worshipful and famous.

The King, Queen, and nobles, being ready to depart, after great thanks and gifts given to Jack of Newbury His Majesty would have made him knight, but he meekly refused it, saying, "I beseech Your Grace let me live a poor clothier among my people, in whose maintenance I take more felicity, than in all the vain titles of gentility: for these are the labouring ants whom I seek to defend, and these be the bees which I keep: who labour in this life, nor for ourselves, but for the glory of God, and to do service to our dread sovereign."

"Thy knighthood need be no hindrance of thy faculty," quoth the King.

"O my dread sovereign," said Jack, "honour and worship may be compared to the Lake of Lethe, which makes men forget themselves that taste thereof: and to the end I may still keep in mind from whence I came, and what I am, I beseech Your Grace let me rest in my russet coat, a poor clothier to my dying day."

"Seeing then," said the King, "that a man's mind is a kingdom to himself, I will leave thee to the riches of thy own content, and so farewell."

The Queen's Majesty taking her leave of the good wife with a princely kiss, gave her in token of remembrance a most precious and rich diamond set in gold, about the which was also curiously set six rubies and six emeralds in one piece, valued at nine hundred marks: and so Her Grace departed.

But in this mean space, Will Summers kept company among the maids, and betook himself to spinning as they did, which among them was held as a forfeit of a gallon of wine, but William by no means would pay it, except they would take it out in kisses, rating every kiss at a farthing.

"This payment we refuse for two causes," quoth the maids: "the one for that we esteem not kisses at so base a rate; and the other, because in so doing we should give as much as you."

CHAP. IIII

How the maidens served Will Summers for his sauciness.

The maidens consented together, seeing Will Summers was so busy both with their work and in his words, and would not pay his forfeiture, to serve him as he deserved: first therefore they bound him hands and feet, and set him upright against a post, tying him thereto: which he took in ill part, notwithstanding he could not resist them. And because he let his tongue run at random, they set a fair gag in his mouth, such a one as he could not for his life put away: so that he stood as one gaping for wind. Then one of them got a couple of dogs' droppings, and putting them in a bag, laid them in soak in a basin of water, while the rest turned down the collar of his jerkin, and put an house-cloth about his neck instead of a fine towel: then came the other maid with a basin and water in the same, and with the perfume in the pudding-bag, flapped him about the face and lips, till he looked like a tawny Moor, and with her hand washed him very orderly: the smell being somewhat strong, Will could be no means abide it, and for want of other language, cried, "Ah ha ha ha." Fain he would have spit, and could not, so that he was fain to swallow down such liquor as he never tasted the like. When he had a pretty while been washed in this sort, at the length he crouched down upon his knees, yielding himself to their favour: which the maidens perceiving, pulled the gag out of his mouth.

He had no sooner the liberty of his tongue, but that he curst and swore like a devil: the maids that could scant stand for laughing, at last asked how he liked his washing?

"God's 'ounds," quoth he, "I was never thus washed, nor ever met with such barbers since I was born: let me go," quoth he, "and I will give you whatsoever you will demand," wherewith he cast them an English crown.

"Nay," quoth one of the maids, "you are yet but washed, but we will shave you ere ye go."

"Sweet maids," quoth he, "pardon my shaving, let it suffice that you have washed me: if I have done a trespass to your trade, forgive it me, and I will never hereafter offend you."

"Tush," said the maids, "you have made our wheels cast their bands, and bruised the teeth of our cards in such sort, as the offence may not be remitted without great penance. As for your gold, we regard it not: therefore as you are perfumed fit for the dogs, so we enjoin you this night to serve all our hogs, which penance, if you will swear with all speed to perform, we will let you loose."

"O," quoth Will, "the huge elephant was never more fearful of the silly sheep,[48] than I am of your displeasures: therefore let me loose, and I will do it with all diligence."

Then they unbound him, and brought him among a great company of swine, which when Will had well viewed over, he drove out of the yard all the sows:

"Why how now," quoth the maids, "what mean you by this?"

"Marry," quoth Will, "these be all sows, and my penance is but to serve the hogs."

"Is it true," quoth they, "have you overtaken us in this sort? Well, look there be not one hog unserved we would advise you."

William Summers stripped up his sleeves very orderly, and clapped an apron about his motley hosen, and taking a pail served the hogs handsomely. When he had given them all meat, he said thus:

> My task is duly done,
> My liberty is won,
> The hogs have eat their crabs,
> Therefore farewell you drabs.

"Nay soft friend," quoth they, "the veriest hog of all hath yet had nothing."

"Where the devil is he," said Will, "that I see him not?"

"Wrapped in a motley jerkin," quoth they, "take thyself by the nose, and thou shalt catch him by the snout."

"I was never so very a hog," quoth he, "but I would alway spare from my own belly to give a woman."

"If thou do not," say they, "eat (like the prodigal child) with thy fellow hogs, we will so shave thee, as thou shalt dearly repent thy disobedience."

He seeing no remedy, committed himself to their mercy: and so they let him go. When he came to the court, he shewed to the King all his adventure among the weaver's maidens, whereat the King and Queen laughed heartily.

CHAP. V

Of the pictures which Jack of Newbury had in his house, whereby he encouraged his servants to seek for fame and dignity.

In a fair large parlour which was wainscotted round about, Jack of Newbury had fifteen fair pictures hanging, which were covered with curtains of green silk, fringed with gold, which he would often shew to his friends and servants.

In the first was the picture of a shepherd, before whom kneeled a great king named Viriat,[49] who sometime governed the people of Portugal.

"See here," quoth Jack, "the father a shepherd, the son a sovereign. This man ruled in Portugal, and made great wars against the Romans, and after that invaded Spain, yet in the end was traitorously slain."

The next was the portraiture of Agathocles, which for his surpassing wisdom and manhood, was created King of Sicilia, and maintained battle against the people of Carthage. His father was a poor potter, before whom he also kneeled. And it was the use of this king, that whensoever he made a banquet, he would have as well vessels of earth as of gold set upon the table, to the intent he might always bear in mind the place of his beginning, his father's house and family.

The third was the picture of Iphicrates an Athenian born, who vanquished the Lacedaemonians in plain and open battle. This man was captain general to Artaxerxes, King of Persia, whose father was notwithstanding a cobbler and there likewise pictured. Eumenes was also a famous captain to Alexander the Great, whose father was no other than a carter.

The fourth was the similitude of Aelius Pertinax, sometime Emperor of Rome, yet was his father but a weaver: and afterward, to give example to others of low condition to bear minds of worthy men, he caused the shop to be beautified with marble curiously cut, wherein his father before him was wont to get his living.

The fifth was the picture of Diocletian, that so much adorned Rome with his magnifical and triumphant victories. This was a famous emperor, although no other than the son of a bookbinder.

Valentinian stood the next, painted most artificially, who was also crowned emperor, and was but the son of a poor ropemaker: as in the same picture was expressed; where his father was painted by him, using his trade.

The seventh was the Emperor Probus, whose father being a gardener, was pictured by him holding a spade.

The eighth picture was of Marcus Aurelius, whom every age honoureth, he was so wise and prudent an emperor; yet was he but a clothweaver's son.

The ninth was the portraiture of the valiant Emperor Maximinus, the son of a blacksmith, who was there painted as he was wont to work at the anvil.

In the tenth table was painted the Emperor Gabianus, who at the first was but a poor shepherd.

Next to this picture, was placed the pictures of two popes of Rome, whose wisdom and learning advanced them to that dignity. The first was the lively counterfeit of Pope John the 22 whose father was a shoemaker: he being elected pope, increased their rents and patrimony greatly.

The other was the picture of Pope Sixtus the fourth of that name, being a poor mariner's son.

The thirteenth picture was of Lamusius King of Lombardy, who was no better than the son of a common strumpet: being painted like a naked child walking in the water, and taking hold of the point of a lance, by the which he held fast, and saved himself. The reason whereof was this: After his lewd mother was delivered of him, she unnaturally threw him into a deep stinking ditch, wherein was some water. By hap King Agilmond passed that way, and found this child almost drowned; who moving him softly with the point of his lance, the better to perceive what he was, the child (though then newly born) took hold thereof with one of his pretty hands, not suffering it to slide or slip away again: which thing the King considering, being amazed at the strange force of this young little infant, caused it to be taken up, and carefully to be fostered. And because the place where he found him was called Lama, he named the child Lamusius: who afterward grew to be so brave a man, and so much favoured of Fortune, that in the end he was crowned King of the Lombards, who lived there in honour, and in his succession after him, even until the time of the unfortunate King Albovina, when all came to ruin, subversion and destruction.

In the fourteenth picture Primislas King of Bohemia was most artificially drawn; before whom there stood an horse without bridle or saddle, in a field where husbandmen were at plough. "The cause why this King was thus painted," quoth Jack, "was this. At that time the King of the Bohemians died without issue, and great strife being amongst the nobility for a new king, at length they all consented that a horse should be let into the field, without bridle or saddle, having all determined with most assured purpose to make him their king, before whom this horse rested: At what time it came to pass, that the horse first stayed himself before this Primislas, being a simple creature, who was then busy driving the plough, they presently made him their sovereign, who ordered himself and his kingdom very wisely. He ordained many good laws, he compassed the city of Prague with strong walls, besides many other things, meriting perpetual laud and commendations."

The fifteenth was the picture of Theophrastus, a philosopher, a counsellor of kings, and companion of nobles, who was but son of a tailor.

"Seeing then my good servants, that these men have been advanced to high estate and princely dignities, by wisdom, learning and diligence, I would wish you to imitate the like virtues, that you might attain the like honours: for which of you doth know what good fortune God hath in store for you? there is none of you so poorly born, but that men of baser birth have come to great honours. The idle hand shall ever go in a ragged garment, and the slothful live in reproach: but such as do lead a virtuous life, and govern themselves discreetly shall of the best be esteemed, and spend their days in credit."

CHAP. VI

How all the clothiers in England joined together, & with one consent complained to the King of their great hindrance sustained for want of traffic into other countries, whereupon they could get no sale for their cloth.

By means of the wars which our King had with other countries, many merchant strangers were prohibited for coming to England, as also our own merchants (in like sort) were forbidden to have dealings with France or the Low Countries: by means whereof the clothiers had most of their cloth lying on their hands, and that which they sold was at so low a rate, that the money scantly paid for the wool and workmanship. Whereupon they sought to ease themselves by abating the poor workmen's wages. And when that did not prevail, they turned away many of their people, weavers, shearmen, spinsters and carders, so that where there was a hundred looms kept in one town, there was scant fifty: and he that kept twenty put down ten. Many a poor man (for want of work) was hereby undone, with his wife and children, and it made many a poor widow to sit with a hungry belly. This bred great woe in most places in England. In the end Jack of Newbury intended (in the behalf of the poor) to make a supplication to the King: and to the end he might do it the more effectually, he sent letters to all the chief clothing towns in England to this effect.

The Letter

"Well beloved friends and brethren, having a taste of the general grief, and feeling (in some measure) the extremity of these times, I fell into consideration by what means we might best expel these sorrows, and recover our former commodity.

"When I had well thought hereon, I found that nothing was more needful herein, than a faithful unity among ourselves. This sore of necessity can no way be cured but by concord: for like as the flame consumes the candle, so men through discord waste themselves. The poor hate the rich, because they will not set them on work; and the rich hate the poor, because they seem burdenous: so both are offended for want of gain. When Belinus and Brennus[50] were at strife, the queen their mother in their greatest fury persuaded them to peace, by urging her conception of them in one womb, and mutual cherishing of them from their tender years: so let our art of clothing, which like a kind mother hath cherished us with the excellency of her secrets, persuade us to an unity. Though our occupation be decayed, let us not deal with it as men do by their old shoes, which after they have long born them out of the mire, do in the end fling them on the dunghill: or as the husbandman doth by his bees, who for their honey burns them. Dear friends, consider that our trade will maintain us, if we will uphold it: and there is nothing base, but that which is basely used.

"Assemble therefore yourselves together, and in every town tell the number of those that have their living by means of this trade, note it in a bill, and send it to me. And because suits in courts are like winter nights, long and wearisome, let there be in each place a weekly collection made to defray charges: for I tell you, noblemen's secretaries and cunning lawyers have slow tongues and deaf ears, which must be daily nointed [51] with the sweet oil of angels. Then let two honest discreet men be chosen and sent out of every town to meet me at Blackwell Hall [52] in London on All Saints' Eve, and then we will present our humble petition to the King. Thus I bid you heartily farewell."

Copies of this letter being sealed, they were sent to all the clothing towns of England, and the weavers both of linen and woolen gladly received them: so that when all the bills were brought together, there were found of the clothiers, and those they maintained, three score thousand and six hundred persons. Moreover, every clothing town sending up two men to London, they were found to be an hundred and twelve persons, who in very humble sort fell down before His Majesty walking in S. James his Park, and delivered to him their petition.

The King presently perusing it, asked if they were all clothiers?

Who answered (as it were one man) in this sort: "We are (most gracious King) all poor clothiers, and Your Majesty's faithful subjects."

"My lords," quoth the King, "let these men's complaint be thoroughly looked into, and their griefs redressed: for I account them in the number of my best commonwealth's men. As the clergy for the soul, the soldier for defence of his country, the lawyer to execute justice, the husbandman to feed the belly: so is the skillful clothier no less necessary for the clothing of the back, whom we may reckon among the chief yeomen of our land: and as the crystal sight of the eye is tenderly to be kept from harms because it gives the whole body light: so is the clothier's whose cunning hand provides garments to defend our naked parts from the winter's nipping frost. Many more reasons there are, which may move us to redress their griefs: but let it suffice that I command to have it done."

With that, His Grace delivered the petition to the Lord Chancellor, and all the clothiers cried, "God save the King."

But as the King was ready to depart, he suddenly turned about, saying: "I remember there is one Jack of Newbury, I muse he had not his hand in this business, who professed himself to be a defender of true labourers."

Then said the Duke of Somerset:[53] "It may be his purse is answerable for his person."

"Nay," quoth the Lord Cardinal, "all his treasure is little enough to maintain wars against the butterflies."

With that Jack shewed himself unto the King, and privately told His Grace of their grief anew.

To whom His Majesty said: "Give thy attendance at the council chamber, where thou shalt receive answer to thy content." And so His Highness departed.

Finally, it was agreed that the merchants should freely

traffic one with another, and that proclamation thereof should be made as well on the other side the sea, as in our land: but it was long before this was effected, by reason the Cardinal being Lord Chancellor, put off the matter from time to time.

And because the clothiers thought it not best to depart before it was ended, they gave their daily attendance at the Cardinal's house: but spent many days to no purpose: sometime they were answered, My Lord was busy, and could not be spoke withal; or else he was asleep, & they durst not wake him: or at his study, and they would not disturb him: or at his prayers, and they durst not displease him: and still one thing or other stood in the way to hinder them. At last, Patch the Cardinal's fool, being (by their often repair thither) well acquainted with the clothiers, came unto them and said: "What, have you not spoken with my lord yet?"

"No truly," quoth they, "we hear say he is busy, and we stay till His Grace be at leisure."

"Is it true?" said Patch, and with that in all haste he went out of the hall, and at last came in again with a great bundle of straw on his back.

"Why how now Patch," quoth the gentlemen, "what wilt thou do with that straw?"

"Marry," quoth he, "I will put it under these honest men's feet, lest they should freeze ere they find my Lord at leisure."

This made them all to laugh, and caused Patch to bear away his straw again. "Well, well," quoth he, "if it cost you a groat's worth of faggots at night, blame not me."

"Trust me," said Jack of Newbury, "if my Lord Cardinal's father had been no hastier in killing of calves, than he is in dispatching of poor men's suits, I doubt he had never worn a miter."

This he spake betwixt themselves softly, but yet not so softly, but that he was overheard by a flattering fellow that stood by, who made it known to some of the gentlemen, and they straight certified the Cardinal thereof.

The Cardinal (who was of a very high spirit, and a lofty

aspiring mind) was marvellously displeased at Jack of Newbury: wherefore in his rage he commanded and sent the clothiers all to prison, because the one of them should not sue for the other's releasement. Four days lay these men in the Marshalsea, till at last they made their humble petition to the King for their release: but some of the Cardinal's friends kept it from the King's sight. Notwithstanding, the Duke of Somerset, knowing thereof, spake with the Lord Cardinal about the matter, wishing he would speedily release them, lest it breed him some displeasure: "For you may perceive," quoth the Duke, "how highly the King esteems men of that faculty."

"Sir," quoth the Cardinal, "I doubt not but to answer their imprisonment well enough, being persuaded that none would have given me such a quip but an heretic: and I dare warrant you were this Jack of Newbury well examined, he would be found to be infected with Luther's spirit, against whom our King hath of late written a most learned book,[54] in respect whereof, the Pope's Holiness hath entitled His Majesty *Defender of the Faith:* therefore I tell you such fellows are fitter to be faggots for fire, than fathers of families: notwithstanding (at Your Grace's request) I will release them."

Accordingly the Cardinal sent for the clothiers afore him to Whitehall,[55] his new built house by Westminster, and there bestowing his blessing upon them, said: "Though you have offended me I pardon you; for as Stephen[56] forgave his enemies that stoned him, and our Saviour those sinful men that crucified him, so do I forgive you that high trespass committed in disgrace of my birth: for herein do men come nearest unto God, in shewing mercy and compassion. But see hereafter you offend no more. Touching your suit it is granted, and tomorrow shall be published through London."

This being said they departed: and according to the Cardinal's words, their business was ended. The Stillyard merchants joyful hereof, made the clothiers a great banquet.

After which, each man departed home, carrying tidings of their good success; so that within short space, clothing was again very good, and poor men as well set on work as before.

How a young Italian merchant coming to Jack of New-bury's house, was greatly enamoured of one of his maidens, and how he was served.

Among other servants which Jack of Newbury kept, there was in his house threescore maidens, which every Sunday waited on his wife to church and home again, who had divers offices. Among other, two were appointed to keep the beams and weights, to weigh out wool to the carders and spinsters, and to receive it in again by weight. One of them was a comely maiden, fair and lovely, born of wealthy parents, and brought up in good qualities, her name was Joan: so it was, that a young wealthy Italian merchant, coming oft from London thither to bargain for cloth (for at that time clothiers most commonly had their cloth bespoken, and half paid for aforehand). This Master Benedick fell greatly en-amoured of this maiden: and therefore offered much cour-tesy to her, bestowing many gifts on her, which she received thankfully: and albeit his outward countenance shewed his inward affection, yet Joan would take no knowledge thereof. Half the day sometime would he sit by her, as she was weigh-ing wool, often sighing and sobbing to himself, yet saying nothing, as if he had been tongueless, like the men of Coro-mandae;[57] and the loather to speak, for that he could speak but bad English. Joan on the other side that well perceived his passions, did as it were triumph over him, as one that were boundslave to her beauty, and although she knew well enough before that she was fair, yet did she never so highly esteem of herself as at this present: so that when she heard him either sigh, or sob, or groan, she would turn her face in a careless sort, as if she had been born (like the woman of Taproband)[58] without ears.

When Master Benedick saw she made no reckoning of his sorrows, at length he blabbered out this broken English, and spake to her in this sort. "Metressa Joan, be me tra and fa, me love you wod all mine heart, and if you no shall love me again, me know me shall die, sweet Mistress love a me, & be me fa and tra you sal lack noting. First; me will give you de silk for make you a frog: second, de fin fin camree for make you ruffs; and the turd shall be for make fin handker-cher, for wipe your nose."

She mistaking his speech, began to be choleric, wishing him to keep that bodkin to pick his teeth.

"Ho ho Metressa Joan," quoth he, "be Got, you be angry. Oh Metressa Joan, be no chafe with you frien for noting."

"Good sir," quoth she, "keep your friendship for them that cares for it, and fix your love on those that can like you, as for me I tell you plain, I am not minded to marry."

"Oh 'tis no matter for marry, if you will come in my chamber, beshit my bed, and let me kiss you."

The maid though she were very much displeased, yet at these words, she could not forbear laughing for her life.

"Ah ah Metresse Joan: me is very glad to see you merry, hold your hand I say, and there is four crown because you laugh on me."

"I pray you sir keep your crowns, for I need them not."

"Yes be Got you shall have them Metressa Joan, to keep in a pox for you."

She that could not well understand his broken language, mistook his meaning in many things: & therefore willed him not to trouble her any more. Notwithstanding such was his love toward her, that he could not forbear her company, but made many journeys thither for her sake. And as a certain spring in Arcadia makes men to starve that drink of it: so did poor Benedick, feeding his fancy on her beauty: for when he was in London, he did nothing but sorrow, wish-ing he had wings like the monsters of Tartaria,[59] that he might fly to and fro at his pleasure. When any of his friends did tell her of his ardent affection toward her, she wished them to rub him with the sweat of a mule, to assuage his amorous passion, or to fetch him some of the water in Boetia,[60] to cool & extinguish the heat of his affection: "For," quoth she, "let him never hope to be helped by me."

"Well," quoth they, "before he saw thy alluring face, he was a man reasonable and wise, but is now a stark fool, being by thy beauty bereft of wit, as if he had drunk of the river Cea,[61] & like bewitching Circe thou hast certainly transformed him from a man to an ass. There are stones in Pontus,"[62] quoth they, "that the deeper they be laid in the water, the fiercer they burn: unto the which fond lovers may fitly be compared, who the more they are denied, the hotter is their desire: but seeing it is so, that he can find no favour at your hand, we will shew him what you have said, and either draw him from his dumps, or leave him to his own will."

Then spake one of the weavers that dwelt in the town, and was a kinsmen to this maid, "I muse," quoth he, "that Master Benedick will not be persuaded, but like the moth, will play with the flame that will scorch his wings. Methinks, he should forbear to love, or learn to speak, or else woo such as can answer him in his language: for I tell you, that Joan my kinswoman, is no taste for an Italian."

These speeches were told to Benedick with no small addition. When our young merchant heard the matter so plain, he vowed to be revenged of the weaver, and to see if he could find any more friendship of his wife: therefore dissembling his sorrow and covering his grief, with speed he took his journey to Newbury, and pleasantly saluted Mistress Joan: and having his purse full of crowns, he was very liberal to the workfolks, especially to Joan's kinsman, insomuch that he got his favour many times to go forth with him, promising him very largely to do great matters, and to lend him a hundred pound, wishing him to be a servant no longer, beside he liberally bestowed on his wife many gifts, and if she washed him but a band, he would give her an angel: if he did but send her child for a quart of wine, he would give him a shilling for his pains. The which his courtesy changed the weaver's mind, saying he was a very honest gentleman, and worthy to have one far better than his kinswoman.

This pleased Master Benedick well to hear him say so, notwithstanding he made light of the matter, and many times when the weaver was at his master's at work, the merchant would be at home with his wife, drinking and making merry. At length time bringing acquaintance, and often conference breeding familiarity, Master Benedick began somewhat boldly to jest with Gillian, saying that her sight and sweet countenance, had quite reclaimed his love from Joan, and that she only was the mistress of his heart: and if she would lend him her love, he would give her gold from Arabia, orient pearls from India, and make her bracelets of most precious diamonds. "Thy garments shall be of the finest silk that is made in Venice, and thy purse shall still be stuffed with angels. Tell me thy mind my love, and kill me not with unkindness, as did thy scornful kinswoman, whose disdain had almost cost me my life." [63]

"O Master Benedick, think not the wives of England can be won by rewards, or enticed with fair words, as children are with plums: it may be that you being merrily disposed, do speak this to try my constancy. Know then, that I esteem more the honour of my good name, than the sliding wealth of the world."

Master Benedick hearing her say so, desired her, that considering it was love that forced his tongue to bewray his heart's ardent affection, that yet she would be secret: and so for that time took his leave.

When he was gone, the woman began to call her wits together, and to consider of her poor estate, and withal the better to note the comeliness of her person, and the sweet favour of her face: which when she had well thought upon, she began to harbour new thoughts, and to entertain contrary affections, saying, "Shall I content myself to be wrapped

in sheep's russet that may swim in silks, & sit all day carding
for a groat, that can have crowns at my command? No,"
quoth she, "I will no more bear so base a mind, but take
Fortune's favours while they are to be had. The sweet
rose doth flourish but one month, nor women's beauties
but in young years. As the winter's frost consumes the summer flowers, so doth old age banish pleasant delight. O
glorious gold," quoth she, "how sweet is thy smell? how
pleasing is thy sight? Thou subduest princes, and overthrow-
est kingdoms, then how should a silly woman withstand thy
strength?" Thus she rested meditating on preferment, pur-
posing to hazard her honesty to maintain herself in bravery:
even as occupiers corrupt their consciences to gather riches.

Within a day or two Master Benedick came to her again,
on whom she cast a smiling countenance: which he perceiving (according to his old custom) sent for wine, and very
merry they were. At last, in the midst of their cups, he
cast out his former question: and after farther conference,
she yielded, and appointed a time when he should come to
her; for which favour, he gave her half a dozen portigues.

Within an hour or two after, entering into her own conscience, bethinking how sinfully she had sold herself to
folly, began thus to expostulate. "Good lord," quoth she,
"shall I break that holy vow which I made in marriage, and
pollute this body of mine which the Lord hath sanctified?
Can I break the commandment of my God, and not rest
accursed? or be a traitor to my husband, & suffer no shame?
I heard once my brother read in a book, that Bucephalus,[64]
Alexander's steed, being a beast, would not be backed by any
but the emperor, and shall I consent to any but my husband?
Artemisia[65] being a heathen lady, loved her husband so well,
that she drunk up his ashes, and buried him in her own
bowels, and should I, being a Christian, cast my husband out
of my heart? The women of Rome were wont to crown their
husbands' heads with bays, in token of victory, and shall I
give my husband horns in token of infamy? An harlot is

hated of all virtuous-minded people, and shall I make myself a whore? O my God forgive my sin," quoth she, "and cleanse my heart from these wicked imaginations."

And as she was thus lamenting, her husband came home: at whose sight her tears were doubled, like unto a river whose stream is increased by showers of rain. Her husband seeing this, would needs know the cause of her sorow: but a great while she would not shew him, casting many a piteous look upon him, and shaking her head, at last she said, "O my dear husband, I have offended against God and thee, and made such a trespass by my tongue, as hath cut a deep scar in my conscience, and wounded my heart with grief like a sword: like Penelope so have I been wooed, but like Penelope I have not answered."

"Why woman," quoth he, "what is the matter? If it be but the bare offence of thy tongue, why shouldest thou so grieve? considering that women's tongues are like lamb's tails, which seldom stand still: and the wise man saith, Where much talk is, must needs be some offence. Women's beauties are fair marks for wandering eyes to shoot at: but as every archer hits not the white, so every wooer wins not his mistress' favour. All cities that are besieged are not sacked, nor all women to be misliked that are loved. Why wife, I am persuaded thy faith is more firm, and thy constancy greater to withstand lovers' alarums, than that any other but myself should obtain the fortress of thy heart."

"O sweet husband," quoth she, "we see the strongest tower, at length falleth down by the cannon's force, though the bullets be but iron: then how can the weak bulwark of a woman's breast make resistance, when the hot cannons of deep persuading words are shot off with golden bullets, and every one as big as a portigue?"

"If it be so wife, I may think myself in a good case, and you to be a very honest woman. As Mars and Venus danced naked together in a net, so I doubt, you and some knave have played naked together in a bed: but in faith thou quean, I will send thee to salute thy friends without a nose: and as thou hast sold thy honesty, so will I sell thy company."

"Sweet husband, though I have promised, I have performed nothing: every bargain is not effected, and therefore as Judas brought again the thirty silver plates, for the which he betrayed his master: so repenting my folly, I'll cast him again his gold, for which I should have wronged my husband."

"Tell me," quoth her husband, "what he is."

"It is Master Benedick," quoth she, "which for my love have left the love of our kinswoman, and hath vowed himself forever to live my servant."

"O dissembling Italian," quoth he, "I will be revenged on him for this wrong. I know that any favour from Joan our kinswoman will make him run like unto a man bitten with a mad dog: therefore be ruled by me, and thou shalt see me dress him in his kind."

The woman was very well pleased, saying, he would be there that night.

"All this works well with me," quoth her husband, "and to supper will I invite Joan my kinswoman, and in the mean space make up the bed in the parlour very decently."

So the goodman went forth, and got a sleepy drench from the pothecary's, the which he gave to a young sow, which he had in his yard, and in the evening laid her down in the bed in the parlour, drawing the curtains round about.

Supper time being come, Master Benedick gave his attendance, looking for no other company but the good wife: Notwithstanding at the last Mistress Joan came in with her kinsman, and sat down to supper with him.

Master Benedick musing at their sudden approach, yet nevertheless glad of Mistress Joan's company, past the supper time with many pleasant conceits, Joan shewing herself that night more pleasant in his company than at any time before: wherefore he gave the good man great thanks.

"Good Master Benedick, little do you think how I have travelled in your behalf to my kinswoman, and very much ado

I had to bring the peevish wench into any good liking of your love: notwithstanding by my very great diligence and persuasions, I have at length won her good will to come hither, little thinking to find you here, or any such good cheer to entertain her: all which I see is fallen out for your profit. But trust me, all the world cannot now alter her mind, nor turn her love from you: In regard whereof, she hath promised me to lie this night in my house, for the great desire she hath of your good company: and in requital of all your great courtesies shewed to me, I am very well content to bring you to her bed. Marry this you must consider, and so she bade me tell you, that you should come to bed with as little noise as you could, and tumble nothing that you find for fear of her best gown and her hat, which she will lay hard by the bedside, next her best partlet, and in so doing, you may have company with her all night, but say nothing in any case till you be abed:"

"O," quoth he, "Mater Jan, be Got Mater Jan, me will not spoil her clothes for a tousand pound, ah me love Metres Joan more than my wife."

Well, supper being done, they rose from the table. Master Benedick embracing Mistress Joan, thanked her for her great courtesy and company, and then the good man and he walked into the town, and Joan hied her home to her master's, knowing nothing of the intended jest. Master Benedick thought every hour twain, till the sun was down, and that he were abed with his beloved. At last he had his wish, and home he came to his friend's house.

Then said John, "Master Benedick you must not in any case have a candle when you go into the chamber, for then my kinswoman will be angry, and dark places fits best lovers' desires."

"O Mater Jan," quoth he, "it's no such matter for light, me shall find Metres Joan well enough in the dark."

And entering in the parlour, groping about, he felt a gown and hat. "O Metres Joan," quoth he, "here is your gown and hat, me shall no hurt for a tousand poun."

Then kneeling down by the bedside instead of Mistress Joan, he saluted the sow in this sort. "O my love and my delight, it is thy fair face that hath wounded my heart, thy gray sparkling eyes, and thy lily-white hands, with the comely proportion of thy pretty body, that made me in seeking thee to forget myself, & to find thy favour, lose my own freedom: but now is the time come wherein I shall reap the fruits of a plentiful harvest. Now my dear, from thy sweet mouth let me suck the honey balm of thy breath, and with my hand stroke those rosy cheeks of thine, wherein I have took such pleasure, Come with thy pretty lips and entertain me into thy bed with one gentle kiss: Why speakest thou not my sweetheart, and stretch out thy alabaster arms to enfold thy faithful friend? Why should ill-pleasing sleep close up the crystal windows of thy body so fast, and bereave thee of thy five lordly attendants wherewith thou wast wont to salute thy friends? let it not offend thy gentle ears that I thus talk to thee. If thou hast vowed not to speak, I will not break it: and if thou wilt command me to be silent, I will be dumb: but thou needest not fear to speak thy mind, seeing the cloudy night concealeth everything."

By this time Master Benedick was unready, and slipped into bed, where the sow lay swathed in a sheet, and her head bound in a great linen cloth: As soon as he was laid, he began to embrace his new bedfellow, and laying his lips somewhat near her snout, he felt her draw her breath very short.

"Why how now love," quoth he, "be you sick, be Got Mistress Joan your breat be very strong: have you no cack[66] a bed?"

The sow feeling herself disturbed, began to grunt and keep a great stir: whereat Master Benedick (like a madman) ran out of the bed, crying, "De devil de devil." The good man of the house (being purposely provided) came rushing in with half a dozen of his neighbours, asking what was the matter.

"Got ound," quoth Benedick, "here be de great devil cry hoh, hoh, hoh, be Gossen I tink you play the knave wid me, and me wil be revenge be Got."

"Sir," quoth he, "I knowing you loved mutton,[67] thought pork nothing unfit: & therefore provided you a whole sow, and as you like this entertainment, spend portigues. Walk, walk, Berkshire maids will be no Italians' strumpets, nor the wives of Newbury their bawds."

"Berkshire dog," quoth Benedick, "owl face shack[68] hang dou and dy veife, have it not be for me love to sweet Metresse Joan, I will no come in your houz: but farewell tell I cash you, be Goz bode,[69] I make your hog nose bud." [70]

The good man and his neighbours laughed aloud, away went Master Benedick, and for very shame departed from Newbury before day.

CHAP. VIII

How Jack of Newbury keeping a very good house, both for his servants and relief of the poor, won great credit thereby: and how one of his wife's gossips found fault therewith.

"Good morrow good gossip: now by my truly I am glad to see you in health. I pray you how doth Master Winchcombe? What never a great belly yet? now fie: by my fa your husband is waxed idle."

"Trust me gossip," saith Mistress Winchcombe, "a great belly comes sooner than a new coat: but you must consider we have not been long married: But truly gossip you are welcome: I pray you to sit down, and we will have a morsel of something by and by."

"Nay truly gossip, I cannot stay," quoth she, "in troth I must be gone: for I did but even step in to see how you did."

"You shall not choose but stay a while," quoth Mistress Winchcombe: and with that a fair napkin was laid upon the little table in the parlour, hard by the fireside, whereon was set a good cold capon, with a great deal of other good cheer, with ale and wine plenty."

"I pray you good gossip eat, and I beshrew you if you spare," quoth the one.

"I thank you heartily good gossip," saith the other. "But good gossip I pray you tell me: doth your husband love you well, and make much of you?"

"Yes truly, I thank God," quoth she.

"Now by my troth," said the other, "it were a shame for him if he should not: for though I say it before your face, though he had little with you, you were worthy to be as good a man's wife as his."

"Trust me, I would not change my John for my lord marquess," quoth she, "a woman can be but well, for I live at heart's ease, & have all things at will, & truly he will not see me lack anything."

"Marry God's blessing on his heart," quoth her gossip, "it is a good hearing: but I pray you tell me, I heard say, your husband is chosen for our burgess in the parliament house, is it true?"

"Yes verily," quoth his wife: "I wis it is against his will: for it will be no small charges unto him."

"Tush woman, what talk you of that? thanks be to God, there is never a gentleman in all Berkshire that is better able to bear it. But hear you, gossip, shall I be so bold to ask you one question more?"

"Yes, with all my heart," quoth she.

"I heard say that your husband would now put you in your hood and silk gown, I pray you is it true?"

"Yes in truth," quoth Mistress Winchcombe, "but far against my mind gossip: my French hood [71] is bought already, and my silk gown is a making: likewise the goldsmith hath brought home my chain and bracelets: but I assure you gossip, if you will believe me, I had rather go an hundred miles, than wear them: for I shall be so ashamed that I shall not look upon any of my neighbours for blushing."

"And why, I pray you?" quoth her gossip. "I tell you dear woman, you need not be anything abashed or blush at the matter, especially seeing your husband's estate is able to maintain it: now trust me truly, I am of opinion you will become it singular well."

"Alas," quoth Mistress Winchcombe, "having never been used to such attire, I shall not know where I am, nor how to behave myself in it: and beside, my complexion is so black, that I shall carry but an ill-favoured countenance under a hood."

"Now, without doubt," quoth her gossip, "you are to blame to say so: beshrew my heart if I speak it to flatter, you are a very fair and well-favoured young woman, as any is in Newbury. And never fear your behaviour in your hood: for I tell you true, as old and withered as I am myself, I could become a hood well enough, and behave myself as well in such attire, as any other whatsoever, and I would not learn of never a one of them all: what woman, I have been a pretty wench in my days, and seen some fashions Therefore you need not to fear, seeing both your beauty and comely personage deserves no less than a French hood: and be of good comfort. At the first (possible) folks will gaze something at you: but be not you abashed for that, it is better they should wonder at your good fortune, than lament at your misery: but when they have seen you two or three times in that attire, they will afterward little respect it: for every new thing at the first seems rare, but being once a little used, it grows common."

"Surely gossip you say true," quoth she, "and I am but a fool to be so bashful: it is no shame to use God's gifts for our credits, and well might my husband think me unworthy to have them, if I would not wear them: and though I say it, my hood is a fair one, as any woman wears in this country, and my gold chain and bracelets are none of the worst sort, and I will shew them you, because you shall give your opinion upon them:" and therewithal she stepped into her chamber and fetched them forth.

When her gossip saw them, she said, "Now beshrew my fingers but these are fair ones indeed. And when do you mean to wear them gossip?"

"At Whitsuntide," [72] quoth she, "if God spare me life."

"I wish that well you may wear them," said her gossip, "and I would I were worthy to be with you when you dress yourself, it should be never the worse for you. I would order the matter so, that you should set everything about you in such sort, as never a gentlewoman of them all should stain you."

Mistress Winchcombe gave her great thanks for her favour, saying, that if she needed her help, she would be bold to send for her.

Then began her gossip to turn her tongue to another tune, and now to blame her for her great housekeeping. And thus she began: "Gossip, you are but a young woman, and one that hath had no great experience of the world, in my opinion you are something too lavish in expenses: pardon me good gossip, I speak but for good will: and because I love you, I am the more bold to admonish you: I tell you plain, were I the mistress of such a house, having such large allowance as you have, I would save 20. pound a year that you spend to no purpose."

"Which way might that be?" quoth Mistress Winchcombe. "Indeed I confess I am but a green housewife, and one that hath had but small trial in the world, therefore I would be very glad to learn anything that were for my husband's profit and my commodity."

"Then listen to me," quoth she: "you feed your folks with the best of the beef, and the finest of the wheat, which in my opinion is a great oversight: neither do I hear of any knight in this country that doth it. And to say the truth, how were they able to bear that port which they do, if they saved it not by some means? Come thither, and I warrant you that you shall see but brown bread on the board: if it be wheat and rye mingled together, it is a great matter, and the bread highly commended: but most commonly they eat either barley bread, or rye mingled with pease, and such like coarse grain: which is doubtless but of small price, and there is no other bread allowed, except at their own board. And in like manner for their meat: it is well known, that necks and points of beef is their ordinary fare: which because it is commonly lean, they seethe therewith now and then a piece of bacon or pork, whereby they make their pottage fat, and therewith drives out the rest with more content. And thus must you learn to do. And beside that, the midriffs of the oxen, and the cheeks, the sheep's heads, and the gathers, which you give away at your gate, might serve them well enough: which would be a great sparing to your other meat, and by this means you would save in the year much money, whereby you might the better maintain your hood and silk gown. Again, you serve your folks with such superfluities, that they spoil in a manner as much as they eat: believe me were I their dame, they should have things more sparingly, and then they would think it more dainty."

"Trust me gossip," quoth Mistress Winchcombe, "I know your words in many things to be true: for my folks are so corn-fed, that we have much ado to please them in their diet: one doth say this is too salt, and another saith this is too gross, this is too fresh, and that too fat, and twenty faults they will find at their meals: I warrant you they make such parings of their cheese, and keep such chipping of their bread, that their very orts would serve two or three honest folks to their dinner."

"And from whence I pray you proceeds that," quoth her gossip, "but of too much plenty? but yfaith were they my servants, I would make them glad of the worst crumbs they cast away, and thereupon I drink to you, and I thank you for my good cheer with all my heart."

"Much good may it do you good gossip," said Mistress Winchcombe: "and I pray you when you come this way, let us see you."

"That you shall verily," quoth she, and so away she went.

After this, Mistress Winchcombe took occasion to give her folks shorter commons, and coarser meats than they were wont to have: which at length being come to the good man's ear, he was very much offended therewith, saying: "I will not have my people thus pinched of their victuals. Empty platters makes greedy stomachs, and where scarcity is kept, hunger is nourished: and therefore wife as you love me, let me have no more of this doings."

"Husband," quoth she, "I would they should have enough: but it is sin to suffer, and a shame to see the spoil they make: I could be very well content to give them their bellies full, and that which is sufficient, but it grieves me, to tell you true, to see how coy they are, and the small care they have in wasting of things: and I assure you, the whole town cries shame of it, and it hath bred me no small discredit for looking no better to it. Trust me no more, if I was not checked in my own house about this matter, when my ears did burn to hear what was spoken."

"Who was it that checked thee, I pray thee tell me? was it not your old gossip, Dame Dainty, Mistress Trip and Go? I believe it was."

"Why man if it were she, you know she hath been an old housekeeper, and one that hath known the world, and that she told me was for good will."

"Wife," quoth he, "I would not have thee to meddle with such light-brained housewives, and so I have told thee a good many times, and yet I cannot get you to leave her company."

"Leave her company? why husband, so long as she is an honest woman, why should I leave her company? She never gave me hurtful counsel in all her life, but hath always been ready to tell me things for my profit, though you take it not so. Leave her company? I am no girl I would you should well know, to be taught what company I should keep: I keep none but honest company, I warrant you. Leave her company ketha? [73] Alas poor soul, this reward she hath for her good will. I wis, I wis, she is more your friend, than you are your own."

"Well, let her be what she will," said her husband: "but if she come any more in my house, she were as good no. And therefore take this for a warning I would advise you:" and so away he went.

How a draper in London, who owed Jack of Newbury much money, became bankrupt, whom Jack of Newbury found carrying a porter's basket on his neck, and how he set him up again at his own cost, which draper afterward became an alderman of London.

There was one Randoll Pert a draper, dwelling in Watling Street, that owed Jack of Newbury five hundred pounds at one time, who in the end fell greatly to decay, insomuch that he was cast in prison, and his wife with her poor children turned out of doors. All his creditors except Winchcombe had a share of his goods, never releasing him out of prison, so long as he had one penny to satisfy them. But when this tidings was brought to Jack of Newbury's ear, his friends counselled him to lay his action against him.

"Nay," quoth he, "if he be not able to pay me when he is at liberty, he will never be able to pay me in prison: and therefore it were as good for me to forbear my money without troubling him, as to add more sorrow to his grieved heart, and be never the nearer. Misery is trodden down by many, and once brought low, they are seldom or never relieved: therefore he shall rest for me untouched, and I would to God he were clear of all other men's debts, so that I gave him mine to begin the world again."

Thus lay the poor draper a long time in prison, in which space, his wife which before for daintiness would not foul her fingers, nor turn her head aside, for fear of hurting the set of her neckenger,[74] was glad to go about and wash bucks[75] at the Thames' side, and to be a charwoman in rich men's houses, her soft hand was now hardened with scouring, and instead of gold rings upon her lily fingers, they were now filled with chaps, provoked by the sharp lee, and other drudgeries.

At last, Master Winchcombe being (as you heard) chosen against the Parliament a burgess for the town of Newbury and coming up to London for the same purpose, when he was alighted at his inn, he left one of his men there to get a porter to bring his trunk up to the place of his lodging. Poor Randoll Pert, which lately before was come out of prison, having no other means of maintenance, became a porter to carry burthens from one place to another, having an old ragged doublet, and a torn pair of breeches, with his hose out at the heels, and a pair of old broken slip-shoes[76] on his feet, a rope about his middle instead of a girdle, and on his head an old greasy cap, which had so many holes in it, that his hair started through it: who as soon as he heard one call for a porter, made answer straight: "Here master, what is it that you would have carried?"

"Marry," quoth he, "I would have this trunk born to the Spread Eagle at Ivybridge."

"You shall master," quoth he, "but what will you give me for my pains?"

"I will give thee two pence."

"A penny more and I will carry it," said the porter: and so being agreed, away he went with his burthen, till he came to the Spread Eagle door, where on a sudden espying Master Winchcombe standing, he cast down the trunk, and ran away as hard as ever he could.

Master Winchcombe wondering what he meant thereby, caused his man to run after him, and so fetch him again: but when he saw one pursue him, he ran then the faster; and in running, here he lost one of his slip-shoes, and then another: ever looking behind him, like a man pursued with a deadly weapon, fearing every twinkling of an eye to be thrust through. At last his breech, being tied but with one point, what with the haste he made, and the weakness of the thong, fell about his heels: which so shackled him, that down he fell in the street all along, sweating and blowing, being quite worn out of breath: and so by this means the serving-man overtook him, and taking him by the sleeve, being as windless as the other, stood blowing and puffing a great while ere they could speak one to another.

"Sirrah," quoth the serving-man, "you must come to my master, you have broken his trunk all to pieces, by letting it fall."

"O for God's sake," quoth he, "let me go, for Christ's sake let me go, or else Master Winchcombe of Newbury will arrest me, and then I am undone forever."

Now by this time Jack of Newbury had caused his trunk to be carried into the house, and then he walked along to know what the matter was: and when he heard the porter say that he would arrest him, he wondered greatly, and having quite forgot Pert's favour, being so greatly changed by imprisonment and poverty, he said, "Wherefore should I arrest thee? tell me good fellow: for my own part I know no reason for it."

"O sir," quoth he, "I would to God I knew none neither."

Then asking him what his name was: the poor man falling down on his knees, said: "Good Master Winchcombe bear with me and cast me not into prison: my name is Pert, and I do not deny but that I owe you five hundred pound: yet for the love of God take pity upon me."

When Master Winchcombe heard this, he wondered greatly at the man, and did as much pity his misery, though as yet he made it not known, saying: "Passion of my heart man, thou wilt never pay me thus: never think being a porter to pay five hundred pound debt. But this hath your prodigality brought you to, your thriftless neglecting of your business, that set more by your pleasure than your profit." Then looking better upon him, he said: "What, never a shoe to thy foot, hose to thy leg, band to thy neck, nor cap to thy head? O Pert, this is strange: but wilt thou be an honest man, & give me a bill of thy hand for my money?"

"Yes sir, with all my heart," quoth Pert.

"Then come to the scrivener's," quoth he, "and dispatch it, and I will not trouble thee."

Now when they were come thither, with a great many following them at their heels, Master Winchcombe said: "Hearest thou scrivener? this fellow must give me a bill of his hand for five hundred pounds, I pray thee make it as it should be."

The scrivener looking upon the poor man, and seeing him in that case, said to Master Winchcombe: "Sir, you were better to let it be a bond, and have some sureties bound with him."

"Why scrivener," quoth he, "doest thou think this is not a sufficient man of himself for five hundred pound?"

"Truly sir," said the scrivener, "if you think him so, you and I are of two minds:"

"I'll tell thee what," quoth Master Winchcombe, "were it not that we are all mortal, I would take his word as soon as his bill or bond; the honesty of a man is all."

"And we in London," quoth the scrivener, "do trust bonds far better than honesty. But sir, when must this money be paid?"

"Marry scrivener, when this man is sheriff of London."

At that word the scrivener and the people standing by laughed heartily, saying: "In truth sir, make no more ado but forgive it him: as good to do the one as the other."

"Nay, believe me," quoth he, "not so: therefore do as I bid you."

Whereupon the scrivener made the bill to be paid when Randoll Pert was sheriff of London, and thereunto set his own hand for a witness, and twenty persons more that stood by, set to their hands likewise.

Then he asked Pert what he should have for carrying his trunk.

"Sir," quoth he, "I should have three pence, but seeing I find you so kind, I will take but two pence at this time."

"Thanks good Pert," quoth he, "but for thy three pence, there is three shillings: and look thou come to me tomorrow morning betimes."

The poor man did so, at what time Master Winchcombe had provided him out of Burchin Lane,[77] a fair suit of apparel, merchant-like, with a fair black cloak, and all other things fit to the same: then he took him a shop in Canweek Street, and furnished the same shop with a thousand pounds' worth of

cloth: by which means, and other favours that Master Winchcombe did him, he grew again into great credit, and in the end
became so wealthy, that while Master Winchcombe lived he
was chosen sheriff,[78] at what time he paid five hundred pounds
every penny, and after died an alderman of the city.

CHAP. X

*How Jack of Newbury's servants were revenged of their
dame's tattling gossip.*

Upon a time it came to pass, when Master Winchcombe was
far from home, and his wife gone abroad: That Mistress Many
Better, Dame Tittle, Tattle, Gossip Pintpot, according to her
old custom, came to Mistress Winchcombe's house, perfectly
knowing of the good man's absence, and little thinking the
good wife was from home: where knocking at the gate,
Tweedle stept out and asked who was there? where hastily
opening the wicket, he suddenly discovered the full proportion of this foul beast, who demanded if their mistress were
within.

"What Mistress Frank," quoth he, "in faith welcome: how
have you done a great while? I pray you come in."

"Nay, I cannot stay," quoth she. "Notwithstanding, I did
call to speak a word or two with your mistress, I pray you
tell her that I am here."

"So I will," quoth he, "so soon as she comes in."

Then said the woman, "What is she abroad? why then farewell good Tweedle."

"Why what haste, what haste, Mistress Frank," quoth he,
"I pray you stay and drink ere you go. I hope a cup of new
sack will do your old belly no hurt:"

"What," quoth she, "have you new sack already? Now by
my honesty I drunk none this year, and therefore I do not
greatly care if I take a taste before I go:" and with that she
went into the wine cellar with Tweedle, where first he set
before her a piece of powdered [79] beef as green as a leek: And
then going into the kitchen, he brought her a piece of roasted
beef hot from the spit.

Now certain of the maidens of the house, and some of the young men, who had long before determined to be revenged of this prattling housewife: came into the cellar one after another, one of them bringing a great piece of a gammon of bacon in his hand: and everyone bade Mistress Frank welcome: and first one drunk to her, and then another, and so the third, the fourth, and the fifth: so that Mistress Frank's brains waxed as mellow as a pippin at Michaelmas, and so light, that sitting in the cellar, she thought the world ran round. They seeing her to fall into merry humours, whetted her on in merriment as much as they could, saying, "Mistress Frank, spare not I pray you, but think yourself as welcome as any woman in all Newbury, for we have cause to love you, because you love our mistress so well."

"Now by my troth," quoth she, lisping in her speech (her tongue waxing somewhat too big for her mouth), "I love your mistress well indeed, as if she were mine own daughter."

"Nay but hear you," quoth they, "she begins not to deal well with us now."

"No my lambs," quoth she, "why so?"

"Because," quoth they, "she seeks to bar us of our allowance, telling our master, that he spends too much in housekeeping."

"Nay then," quoth she, "your mistress is both an ass, and a fool: and though she go in her hood, what care I? she is but a girl to me: Twittle twattle, I know what I know: go to, drink to me. Well Tweedle, I drink to thee with all my heart: why thou whoreson, when wilt thou be married? O that I were a young wench for thy sake: but 'tis no matter, though I be but a poor woman, I am a true woman. Hang dogs, I have dwelt in this town these thirty winters."

"Why then," quoth they, "you have dwelt here longer than our master."

"Your master?" quoth she. "I knew your master a boy, when he was called Jack of Newbury, aye Jack, I knew him called plain Jack: and your mistress, now she is rich, and I am poor, but it's no matter, I knew her a draggle-tail girl, mark ye?"

"But now," quoth they, "she takes upon her lustily, and hath quite forgot what she was."

"Tush, what will you have of a green thing?" quoth she. "Here I drink to you, so long as she goes where she list a gossiping: and it's no matter, little said is soon amended: But hear you my masters, though Mistress Winchcombe go in her hood, I am as good as she, I care not who tell it her; I spend not my husband's money in cherries and codlings, go to, go to, I know what I say well enough: I thank God I am not drunk: Mistress Winchcombe, mistress? No, Nan Winchcombe, I will call her name, plain Nan: what I was a woman when she was sir-reverence[80] a paltry girl, though now she goes in her hood and chain of gold: what care I for her? I am her elder, and I know more of her tricks: nay I warrant you, I know what I say, 'tis no matter, laugh at me and spare not, I am not drunk I warrant:" and with that being scant able to hold open her eyes, she began to nod, and to spill the wine out of the glass: which they perceiving, let her alone, going out of the cellar till she was sound asleep, and in the mean space they devised how to finish this piece of knavery.

At last they all consented to lay her forth at the back side of the house, half a mile off, even at the foot of a stile, that whosoever came next over, might find her: notwithstanding, Tweedle stayed hard by to see the end of this action. At last comes a notable clown[81] from Greenham, taking his way to Newbury: who coming hastily over the stile, stumbled at the woman, and fell down clean over her. But in his starting up, seeing it was a woman, cried out, "Alas, alas."

"How now, what is the matter?" quoth Tweedle.

"O," quoth he, "here lies a dead woman."

"A dead woman," quoth Tweedle, "that's not so I trow," and with that he tumbled her about:

"Bones of me," quoth Tweedle, " 'tis a drunken woman, and one of the town undoubtedly: in troth it is a great pity she should lie here."

"Why do you know her?" quoth the clown.

"No not I," quoth Tweedle, "nevertheless, I will give thee half a groat, and take her in thy basket, and carry her throughout the town, and see if anybody know her."

Then said the other, "Let me see the money, and I will: For by the Mass, che earned not half a groat this great while."

"There it is," quoth Tweedle: then the fellow put her in his basket, and so lifted her upon his back.

"Now by the Mass she stinks vilely of drink, or wine, or something. But tell me, what shall I say when I come into the town?" quoth he.

"First," quoth Tweedle, "I would have thee so soon as ever thou canst get to the town's end, with a lusty voice to cry, Oyes, and then say, Who knows this woman, who? And though possible some will say, I know her, and I know her; yet do not thou set her down till thou comest to the market cross, and there use the like words: and if any be so friendly, to tell thee where she dwells, then just before her door cry so again: and if thou perform this bravely, I will give thee half a groat more."

"Master Tweedle," quoth he, "I know you well enough, you dwell with Master Winchcombe, do you not? I'faith if I do it not in the nick, give me never a penny:"

And so away he went, till he came to the town's end, and there he cries out as boldly as any bailiff's man, "Oyes, who knows this woman, who?"

Then said the drunken woman in the basket, her head falling first on one side, and then on the other side, "Who co me, who?"

Then said he again, "Who knows this woman, who?"

"Who co me, who?" quoth she, and look how oft he spoke the one, she spoke the other: saying still, "Who co me, who co me, who?" Whereat all the people in the street fell into such a laughter, that the tears ran down again.

At last one made answer, saying: "Good fellow, she dwells in the North Brook Street, a little beyond Master Winchcombe's."

The fellow hearing that, goes down thither in all haste, and there in the hearing of a hundred people, cries, "Who knows this woman, who?"

Whereat her husband comes out, saying: "Marry that do I too well, God help me."

Then said the clown, "If you know her, take her: for I know her not but for a drunken beast."

And as her husband took her out of the basket, she gave him a sound box on the ear, saying, "What you queans, do you mock me?" and so was carried in.

But the next day, when her brain was quiet, and her head cleared of these foggy vapours, she was so ashamed of herself, that she went not forth of her doors a long time after: and if anybody did say unto her, "Who co me, who?" she would be so mad and furious, that she would be ready to draw her knife and stick them, and scold as if she strove for the best game at the cucking-stool.[82] Moreover, her prattling to Mistress Winchcombe's folks of their mistress, made her on the other side to fall out with her, in such sort, that she troubled them no more, either with her company or her counsel.

CHAP. XI

How one of Jack of Newbury's maids became a lady.

At the winning of Morless in France, the noble Earl of Surrey being at that time Lord High Admiral of England, made many knights: among the rest was Sir George Rigley, brother to Sir Edward Rigley,[83] and sundry other, whose valours far surpassed their wealth: so that when peace bred a scarcity in their purse, and that their credits grew weak in the city, they were enforced to ride into the country, where at their friends' houses they might have favourable welcome, without coin[84] or grudging.

Among the rest, Jack of Newbury that kept a table for all comers, was never lightly without many such guests: where they were sure to have both welcome and good cheer, and their mirth no less pleasing than their meat was plenty. Sir George having lain long at board in this brave yeoman's house, at length fell in liking of one of his maidens, who was as fair as she was fond. This lusty wench he so allured with hope of marriage, that at length she yielded him her love, and therewithal bent her whole study to work his content: but in the end, she so much contented him, that it wrought altogether her own discontent: to become high, she laid herself so low, that the knight suddenly fell over her, which fall became the rising of her belly. But when this wanton perceived herself to be with child, she made her moan unto the knight in this manner.

"Ah Sir George, now is the time to perform your promise, or to make me a spectacle of infamy to the whole world forever: in the one you shall discharge the duty of a true knight, but in the other shew yourself a most perjured person. Small honour will it be to boast in the spoil of poor maidens, whose innocency all good knights ought much rather to defend."

"Why thou lewd paltry thing," quoth he, "comest thou to father thy bastard upon me? Away ye dunghill carrion, away: Hear you good huswife, get you among your companions, and lay your litter where you list: for if you trouble me any more, by heaven I swear, thou shalt dearly abide it:" and so bending his brows like the angry god of war, he went his ways, leaving the child-breeding wench to the hazard of her fortune, either good or bad.

This poor maiden seeing herself for her kindness thus cast off, shed many tears of sorrow for her sin, inveighing, with many bitter groans, against the unconstancy of love-alluring men. But in the end, when she saw no other remedy, she made her case known unto her mistress: who after she had given her many bitter checks and taunts, threatening to turn her out of doors, she opened the matter to her husband.

So soon as he heard thereof, he made no more to do, but presently posted to London after Sir George, and found him at my Lord Admiral's. "What, Master Winchcombe," quoth he, "you are heartily welcome to London, and I thank you for my good cheer. I pray you how doth your good wife, and all our friends in Berkshire?"

"All well and merry, I thank you good Sir George," quoth he: "I left them in health, and I hope they do so continue. And trust me sir," quoth he, "having earnest occasion to come up to talk with a bad debtor, in my journey it was my chance to light in company of a gallant widow: a gentlewoman she is, of wondrous good wealth, whom grisly death hath bereft of a kind husband, making her a widow, ere she had been half a year a wife: her land, Sir George, is as well worth a hundred pound a year as one penny, being as fair and comely a creature, as any of her degree in our whole country: Now sir, this is the worst, by the reason that she doubts herself to be with child, she hath vowed not to marry these twelve months: but because I wish you well, and the gentlewoman no hurt, I came of purpose from my business to tell you thereof: Now Sir George, if you think her a fit wife for you, ride to her, woo her, win her, and wed her."

"I thank you good Master Winchcombe," quoth he, "for your favour ever toward me, and gladly would I see this young widow if I wist where."

"She dwelleth not half a mile from my house," quoth Master Winchcombe, "and I can send for her at any time if you please."

Sir George hearing this, thought it was not best to come there, fearing Joan would father a child upon him, and therefore answered, he had no leisure to come from my lord: "But," quoth he, "would I might see her in London, on the condition it cost me twenty nobles."

"Tush Sir George," quoth Master Winchcombe, "delays in love are dangerous, and he that will woo a widow, must take time by the forelock, and suffer none other to step before him, lest he leap without the widow's love. Notwithstanding, seeing now I have told you of it, I will take my gelding and get me home: if I hear of her coming to London, I will send you word, or perhaps come myself: till when, adieu good Sir George."

Thus parted Master Winchcombe from the knight: and being come home, in short time he got a fair taffeta gown, and a French hood for his maid, saying: "Come ye drab, I must be fain to cover a foul fault with a fair garment, yet all will not hide your great belly: but if I find means to make you a lady, what will you say then?"

"O master," quoth she, "I shall be bound while I live to pray for you."

"Come then minion," quoth her mistress, "and put you on this gown and French hood: for seeing you have lain with a knight, you must needs be a gentlewoman."

The maid did so: and being thus attired, she was set on a fair gelding, and a couple of men sent with her up to London: and being well instructed by her master and dame what she should do, she took her journey to the city in the term time,[85] and lodged at the Bell in the Strand: and Mistress Loveless must be her name, for so her master had warned her to call herself: Neither did the men that waited on her, know the contrary; for Master Winchcombe had borrowed them of their master, to wait upon a friend of his to London, because he could not spare any of his own servants at that time: notwithstanding, they were appointed for the gentlewoman's credit, to say they were her own men. This being done, Master Winchcombe sent Sir George a letter, that the gentlewoman which he told him of, was now in London, lying at the Bell in the Strand, having great business at the term.

With which news Sir George's heart was on fire, till such time as he might speak with her: three or four times went he thither, and still she would not be spoken withal, the which close keeping of herself, made him the more earnest in his suit.

At length he watched her so narrowly, that finding her going forth in an evening, he followed her. she having one man before, and another behind: carrying a very stately gate in the street, it drove him into the greater liking of her, being the more urged to utter his mind. And suddenly stepping before her, he thus saluted her, "Gentlewoman, God save you, I have often been at your lodging, and could never find you at leisure."

"Why sir," quoth she (counterfeiting her natural speech), "have you any business with me?"

"Yes fair widow," quoth he, "as you are a client to the law, so am I a suitor for your love: and may I find you so favourable to let me plead my own case at the bar of your beauty, I doubt not but to unfold so true a tale, as I trust will cause you to give sentence on my side."

"You are a merry gentleman," quoth she: "but for my own part, I know you not; nevertheless, in a case of love, I will be no let to your suit, though perhaps I help you little therein. And therefore sir, if it please you to give attendance at my lodging, upon my return from the Temple,[86] you shall know more of my mind," and so they parted.

Sir George receiving hereby some hope of good hap, stayed for his dear at her lodging door: whom at her coming she friendly greeted, saying, "Surely sir, your diligence is more than the profit you shall get thereby: but I pray you how shall I call your name?"

"George Rigley," quoth he, "I am called, and for some small deserts I was knighted in France."

"Why then Sir George," quoth she, "I have done you too much wrong to make you thus dance attendance on my worthless person. But let me be so bold to request you to tell me, how you came to know me: for my own part I cannot remember that ever I saw you before."

"Mistress Loveless," said Sir George, "I am well acquainted with a good neighbour of yours, called Master Winchcombe, who is my very good friend, and to say the truth, you were commended unto me by him."

"Truly Sir George," said she, "you are so much the better welcome: Nevertheless, I have made a vow not to love any man for this twelve months' space. And therefore sir, till then I would wish you to trouble yourself no further in this matter till that time be expired: and then if I find you be not entangled to any other, and that by trial I find out the truth of your love, for Master Winchcombe's sake your welcome shall be as good as any other gentleman's whatsoever."

Sir George having received this answer, was wondrous woe, cursing the day that ever he meddled with Joan, whose time of deliverance would come long before a twelve month were expired, to his utter shame, and overthrow of his good fortune: for by that means should he have Master Winchcombe his enemy, and therewithal the loss of this fair gentlewoman. Wherefore to prevent this mischief, he sent a letter in all haste to Master Winchcombe, requesting him most earnestly to come up to London, by whose persuasion he hoped straight to finish the marriage. Master Winchcombe fulfilled his request, and then presently was the marriage solemnized at the Tower of London, in presence of many gentlemen of Sir George's friends. But when he found it was Joan whom he had gotten with child, he fretted and fumed, stamped, and stared like a devil.

"Why," quoth M. Winchcombe, "what needs all this? Came you to my table to make my maid your strumpet? had you no man's house to dishonour but mine? Sir, I would you should well know, that I account the poorest wench in my house too good to be your whore, were you ten knights: and seeing you took pleasure to make her your wanton, take it no scorn to make her your wife: and use her well too, or you shall hear of it. And hold thee, Joan," quoth he, "there is a hundred pounds for thee: And let him not say thou camest to him a beggar."

Sir George seeing this, and withal casting in his mind what friend Master Winchcombe might be to him, taking his wife by the hand, gave her a loving kiss, and Master Winchcombe great thanks. Whereupon he willed him for two years space to take his diet and his lady's at his house: which the knight accepting, rode straight with his wife to Newbury.

Then did the mistress make curtsy to the maid, saying: "You are welcome madam," giving her the upper hand in all places. And thus they lived afterward in great joy: and our king hearing how Jack had matched Sir George, laughing heartily thereat, gave him a living forever, the better to maintain my lady his wife.

FINIS

NOTES

Notes

Gascoigne: THE ADVENTURES OF MASTER F. J.

Page	Note	
29	26	A writ commanding a stay of legal proceedings.
32	27	Afterward.
34	28	Ignorant, foolish.
34	29	Roll, toss.
35	30	In the Piedmontese style.
35	31	All went well.
37	32	Trimming.
39	33	Lurch.
39	34	Painted.
39	35	Misprint for *bumbast* or *bombast*, meaning stuffing.
39	36	Pads.
39	37	Hairnets.
39	38	Slashes in sleeves to show color beneath.
39	39	Curls.
39	40	Appearance.
40	40a	Lose.
40	41	That is, about.
40	41a	That is, on.
41	42	Inexpressible.
41	43	Sharing.
46	44	Misprint for *restore?*
46	45	Health.
47	46	Portcullis.
48	47	Residence.
49	48	Scarcely.
49	49	Porcupine's.
51	50	Blame.
51	50a	Zoroaster?
51	51	Unhappy lovers.
51	52	Maiden warrior in Ariosto's ORLANDO FURIOSO; her lover, Rogero, gives her frequent cause for jealousy.
52	53	Pillowcase.
52	54	Water distilled from damask roses.
54	54a	Misprint for *proposition?*

Page	Note	
55	55	Selfishly.
55	56	The fountain of hate.
55	57	Difficult.
57	58	Old maids were believed to be condemned to leading apes in hell in mockery of their not having led children on earth.
58	59	Misprint for *unworthiness?*
60	60	Cure.
62	61	That is, the eleventh article in her code of love.
62	62	That is, religion of love.
62	63	Alto.
63	64	In one voice.
66	65	That is, adieu.
67	66	Mistaken.
71	66a	That is, behave courteously.
76	67	The nightingale was thought to sing with a thorn at her throat to keep herself awake at night.
77	68	In other words, if there were a will, there would be a way.
77	69	According to her custom.
78	70	Slang for prostitute.
78	71	That is, conformity to the conventional behavior of lovers.
78	72	Arrogance.

Lyly: EUPHUES: THE ANATOMY OF WIT

Page	Note	
92	1	Most painful, keenest.
92	2	For *who* in Bond's text.
92	3	An obsolete variation of *reckless*.
92	4	*But* in Bond's text omitted.
92	5	Throughout EUPHUES Venus is the symbol of sensual love, and Vesta, the goddess of the hearth, is the symbol of chastity or domestic bliss.
92	6	Lyly has in mind Ovid as the author of THE ART OF LOVE, in contrast to Aristotle as the moral philosopher. Hector, the eldest son of Priam, King of Troy, is the serious warrior, in contrast to his brother Paris, the abductor of Helen. Flora, the goddess of flowers and of general fertility, is contrasted to Diana, the goddess of chastity.
93	7	Damocles' flattery of the ruler Dionysius I resulted in the famous sword's being hung over his head; Damon's willingness to sacrifice himself for Pythias, or Phintias, has become proverbial.
93	8	Laelius was inseparable from his friend and leader, Scipio Africanus. To Aristippus, the hedonist philosopher (435–360 B.C.), Lyly attributes here undesirable physical and personal characteristics.
93	9	Chrysippus, the Stoic philosopher (*ca.* 280–206 B.C.), was noted for his zealous attention to study.
94	10	Milo, a celebrated Greek athlete of the sixth century B.C., is reputed to have carried a four-year-old heifer on his shoulders through the stadium at Olympia and then to have eaten the entire animal in a single day.
94	11	Flower beds of fanciful patterns.

Page Note
96   12   Scylla, a six-headed sea monster, lived in a cave opposite Charybdis, a whirlpool. The Syrtes, the dangerous shallow waters along the coasts of Africa, were associated with quicksands, which Lyly projects upon the Symplegades, the clashing rocks at the entrance of the Hellespont.

97   13   The colocynth, or bitter apple.

97   14   A spot caused by rust.

97   15   Churlish.

97   16   Timon of Athens, celebrated as a misanthrope.

99   17   An obsolete form for *asbestos*, in the Middle Ages known as "the unquenchable stone."

100   18   As a result.

101   19   Pressed down or forced in, hence glutted.

101   20   Persons bowed down with age or with heavy wraps.

102   21   The taurus, like many of Lyly's references to natural history, is mentioned in the work of Pliny the Elder (23–79), whose allusions often have no real counterparts.

102   22   Unusual.

103   23   "Those things above us mean nothing to us."

103   24   "A rascal speaks thoughts."

103   25   The English word *sympathy* was not introduced into the language until around 1570 and not generally used until some time later.

103   26   A crooked staff.

104   27   A pun involving the idiom, "to stand on one's dignity."

106   28   An archaic form for *since*.

106   29   For Damon and Pythias, Scipio and Laelius, see above, Notes 7 and 8. Pylades and Orestes, Theseus and Pirithous were famous friends in Greek mythology. The friendship of Titus and Gysippus was described in a story by Boccaccio.

Page	Note	
107	30	A variant of *banns*, the notice of proposed marriage.
109	31	Desire.
110	32	An obsolete variant of *ostrich*.
112	33	Lyly probably has in mind the stones of Cilicia, which Pliny refers to as making good whetstones.
116	34	Probably from *cocker-mate*, childhood companion.
117	35	For the sake of a pun, Lyly drops the final letter from *bittern*.
118	36	Mushroom.
118	37	The part of the amnion which covers the head of the child at birth; hence a headdress which obscures sight.
118	38	Candaules, a monarch of Lydia, revealed the queen naked to Gyges. At the instigation of the angry queen, Gyges slew Candaules and became ruler.
118	39	By robbing Menelaus of his wife Helen.
119	40	A region of southwestern Asia Minor, colonized by the Greeks and ruled later by the Romans. Lyly's source for this story is unknown.
119	41	Lucretia, the wife of Tarquinius Collatinus, was outraged by Sextus, the son of Tarquinius Superbus, the last King of Rome (sixth century B.C.); having told her husband, she ended her own life. This incident contributed to a popular uprising among the Tarquins and to the establishment of the Roman republic. The Tarquinius referred to by Lyly is Sextus, the son of Superbus.
120	42	To put off her suitors while Ulysses was away, Penelope pretended that she could not marry until she had finished weaving a shroud for her father-in-law Laertes, but each night she unraveled the day's work so that the shroud would never be completed.

120   43   *Take heart at grass,* that is, cheer up, survives in the idiom *take heart of grace.*

120   44   Strong broths.

122   45   Ovid, Tibullus, and Propertius, Roman poets born in the half century before Christ, all composed poems dealing with love.

123   46   For *for* in Bond's text.

125   47   Mirror.

126   48   Whispering to.

126   49   Swooned.

127   50   Firewood.

128   51   The sea god Proteus had the power to change shape if caught; Lyly's choice of Pygmalion as a foil seems arbitrary rather than meaningful. Aeneas deserted Dido in order to complete his mission of founding Rome; the intense love of prince Troilus of Troy for the lady Cressida resulted in many difficulties for the lovers. The natural history which precedes comes from source books or folk lore, and is valid only in part.

128   52   This early variant of *housewife* was used often to refer to a worthless or pert female; it has developed into the word *hussy.*

129   53   According to a well known fable, the foolish geese who attended the words of a fox proclaiming his piety were eaten by him. A Renaissance travel story described crocodiles as producing tears in order to attract the attention of men and thus to devour them.

129   54   See Note 58 to THE ADVENTURES OF MASTER F. J.

130   55   Athon is Mount Athos in Macedonia; Hybla is a town in Sicily.

131   56   Returning from the Trojan War, Demophon met and fell in love with Phyllis, a Thracian princess; he left her, promising to return when he settled his affairs in Athens, but tired of waiting, she

hanged herself. For Dido and Aeneas, see above, Note 51. Theseus escaped the Labyrinth by following a piece of cord given him by the Cretan princess Ariadne, but fleeing with her, he somehow left her on the island of Naxos. Jason, whom Medea helped to survive the adventure of obtaining the Golden Fleece, later deserted her for a younger woman.

131   57   This stone, like the herb araxa and the stone of Mount Tmolus below, seems to be Lyly's own invention.

132   58   Lyly took this story from Plutarch's life of Lysander, the Spartan general of the fifth century B.C.

133   59   Brooches and bracelets, tape and braid.

135   60   His decoy for attracting Lucilla.

137   61   An obsolete form of *Portugal;* here, however, the Portuguese.

139   62   Lyly contrasts the Vestal Virgins as symbols of chastity to Juno in her function of attendant goddess of brides and of women bearing children.

139   63   No such reference occurs in Homer; it is perhaps taken from North's translation of DIAL OF PRINCES.

140   64   Literally *dis-ease* in the sense of disturbance, or perhaps a pun.

140   65   That is, with regard to the matter of marriage.

140   66   Against.

140   67   Myrrha, or Smyrna, was the mother of Adonis by her own father, Cinyras; for her uncontrollable passion, she was changed into a myrtle tree. Byblis, in love with her brother Caunus, pursued him through various lands until she was turned into a fountain. Phaedra, the wife of Theseus, fell in love with her stepson Hippolytus; the resulting complications led to her suicide.

141   68   An obsolete dialectical past tense of *fling*.

149   83   One myth has Theseus abducting Helen from
             Sparta when she was quite a young girl; chrono-
             logically her relationship with Theseus precedes
             that with Menelaus.

150   84   Venus was married to Vulcan, but was discovered
             naked in the arms of Mars. Captured thus in an
             iron net, the two were displayed to the ridicule
             of the gods.

150   85   The name is attributed to two famous Greek
             courtesans, often confused with each other.

150   86   Pasiphaë, the wife of King Minor of Crete, fell in
             love with a bull and bore him the Minotaur. For
             Myrrha, see Note 67, above.

151   87   Obsolete form for *corrosives*.

151   88   Aristotle, Justinian, and Galen were much re-
             spected in the Renaissance as authorities on moral
             philosophy, law, and medicine. Lyly may have in
             mind specific works by each, but the only precise
             title which he employs is from Galen's com-
             mentary on the APHORISMI of Hippocrates. AXIO-
             MATA PHILOSOPHICA, a book including parts of
             Aristotle, was registered for publication in 1592,
             but AXIOMAES and MAXIMS seem to be titles of
             Lyly's own invention.

154   89   Danaus was the father of fifty daughters, his
             brother Aegyptus of fifty sons. After family dis-
             sension between the two brothers, the sons of
             Aegyptus begged of Danaus the hands of his
             daughters. To avenge his brother's enmity, Danaus
             consented but instructed his daughters to murder
             their husbands on the wedding night. One daugh-
             ter Hypermnestra spared her husband Lynceus.
             At first Danaus punished her by imprisonment, but
             later he relented and released her.

Sidney: THE ARCADIA

Page	Note	
188	22	Bless.
189	23	As if.
189	24	In other words, an assuaging.
191	25	One of the three Furies, or avenging goddesses; the name Alecto means unceasing pursuit.
193	26	Punctuation modernized.
194	27	The reference is to events described early in THE ARCADIA. Pyrocles was shipwrecked on the coast near Arcadia. It was at this point that he assumed the name Daiphantus.

Nashe: THE UNFORTUNATE TRAVELLER

Page	Note	
203	1	Henry VIII landed at Calais on June 30, 1513, and captured Thérouanne and Tournai on August 4 and September 23 of the same year.
203	2	"We seek the heavens in our foolishness." Nashe employs frequent quotations from Latin writers, especially Horace, Ovid, and Virgil, and occasionally Plautus and Terence. The editors have translated these quotations when Nashe himself has not done so in his text. For the specific source of each quotation, the interested student may consult the notes of McKerrow's edition of Nashe.
203	3	Provisions supplied to troops.
203	4	Young herrings.
203	5	"Let us sing somewhat of greater things."
203	6	That is, throw the die so that it slides without turning over.
203	7	A phrase from the rhyme with which the study of the hornbook, a children's primer, was begun.
203	8	"Something lies hidden which is not apparent."
204	9	Without ornamentation of the ivy bush, which was Bacchus's sacred plant and consequently the recognized sign of a tavern.
204	10	"Virtue extends to the stars." Nashe of course puns with *sidera* and *cider*.
204	11	Heavenly water was actually the name of a drug considered an effective restorative.
205	12	A complicated step in the cinquepace, a sixteenth-century dance, was called "the trick of seventeen"; hence, here Nashe suggests an involved lie.
205	13	A unit of weight; with reference to cheese, between two and three hundred pounds.

Page Note

205   14   Coins of small value, from a fraction of a cent to three cents: the doit was a Dutch coin; the dandiprat was English; and the half-souse (cf. sou) and the denier were French.

206   15   Small change.

208   16   Epeminedes, a religious teacher of Crete (*ca.* 500 B.C.), performed many wonders. According to one legend, he slept for forty years; according to another, for fifty-seven.

208   17   Skinflint.

209   18   Shovels.

210   19   Demetrius II of Syria (*ca.* 161–126 B.C.), who made war on the Parthians and was captured by them; the King of the Parthians sent to Demetrius some dice by way of reproaching him for his dissipated ways, which included gambling.

210   20   Probably a die so loaded that either three or four would come uppermost in a roll.

210   21   "Believe me, giving is a matter for good judgment."

211   22   The first case of declension in the Latin grammar book, though *asinus*, ass or stupid fellow, was hardly the word ordinarily used as a model.

211   23   The proverbial phrase was "Tom Drum's entertainment," suggesting a rough reception and a violent expulsion. In THOMAS OF READING, Deloney invented a story around a comic character, Tom Drum, in order to explain the phrase.

211   24   High men, low men, langrets, and fullams were particular kinds of loaded dice.

211   25   Sluggishness.

212   26   That is, thoroughly.

213   27   Ajax, a Greek hero of enormous size, fought the Trojans and wrestled with Ulysses in a contest of strength against cunning.

213   28   The three counselors of the Greeks in the fight

Page Note

against Troy; the killing of Rhesus, the Thracian ally of King Priam, is usually attributed to Ulysses and Diomed alone.

213   29   Architas' dove was of such perfect geometrical proportions that it voluntarily rose up and flew.

214   30   Residence.

214   31   Ulysses feigned madness and Achilles dressed as a woman in order to avoid going away to the Trojan wars; Palamed, the clever inventor of letters, discovered Ulysses' deception.

214   32   Lycaon, who founded a cult to worship Jove, finally tried to trick him into eating human flesh, and also tried to murder him.

214   33   The reference to Taurimontanus and many other colorful stories employed by Nashe are borrowed from Cornelius Agrippa (1486–1535), a German humanist scholar and a reputed magician. Agrippa's DE INCERTITUDINE ET VANITATE OMNIUM SCIENTIARUM, translated by James Sandford in 1569 and 1575, became a popular Renaissance source book. Below, Nashe makes Agrippa a character in the story of Wilton's travels.

215   34   A general phrase for "godspeed on his journey."

215   35   That is, *qui va là,* "who goes there?"

215   36   Devil's breeches were a kind of closely fitting trousers.

215   37   A pun on the Puritan's revulsion from religious symbols and ceremonies and on the use of the cross on the reverse side of many coins.

216   38   One of the farms near London popular with townsmen as a place for excursions.

217   39   Dionysius, the Younger, a tyrant of Syracuse, was defeated by the Corinthians in 344 B.C.; he was sent to Corinth, where he spent his life among actors and prostitutes and, according to some stories, conducted a school. See below, Note 86.

Page	Note	
217	40	Before us.
217	41	That is, flogged.
217	42	"Grief prevents more."
217	43	Flat dishes; perhaps a pun on *battle* and *battel*, a portion of food, is implied.
217	44	A pun on *cue* as a prearranged signal, on *q.* as a symbol for a farthing or for a portion of food worth a farthing, and on *q.* as an abbreviation for quart.
217	45	That is, did them out of their provisions.
218	46	Finical, that is, overfastidious. See also *phinifide* below.
218	47	A stone used for polishing.
218	48	That is, anyhow.
219	49	Fodder instead of grass; hence, "at hard-meat" is indoors or in confinement.
219	50	Slashed, as the fashion was.
219	51	Hose decorated with colored stripes at the sides.
219	52	Stockings that fit the buttocks snugly.
219	53	Leather apron.
219	54	Perhaps *angle*.
220	55	An epidemic of so-called sweating sickness occurred in 1517.
220	56	That is, fasten his laces.
220	57	To do him in.
220	58	The tub was a familiar part of the equipment used to cure venereal diseases; Mother Cornelius, an old woman, kept an establishment for such a cure.
220	59	The hall of the Cooks' Company.
220	60	Lambskin used in making a cheap fur.
221	61	Paracelsus, the Swiss alchemist and physician (1493–1541), reputedly kept a familiar spirit in the pommel of his sword; Nashe puns with this spirit and with "spirit of the buttery," that is, of the wine cellar or of drunkenness.
221	62	"There was more in the artist than in the art."

Page Note

222 63 Banks's bobtail horse, Marocco, a performing animal of the times, is frequently referred to in Renaissance literature.

222 64 That is, as precious stones are precious, red and shining.

222 65 The editors have left Nashe's spelling, which is of course a pun on *fiery faces* and *fieri facias*, the writ of execution against property for collection of debt.

222 66 Properly *in diebus illis*, in those days or once upon a time.

222 67 The legendary descendant of Aeneas and eponymous ancestor of the Britons.

222 68 In 1515, Francis I headed an expedition to recover Milan; the Duke of Milan was supported by a large army of Swiss allies, and the French were supported by the vanguard of the Venetian army. At first the French fared badly, but with the help of the Venetians turned the tide of battle and killed, in all, some 12,000 Swiss soldiers.

223 69 This action is often assigned to the Etruscans, not the Romans.

223 70 In the account which follows, Nashe seems to have combined two stories, one of the battle of Frankenhausen in 1525 and one of the uprising of Münster in 1534; most of his details, however, come from the latter. In each of these conflicts the Anabaptists rose up against the existent royal authority. Jan Beukelssen of Leyden, a tailor (that is, *botcher*, repairer), who had migrated with other Dutch Anabaptists to Münster, was a leader of the insurrection in 1534; he was tortured to death for his part in the rebellion by both the Catholic and the Protestant princes, the former opposing his religious stand and the latter the communal intentions of the Anabaptists

Page	Note	
223	71	Strips of cloth.
223	72	A spool.
223	73	Twilled, that is, woven in a ribbed pattern.
223	74	A strong needle used for sewing up packages.
223	75	A variant spelling of *cowl*, the hood-shaped covering of the chimney of a malt kiln.
224	76	Carrying rods for cowls or tubs.
224	77	Adzes.
224	78	A steel skullcap, a part of armor.
224	79	Here, of course, a fictitious land, but certainly a disreputable one, for the word means both a loose woman and a kind of card game.
225	80	What more?
226	81	The giants in their war with the gods heaped Ossa and Pelion on Olympus in an attempt to scale the heavens.
227	82	Philip II, King of Spain (1556–1598), who was the champion of Catholicism.
227	83	Nashe probably took this story from Agrippa.
227	84	Nashe confuses Cato the Censor's son, born in his father's old age, with his grandson, a wise man like the grandfather.
227	85	Zaccheus, the rich publican of Jericho, received Jesus at his house. Luke 19:1–10.
228	86	Nashe confuses Dionysius the Elder, a tyrant of Syracuse (born 430 B.C.), who in his plunders carried off a golden mantle from a statue of Jupiter among the spoils of Carthage, with his son Dionysius the Younger. See above, Note 39.
229	87	Marlowe's translation of Ovid's AMORES.
229	88	Cnipperdoling or Knipperdolink was one of the leaders of the insurrection in Münster; Müncer was a founder of the Anabaptist sect.
231	89	Light muskets.
231	90	Nashe achieves a paradox from *to dissoul*, meaning

to destroy a soul, and *to join*, meaning to come in contact with for purposes of destruction.

231   91   Leyden was actually tortured to death by burning tongs.

231   92   That is, synonymas or synonyms.

231   93   Ten toes.

232   94   A variation of *errant* and perhaps a pun on *knights errant* and on *arrant* in the sense of notorious.

232   95   Henry Howard, the Earl of Surrey (1517–1547), led a dramatic life: of royal descent, he was proposed as a husband for Princess Mary, but married Frances Vere in 1532; he was in France in 1532–1533 as a part of Henry VIII's household at the Field of Gold and in 1543–1546 as a military leader; he was imprisoned in 1537 for impetuously striking a courtier, in 1542 for involvement in a second quarrel, and in 1543 for rioting in the streets and for eating meat during Lent; he was an outstanding participant in the tournaments in celebration of Henry VIII's third marriage in 1540; and he was executed in 1547 on the probably spurious charges that he was putting forth his father's claim to the throne as successor to Henry VIII even before Henry's death. Despite Nashe's story, Surrey was apparently never in Italy; his association with the country no doubt derives from the strong Italian influence on his poetry. Surrey, as an accomplished poet, is credited with the invention of the English or Shakespearean sonnet and with English blank verse.

232   96   Variant of *choristers*.

233   97   Geraldine, whom Surrey addressed by name in only one sonnet, was perhaps Elizabeth Fitzgerald (1528?–1589), a daughter of the Irish Earl of Kildare, a descendant of the Giraldi of Florence.

She was married to an English knight who died in
1548 and later to an English earl. Surrey probably
knew her as a young girl.

233   98   In fact, Elizabeth Fitzgerald served none of the
Catherines to whom Henry VIII was married.

233   99   That is, executioner.

233   100   Deprived of other images by the thought of "her
rare worth" alone.

234   101   Dissuasion.

234   102   The name of a specific room.

234   103   The reference is of course to Aeneas' leaving Dido,
the Queen of Carthage, in order to complete his
mission as the founder of Rome.

234   104   "Hence these tears . . . ."

235   105   More and Erasmus, the great humanists, met in
England in 1497 and 1508, and at Calais in 1520,
but probably never at Rotterdam.

235   106   Erasmus' IN PRAISE OF FOLLY appeared in 1509;
More's UTOPIA, ca. 1516.

235   107   Nashe may be satirizing Cambridge in Wittenberg
as Lyly does Oxford in Athens, but of course he is
also concerned with actual events at Wittenberg.
Wittenberg was founded by Frederick III, Elector
of Saxony, in 1502; Luther arrived there in 1508
and became professor of theology in 1512. He
posted his important protestation in 1517.

236   108   According to the established form.

236   109   A *pique devant*, or peaked-in-front Van Dyke
beard.

236   110   Marcus Tullius Cicero (106–43 B.C.), the famous
Roman orator.

236   111   How's and wherefore's.

236   112   "It seems that it may be."

236   113   Homer has Nestor remain youthful in behavior
even after the age of sixty; Ovid, however, has
him attain more than two hundred years of age.

Page Note

236 114 "While the boar (loves) the ridges of the moun-
           tain," a phrase from Virgil's ECLOGUES, is completed
           with "always these honors, and your name and
           praises, will remain."

236 115 I have spoken.

236 116 Perhaps the German word *hof*, field, or, with
           houses, farmhouses; perhaps the word *hock*, Rhine
           wine, or, with *houses*, taverns.

237 117 Vanderhulke is said to be a satire of Gabriel
           Harvey, a minor writer and critic contemporary
           with Nashe.

237 118 Double beer is beer of double strength. *Broccing*
           may mean *broking* in the sense of rascally, *broking*
           in the sense of spoken in a broken or dialectical
           language, or *brocking* in the sense of stinking like
           a badger; in any case, the adjective is one of mild
           abuse. The oration, then, is described as a ridicu-
           lous and drunken speech.

237 119 Bombastic.

237 120 Literally, tribute; possibly a malapropism for
           homage.

237 121 *Fisgigging* means gadding about like a frivolous
           woman; *firking*, dancing briskly; *flantado*, flaunt-
           ing. *Amfibologies* is a word of Nashe's coining.

238 122 *Squitter* is an alteration of *skitter*, to void thin ex-
           crement. A squitter-book is a prolific but worth-
           less writer.

238 123 A pun on *to verse*, to write rhymes, and *to verse*,
           to trick.

238 124 Lambskin was worn on the bachelor's hood; min-
           iver, on the master's.

238 125 The adjective *mechal*, adulterous, is from the
           Latin *moechus*, adulterer; Nashe's *maechi*, adulter-
           ers, is a misspelling. His triple pun is on *mechanical*,
           maechi, and *Mecca*, spelled by Nashe *Maecha*.

238 126 "O how great an artist is lost in me." *Artifex*

later meant free craftsman, hence a particular kind of citizen; *carnifex*, however, means only executioner or destroyer. Nashe's joke is obscure.

238 127 This Latin dramatization of the parable of the prodigal son was written by the Hollander Fullonius in 1529 and translated into English in 1540.

238 128 A philosopher (*ca.* 500 B.C.) credited as the first Greek writer to pursue the serious questions of the nature of knowledge and the soul.

239 129 Snapping.

239 130 Andreas Rudolf Bodenstein of Carlstadt (1480–1541), usually referred to as Carlstadt, supported Luther against the criticism of Johann Maier von Eck and became the Protestant leader at Wittenberg; but Carlstadt was even more radical than Luther and later disagreed with him.

239 131 That is, engaged in a noisy debate; the phrase may be derived from *lever le cul*, to drive a person from his seat, an expression employed in a lively Christmas game in which each player is forced from his seat and supplanted by another. Perhaps Luther and Carlstadt follow each other on the platform as they orate.

239 132 "Those things that are above us are nothing to us." This old proverb appears also in Lyly's EUPHUES.

240 133 Marius Nizolius, the Italian scholar, who compiled THESAURUS CICERONIANUS (1535).

240 134 See above, Note 33. Nashe invents several stories of Agrippa's powers.

241 135 Plautus, the celebrated comic poet of Rome (*ca.* 254–184 B.C.), once worked for a baker, who set him to turning a hand mill.

242 136 Thomas Cromwell, Earl of Essex (1485?–1540), is not known to have visited Charles V, though he carried on negotiations with him for the dissolu-

Page Note

tion of Henry VIII's marriage to Katharine of Aragon, Charles's aunt, and against him for the marriage of Anne of Cleves, supported by Charles's Protestant enemies. For his trouble, Cromwell was beheaded by Henry on a charge of treason; Henry had become dissatisfied with Anne and needed a scapegoat.

245   137   The reference may be to Brunquell, a loyal dwarf servant in a minor play of the period.

245   138   Swooned.

246   139   The phrase "angel of light" is from II Corinthians 11:14.

246   140   A counterfeit coin.

246   141   That is, had me hanged.

247   142   That is, his butler or his page.

247   143   A Latin verse, usually the first verse of the Fifty-first Psalm (which began with *Miserere*), set before one who claimed benefit of clergy; by reading the Latin, the claimant might prove himself an ecclesiastic and hence save his neck.

247   144   Originally a dog that bites or worries sheep, then a shifty or knavish fellow.

247   145   That is, an old so-and-so.

248   146   Probably Bergamask, an inhabitant of Bergamo, near Venice; Bergamasks were considered loutish.

248   147   Companions in power or in trade.

248   148   A variant spelling of *lickerous*, pleasant to taste, lustful.

248   149   The one side.

249   150   "Thalia has given us a flexible nature." Ovid, in HEROIDES, attributes the line to the poetess Sappho, who speaks to the ferryman Phaon of a gift which Thalia, one of the Graces, has given to women.

249   151   Two aces, the lowest throw at dice.

250   152   A variant of Circe.

250   153   That is, kept bustling and jabbering.

Page	Note	

250 154 Plain, direct.

251 155 Foolish, duped.

251 156 Understand.

251 157 John Russell (1486?–1555), though never in Venice, was several times a representative of Henry VIII on the continent and was also connected with the Earl of Surrey, once transferring to him his mission of negotiations at Venice when he, Russell, broke his leg en route.

251 158 That is, resident in the capacity of ambassador. In 1527 Russell served this function at the papal court, but not at Venice.

251 159 Pietro Aretino (1492–1554), poet, critic, writer of religious books, friend of artists, was honored by Charles V, Francis I, and Henry VIII, but not precisely as Nashe describes.

251 160 "I have sinned; I confess."

252 161 Bookish terms.

252 162 Martial, the Roman poet (*ca.* 40–*ca.* 104), speaks of his many Muses in his EPIGRAMS.

252 163 Tolerated.

252 164 A work extant in the sixteenth century attacking Moses, Christ, and Mohamet, probably not by Aretino.

252 165 The epitaph in question emphasizes Aretino's unrestrained use of his sharp tongue.

252 166 "The scourge of princes, the truth teller, the divine one, and rare Aretino." Nashe's Italian is clear, though not exact.

253 167 The works referred to are LA UMANITÁ DI CHRISTO (1535), GENESIS (1538), I SETTE SALMI DE LA PENETENTIA DI DAVID (1534), LA VITA DI SAN TOMASO, SIGNOR D'AQUINO (1543), and LA VITA DI MARIA VERGINE (1539).

253 168 Théodore de Bèze, a French Calvinistic theologian

Page Note

1519–1605), who wrote some licentious Latin verse
of which he later repented.

254	169	"Now you are dismissed."
254	170	Ceremonial attire and/or position.
254	171	That is, bade "Much good may it do you!"
255	172	The highest note; hence, *above e-la*, excessive.
256	173	"Shame and love do not come to the same place."
256	174	A piece of wood fastened to the leg.
257	175	The prime mover, that is, God.
257	176	The gods of the world.
257	177	"A girl is a sweet sickness. I myself pursue what flees. Love causes me to follow. O unhappy me. Why did I look? Why am I dying with love? I love impatiently. She will yield to being loved only so much."
258	178	Skirts or bottom edges.
258	179	"From tears come tears."
258	180	Obsolete form for *ostrich*.
258	181	Variant spelling of *curvet*, to leap in a particular fashion.
259	182	Puffed up.
259	183	Fitted together.
259	184	"Winged with a spur."
260	185	"Every lover fights."
260	186	A form of *appointed* in the sense of "designed."
260	187	"He is able to resist at length."
260	188	"Therefore a wonderful thing because a rare thing."
260	189	"A noble spirit perishes by its nobility."
260	190	"Do not trust appearances."
260	191	"There is concern of the future."
260	192	"Gray hairs are my chains."
260	193	False-burden or bass; here, mot.
260	194	"We hope, they shine forth."
261	195	Nashe's misspelling is *florimus*.

Page Note
261   196   "Devoted in vain."
261   197   "I am fed by hope."
262   198   "Monuments of grief will remain."
263   199   "Plenty makes me poor."
263   200   "What are dominions without enjoyment of them?"
264   201   At this time the Duke of Florence was either Alessandro de' Medici (duke from 1532 to 1537) or Cosimo de' Medici (duke from 1537 to 1569).
265   202   The Spanish *beso las manos*, an affected salutation.
265   203   A Roman jurist of this name, a professor of law at Bologna, lived *ca*. 1436.
265   204   Bugs.
265   205   Nashe perhaps refers to the Cimbri, the German tribe, forced to migrate south from North Jutland in the second century B.C.
265   206   At best an inaccurate reference to Saint Augustine's writings.
265   207   Reference unknown.
266   208   One of the stations of the cross in the old passion plays at Rome was called the Casa di Pilato.
266   209   The reference is unknown; *iemmes* should no doubt be read *Gems*.
266   210   The number of reputed wonders varied. With the exception of Pompey's theater, the places Nashe refers to are unknown.
266   211   A special kind of torture instrument.
267   212   Nashe undoubtedly means Thomas Proctor's GORGEOUS GALLERY OF GALLANT INVENTIONS, a poetical miscellany of 1578.
267   213   The spelling of the original text is *slust*, though *flust*, meaning flushed, appears in some texts.
267   214   Perhaps *in consort*, an idiom which merged with *in concert*.
268   215   Mysterious or concealed.

Page	Note	
270	216	A pair of globes designed by Gerardus Mercator in the 1540's was known in England by 1592.
270	217	Thomas Lanquet's chronicle was published in 1549; Nashe refers to a 1522 entry.
271	218	That is, put it into practise.
272	219	Servant.
273	220	Bailiff.
273	221	That is, frequently; *a paternoster while* was the time it took either to say the Lord's prayer or to reach the paternoster beads in the rosary.
273	222	Smash.
274	223	The Roman statesman and literary patron (*ca.* 70–8 B.C.).
274	224	Obsolete form for *started*.
275	225	Relative pronoun *who* possibly omitted here.
275	226	Pander.
276	227	A Renaissance superstition.
277	228	Cephalus, the Attic hero, killed his wife Procris, whom he took for a wild beast when she followed him into the forest to check on his fidelity.
278	229	Nashe gets the story from Agrippa.
281	230	That is, Epicharmus.
282	231	Philemon of Syracuse lived 361–262 B.C.
282	232	German scholar and professor of history (1468–1534).
283	233	"Ah, by the dead Lord!"
283	234	Sickly-looking.
283	235	A variant of *gaskins*, kind of breeches or hose.
283	236	Perhaps loops at the back of the neck on a coat.
284	237	A kind of sop made with the crumbs of bread.
284	238	The exclamation of jugglers commanding an article to move.
284	239	A knight whose achievements belong to the carpet, that is, in the lady's boudoir, rather than to the field of battle.

Page	Note	
284	240	Because they murdered their husbands, Danaus' daughters were condemned in Hades to filling a leaky jar with water.
285	241	A district of Ethiopia, reputedly the section from which the Theban Egyptians came.
286	242	A variant of *penthouses*, in the sense of overhanging balconies, gutters, and so on.
287	243	Fine (and) rosy, commonly used for *wench*.
287	244	Penalty; here, awkward predicament.
288	245	Lotions to cause wounds to heal up.
288	246	Having become clotted.
288	247	A mild laxative, made from the juice of the bark of the manna ash.
288	248	*Not . . . a dodkin*, not a bit.
288	249	Balm.
288	250	Misprint for *my*.
289	251	Overthwart, placed crosswise.
289	252	Lightened.
289	253	Gargles.
289	254	A London district.
289	255	Probably *tittle*.
290	256	Marauders or invading soldiers.
290	257	Seneca, the philosopher (3 B.C.–65 A.D.), bidden by Nero to kill himself, opened his veins and bled to death; Lucan, the poet (39–65), his nephew, committed suicide by a similar method when Nero ordered his death for participation in conspiracy despite his having turned informer.
290	258	Bumpkins.
290	259	That is, from.
290	260	A prostitute's attendant.
290	261	Saucy.
291	262	That is, *liripipe*, the tail of a scholar's hood; hence a lesson.
291	263	From *taratantara*, the Latin onomatope for the sound of a trumpet; hence, loudly or lustily.

Page	Note	
291	264	That is, leading her a dance, from *measure*, a stately dance.
291	265	A word of Nashe's invention, possibly a combination of *Delphian* and *finical*.
291	266	A ballad recorded in the Stationers' Register *ca.* 1590 was about a highwayman who whipped his victims.
291	267	Paris Garden was maintained on the Bankside, London, from the sixteenth to the eighteenth centuries for bearbaiting, bullbaiting, prize fighting, etc. Yarking, or beating, a blind bear often followed bearbaiting.
292	268	Some of Nashe's stereotyped Jewish names are from the Bible (such as Gideon, Benhadad, Zedekiah); others are of his own invention.
292	269	That is, *black sanctus*, a mock hymn.
292	270	Entice.
292	271	Remind.
293	272	Triflingly, from *to pingle*, to struggle or to work in a trifling way.
293	273	One of the women who ministered to Jesus (Luke 8:3).
293	274	Blemish.
296	275	Charles de Bourbon, who was killed while attempting to sack Rome in 1527.
296	276	"He has not been found," the formal return made by a sheriff to a writ ordering the arrest of a defendant not within his bailiwick.
297	277	*Aqua fortis* was nitric acid of commerce; *mercury sublimatum* was corrosive sublimate, or mercuric chloride.
297	278	The water of the smith's forge.
297	279	Specific reference unknown, though it suggests a familiar folk-tale pattern.
298	280	June 29.
299	281	With complete power.

Page	Note	
299	282	That is, everything.
299	283	Crowded.
299	284	Spirits of wine, that is, alcohol.
300	285	Obsolete form for *lifted*.
300	286	Perhaps "in a great to-do."
301	287	Probably a pritchel. This and the following tools are cobbler's implements.
302	288	Nashe's word is *arrant*.
302	289	Stir.
304	290	Usually spelled *bollen*, puffed up.
305	291	Julian the Apostate (331?–363), a Roman emperor, gave up his Christianity for the paganism to which his studies had directed him.
307	292	With small blows.
307	293	Squeezed.
307	294	Henry VIII's camp at the Field of the Cloth of Gold in 1520 was at Guisnes, Francis I's at Ard, and the meeting place of the two rulers in the valley between the towns.

Deloney: JACK OF NEWBURY

		against the invading army of James IV of Scotland and defeated the Scottish forces at Flodden.
345	30	Tournai and Thérouanne.
345	31	Deloney may or may not have had a hand in establishing the version of the traditional ballad which he includes; several versions exist.
346	32	A derogatory phrase for a show-off; here applied to James IV.
347	33	Ornamental trimmings.
347	34	Apparently Deloney refers to Garter King at Arms, the chief member of the Order of the Garter, the highest order of English knighthood.
349	35	This parable of the insects is obviously in part an attack on Henry VIII's advisor Cardinal Wolsey; therefore the confusing reference to Easter may be to April 20, 1523, when Wolsey demanded as taxes the equivalent of one fifth of all goods.
349	36	That is, took it ill.
350	37	Germany.
352	38	Herostratus' attempt to immortalize himself occurred on the night of the birth of Alexander the Great in 356 B.C.
352	39	A variant spelling of *sessed*, that is, *assessed*.
352	40	Henry VIII's famous jester.
352	41	Agents of Henry VII, executed in 1510 by Henry VIII for having armed their friends during Henry VII's last illness.
353	42	That is, not participating in a lowly occupation.
355	43	Although the reference is unknown, there was a family of Kingsmills living near Newbury in the sixteenth century.
355	44	John Stow, the English chronicler, described actual animosity between Wolsey and Paulet in his ANNALS, 1600.
355	45	Again, a traditional ballad which Deloney may or may not have altered.

360 46 The manner referred to is probably gift giving on special occasions.

361 47 Acted to come exactly together, coincided, agreed.

363 48 The elephant's fear of the sheep is a bit of animal lore referred to elsewhere in classical and Renaissance literature.

365 49 The use of pictures as moral examples is commonplace in popular literature. Although Deloney for the most part employs actual historical personages, he frequently confuses the known facts about them; however, his inaccuracies may be due to the source books of the lives of famous people, to one or more of which he undoubtedly went. Viriathus, described variously as a shepherd and a huntsman, became a kind of guerilla chief among the Lusitanians; the harassed Romans arranged his assassination in 140 B.C. Agathocles, who was known more for his cruelty than for his humility, died from poisoning in 289 B.C. Iphicrates defeated the Spartans in 392 B.C. and turned to aiding the Persians two decades later. Eumenes, in effect the private secretary of Philip and his son Alexander, survived each, only to be murdered by an opposing faction in 316 B.C. Aelius, the name of a Roman plebeian gens, appeared in the full names of many distinguished Romans, but Deloney probably has in mind Publius Helvius Pertinax (126–193), reputedly of low birth, who became emperor against his will and was assassinated by a mutiny of his soldiers. Diocletian ruled from 284 to 305; Valentinian I, from 364 to 375; Probus, from 276 to 282, when he was killed by his soldiers. Actually, Marcus Aurelius (121–180) did not have far to rise, for his father was thrice consul of Rome and he himself was early adopted by an emperor and

betrothed to an emperor's daughter. Maximinus, who ruled from 235 to 238, first worked as a shepherd, then entered the army, and finally rose to the highest rank, in part because of the attractiveness of his tremendous size and superhuman strength. John XXII, pope from 1316 to 1334, is known for his politically stormy career rather than for the kindness which Deloney attributes to him. Sixtus IV, pope from 1471 to 1484, was actually born of a poor family. Deloney's Primislas is probably Premysl, reputed ancestor of the kings and dukes who ruled Bohemia from 873 to 1306; Premysl, a peasant, married Libussa, a princess and the foundress of Prague, and became prince of the Bohemian Czechs. Theophrastus, Aristotle's favorite pupil, died in 287 B.C. The editors find no historical evidence for an emperor Gabianus or for a king Lamusius.

369   50   The heroes Belinus and Brennus appear in Elizabethan chronicles and romances. Belinus is probably an invented form suggesting *warrior*, and Brennus, as is true for several leaders of this name among the Gauls, is perhaps a name derived from the Celtic *bran*, a prince.

369   51   That is, anointed.

369   52   Blackwell, or Bakewell, Hall was used as a weekly market place for all kinds of woolen cloths.

370   53   The Duke of Somerset is known to have visited Newbury in 1537 and to have lodged at the house of Jack of Newbury's son.

372   54   In 1521, before the fall of Wolsey, Henry VIII had defended the papacy against Luther.

372   55   Whitehall, at first a lodging of the archbishops of York, was pulled down, begun again by Wolsey, and completed by Henry VIII.

Page Note

372 56 Stephen, an oustanding exponent of primitive Christianity, was stoned by the populace of Jerusalem for his "blasphemy."

373 57 Perhaps the Coromandel Coast of India, but the specific reference is unknown.

373 58 The island of Taprobane is Ceylon, but the story of the woman is unknown.

374 59 The griffins.

375 60 Deloney inverts the legend of a Boetian lake which made men lecherous.

375 61 A river Cea is unknown, although there is an island Cea or Zea in the Aegean Sea.

375 62 The Pontus Euxinus, or Black Sea, to which the Greeks attributed many terrors of navigation.

376 63 Deloney forgets to let Benedick speak his Italianate English.

377 64 The story appeared in North's translation of Plutarch's life of Alexander.

377 65 Artemisia, queen of Caria, married her brother Mausolus, a union sanctioned in her society; according to the traditional story, when he died, she built him a beautiful tomb known as the Mausoleum, but one legend, that followed by Deloney, is that she made herself his tomb.

381 66 _To cack_ is an obsolete phrase meaning "to void excrement."

382 67 Deloney puns with the word _mutton_, which may mean the flesh or meat of the sheep and also flesh for purposes of lust, or, in obsolete slang, a prostitute.

382 68 Italianate English for _jack_, an ordinary fellow.

382 69 By God's bones.

382 70 Bleed.

383 71 A sixteenth-century headpiece of some fashion and dignity.

Rinehart Editions